Fragrances
of the World

Parfums
du Monde

2000

Michael Edwards

Fragrances of the World

Parfums du Monde

2000

Guy Robert
Technical Consultant
Conseiller Technique

Michel Roudnitska
Images

To John Ledes
He encouraged me

À John Ledes
qui m'a encouragé

ISBN 0 9587419 5 6
Copyright © 2000 Michael Edwards

Table des matières

Contents

Utilisation du guide	6
Comprendre le guide	10
Le Cercle des Parfums	11
Nouveautés	12
Hespéridé	14
Vert	20
Marine	24
Florale	28
Fleuri Aldéhydé	40
Fleuri Oriental	44
Oriental Doux	50
Oriental	54
Oriental Boisé	58
Chypre Boisé	64
Chypre Cuir	70
Fougère	74
Index Féminin	84
Index Masculin	96
Parfums de Légende	103
Index des Maisons	104

Using the guide	7
Understanding the guide	8
The Fragrance Wheel	9
New Fragrances	12
Citrus	14
Green	20
Water	24
Floral	28
Soft Floral	40
Floral Oriental	44
Soft Oriental	50
Oriental	54
Woody Oriental	58
Mossy Woods	64
Dry Woods	70
Aromatic Fougère	74
Women's Index	84
Men's Index	96
Perfume Legends	95
House Index	104

Utilisation
du guide

Pour beaucoup d'entre nous, trouver le parfum qui convient est une véritable épreuve, rendue plus difficile encore par une avalanche de nouveaux parfums. Le livre *Parfums du Monde* repose sur cette simple idée : trouver de nouveaux parfums doit être un plaisir et non une tâche.

Ce qui au départ était déjà une innovation, pour guider le personnel des parfumeries et des grands magasins, est devenu le manuel le plus complet qui existe sur les parfums. *Parfums du Monde* classifie plus de 2300 parfums.

Il est le seul guide indiquant l'accord entre les parfums pour femmes et ceux pour hommes par famille de senteurs.

C'est un guide indépendant et impartial dont la publication est rendue possible par des milliers de boutiques et de personnes qui, chaque année, souscrivent à la nouvelle édition. La classification et la liste des parfums sont établies à titre gracieux.

Je suis évaluateur, et non pas parfumeur. Je détermine la classification d'un parfum en fonction de sa personnalité unique, de sa « signature ». J'ai la chance d'être aidé dans ce travail par Guy Robert, l'un des grands parfumeurs modernes et auteur des classiques Calèche et Madame Rochas.

Chaque classification est vérifiée avec les évaluateurs dans les Maisons de parfum ou avec les parfumeurs eux-mêmes. Vérifier prend du temps, mais c'est une étape importante de mon travail, peut-être sa force.

Si vous aimez le parfum, alors *Parfums du Monde* va vous fasciner. Il rendra facile la découverte de nouveaux parfums qui vous plairont. Simplement, consultez l'index pour trouver la famille à laquelle appartient chacun de vos parfums préférés. Vous êtes sûr de trouver dans la même famille d'autres parfums qui vous conviendront.

Parfums du Monde est l'ouvrage de référence pour les parfumeurs et les évaluateurs parce qu'il est exhaustif. Il est le seul guide à inclure la classification des parfums d' "artisans parfumeurs" et des parfumeurs indépendants: tels qu' Annick Goutal, le Comptoir Sud Pacifique, Creed, Dyptique, Jo Malone, L'Artisan Parfumeur, Maître Parfumeur et Gantier, par exemple.

Les professionnels du marketing trouveront dans l'index des Maisons une référence indispensable et sans rivale. Les formateurs, découvrant la valeur de ce guide, pourront l'utiliser comme manuel.

Si vous êtes conseiller en beauté ou associé à la vente, ce guide vous permettra d'aider, de façon simple et efficace, vos clients à choisir de nouveaux parfums qu'ils aimeront.

Posez leur la question: « Quelles sont vos parfums préférés ? » et cherchez ensuite dans l'index alphabétique chacun des parfums mentionnés pour savoir à quelle famille il appartient. Presque toujours, vous trouverez qu'au moins deux des parfums sont dans la même famille.

Il peut arriver qu'une personne donne le nom de trois ou quatre parfums de familles assez différentes. La raison en est bien simple: c'est une personne qui aime le parfum. Elle est plus aventureuse dans ses goûts, car elle a essayé des parfums divers. Ne vous inquiétez pas, demandez-lui simplement le nom de deux ou trois autres parfums qu'elle a portés ou admirés. Invariablement, vous découvrirez la famille qui a pour elle une importance particulière.

Sélectionnez alors trois nouveaux parfums à faire essayer par votre client(e) ou ami(e) - un ou deux dans le même groupe et un ou deux autres qui sont plus frais ou plus riches.

Si vous voulez suggérer une senteur de famille différente, choisissez les deux familles adjacentes dans le Cercle des parfums (voir page 11). Les femmes qui aiment le Fleuri oriental, par exemple, souvent portent aussi Oriental doux. Dans un climat plus froid, elles opteront peut-être pour des parfums plus sensuels au ton Oriental doux.

J'espère surtout que *Parfums du Monde* encouragera chacun à être plus aventureux. Le parfum peut être beaucoup plus qu'un plaisant accessoire. Il est écrit dans le Coran: « Les parfums sont des nourritures qui éveillent l'esprit ». Un grand parfum est une œuvre d'art. Poésie silencieuse, il est l'invisible langage du corps. Il peut rendre nos jours plus heureux, hanter nos nuits et donner sa nuance à nos souvenirs.

Le parfum est une émotion liquide.

Using _the guide_

For most people, finding the right fragrance is a confusing exercise. The avalanche of new fragrances compounds the problem.

Fragrances of the World is dedicated to a simple idea: finding new fragrances should be a pleasure, not a problem.

What started out as a simple yet innovative reference for staff in perfumeries and department stores has evolved into the world's most comprehensive fragrance manual. _Fragrances of the World_ classifies more than 2,300 perfumes.

It is still the only guide that matches women's and men's fragrances, family by family.

The guide is independent and impartial. Its publication is made possible by the thousands of stores and individuals who subscribe to each annual edition. No charge is made for classifying and listing the fragrances.

I am an evaluator, not a perfumer. I personally classify each fragrance by coming to an understanding of its personality and distinctive 'signature'.

I am fortunate to have the help of Guy Robert, one of the great modern perfumers and the creator of classics such as Calèche and Madame Rochas.

Each classification is checked with the evaluators at the fragrance Houses, or with the perfumers themselves. Checking takes time, but it is an essential step and, perhaps, the greatest strength of my work.

If you love fragrance, _Fragrances of the World_ will fascinate you. It makes it easy for you to find new fragrances you will enjoy. Simply go to the Index to discover the family to which each of your favourite fragrances belongs. You are certain to find other fragrances in the same family that will appeal.

Fragrances of the World is an essential reference for perfumers and evaluators because it is so comprehensive. It is the only guide to classify the fragrances of the 'artisan' Houses and independent perfumers: Annick Goutal, Comptoir Sud Pacifique, Creed, Diptyque, Jo Malone, L'Artisan Parfumeur, Maître Parfumeur et Gantier, for example.

Marketing professionals will find the House Index an indispensable competitive reference. Trainers will also discover the value of the guide as a training manual.

If you are a beauty adviser or sales associate, there is no easier way to help your customers find new fragrances they are certain to like.

Ask the question: "What are your favourite fragrances?" Look up each fragrance in the alphabetical Index to find out the family to which it belongs. Most times, you will find that at least two of the fragrances will belong to the same family.

Occasionally, someone will give you the names of three or four fragrances belonging to quite different families. The reason is simple - they love fragrance. Their taste is more adventurous simply because they have tried more fragrances. Don't worry. Just ask for the names of another two or three fragrances that they have worn or admired. Invariably, you will find that one family holds a special appeal.

Now select three new fragrances for your customer or friend to try - one or two from within the same groups and another one or two that are fresher or richer.

If you wish to suggest a fragrance from a different family, consider moving one family up or down on the Fragrance Wheel (see page 9). Women who enjoy Floral Orientals, for example, often wear Soft Florals as well. In cooler weather, they may switch to the more sensual Soft Orientals.

I hope, above all, that _Fragrances of the World_ will encourage people to be more adventurous. Fragrances can be so much more than just a pleasant accessory. "Perfumes are foods that reawaken the spirit," says the Koran. A great perfume is a work of art. It is silent poetry, invisible body language. It can lift our days, haunt our nights and create the milestones of our memories.

Fragrance is liquid emotion.

Understanding

The Four Columns

At the heart of this guide is a fragrance scale so innovative it is copyright. Think of fragrances as musical notes, with the freshest notes on the left of each family page and the richest, deepest notes on the right.

When four fragrances from the same family are compared - one a Fresh interpretation, the second a Crisp, the third a Classical and the fourth a Rich version - one's nose steps down a fragrance scale of Fresh > Crisp > Classical > Rich interpretations. With each step, the fragrance note becomes a little deeper.

Fresh	●	The most effervescent fragrances in the family
Crisp	●●	Lively interpretations with a crisp accent
Classical	●●●	Balanced notes characteristic of the family
Rich	●●●●	The richer, deeper fragrances

Citrus-Fruity, Green, Water and White Flowers

Grouping the Fresh and Crisp fragrances under the headings Citrus-Fruity, Green, Water and White Flowers makes it easier to imagine the scent of each fragrance. **Green** notes, for example, will add the sharp freshness of green leaves, crushed grass. A hint of green will make a fragrance crisp while a touch more will make it fresh.

Citrus-Fruity notes come from citrus oils, from apple and apricot, melon and peach, plum and exotic fruits. Their scent adds a tangy freshness quite different from the sharper Green notes.

Water notes, by contrast, capture the cool freshness of sea air or the pure scent of a waterfall.

The scents of fresh **White Flowers** add the sweet, soft, fresh accents of lily of the valley and jasmine, gardenia, hyacinth, white honeysuckle and freesia.

Women's, Men's and Shared fragrances

Feminine fragrances are printed in black:
L'AIR DU TEMPS   Nina Ricci 1948

Masculine fragrances are printed in blue:
ROMANCE MAN   Ralph Lauren 1999

Shared fragrances, marked ♀, are listed among both women's and men's fragrances

Dates

1948	This indicates the year in which the fragrance was introduced
1962/95	When two dates are shown, the first date is the year in which the fragrance was originally introduced, the second the year in which it was reorchestrated, updated or, on occasion, completely changed

Symbols

*	* An asterisk indicates that the fragrance has been discontinued but is still included in the guide for reference or because stocks are still available in some stores
♀	♀ indicates a Shared fragrance
Ⓛ	Ⓛ indicates a limited edition fragrance

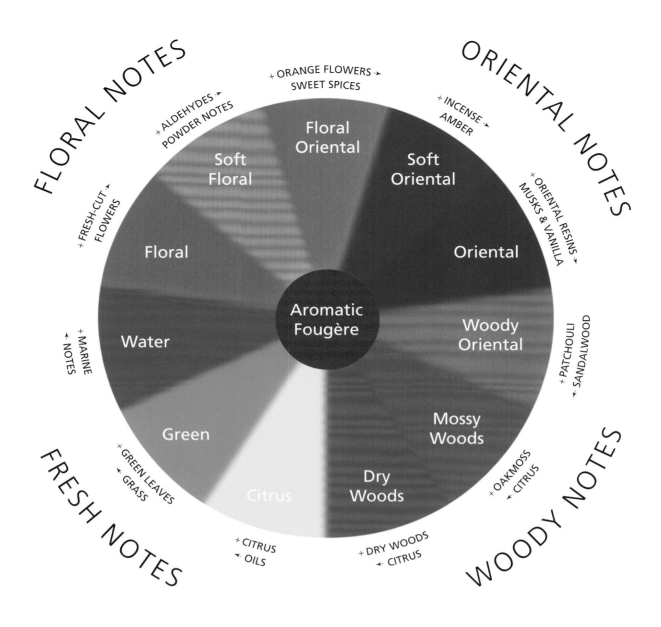

The Fragrance Wheel

Since emotions play such a large part in the sense of smell, people assume there is no logic in their choice of fragrances. Yet it's likely that at least two of their favourite fragrances belong to the same 'family'.

The fragrance families hold the key to everyone's likes and dislikes.

The Fragrance Wheel allows you to see at a glance the relationship between the different families.

To the major groups of fragrances defined by perfumers – Floral, Oriental and Woody – has been added a fourth, the Fresh notes.

Modern perfumery has transformed what were once simply light eaux de cologne into real Citrus fragrances.

The true Green fragrances and the Water fragrances are also included among the Fresh notes.

To help you pinpoint your selection more accurately, the Fragrance Wheel breaks down the four major groups into 12 distinct families. Each family leads to the next. Florals become Soft Florals when blended with sparkling aldehydes and balanced by a soft iris or vanilla drydown. Soft Florals are transformed into Floral Orientals by adding the scents of orange flowers and sweet spices.

Positioned at the hub of the Fragrance Wheel are the Aromatic Fougères. a universal fragrance family that includes elements from many families:

> The freshness of a Citrus
> Floral notes of lavender
> The spicy-sweetness of a Floral Oriental
> The ambery depth of an Oriental
> And the Mossy Woods warmth of sandalwood and oakmoss

This universal appeal makes masculine Aromatic Fougères a perfect match to almost any feminine fragrance.

Comprendre

Les Quatre Colonnes

Au cœur de ce guide se trouve une échelle des parfums si innovatrice qu'elle a été brevetée. Pensez à l'ensemble des parfums comme à une gamme musicale avec, dans chaque famille, à gauche les notes les plus fraîches, et les notes les plus riches, les plus profondes, à droite.

Lorsqu'on compare les parfums d'une même famille - le premier avec une interprétation fraîche, le deuxième vif, le troisième classique et le quatrième profond - le nez descend une gamme du frais au vif, puis au classique et enfin au profond. À chaque étape, le parfum devient un peu plus pénétrant.

Frais	●	Les parfums les plus effervescents dans cette famille
Pétillant	●●	Interprétation vivante avec une touche de vivacité
Classique	●●●	Equilibre des notes caractéristique de cette famille
Profond	●●●●	Les parfums les plus profonds, les plus riches

Notes Hespéridées Fruité, Verts, Marines, Fleurs Blanches

Regrouper les senteurs Frais et Vif sous le nom d'Hespéridé, Fruité, Vert, Marine et Fleurs Blanches permet de mieux imaginer la senteur de chaque parfum. **Vert**, par exemple, ajoute une note de fraîcheur vive, celle des feuilles vertes ou du gazon fraîchement coupé. Une touche de vert rendra le parfum vif, puis une autre encore, frais.

Les notes d'**Hespéridé fruité** proviennent des huiles d'agrumes, auxquelles se joignent la pomme, l'abricot, le melon, la pêche, la prune et les fruits exotiques. Leur senteur ajoute une fraîcheur corsée assez différente des notes vertes plus tranchantes.

Les notes **Marines**, par contre, savent capturer la froide fraîcheur de l'air marin ou l'embrun d'une cascade.

Les senteurs de fraîches **Fleurs blanches** ajoutent à la douceur, au soyeux, un ton frais des muguet, jasmin, gardénia, jacinthe, chèvrefeuille blanc et freesia.

Parfums féminins, parfums masculins et parfums mixtes

Les parfums féminins sont imprimés en noir :
L'AIR DU TEMPS   Nina Ricci 1948

Les parfums masculins sont imprimés en bleu :
ROMANCE MAN   Ralph Lauren 1999

Les parfums mixtes sont marqués de ♂ et sont présents à la fois dans la liste des parfums pour femme et pour homme.

Dates

1948	Indique l'année de lancement du parfum
1962/95	Lorsque deux dates apparaissent, la première est celle du lancement du parfum, la deuxième, celle de sa reprise, mise à jour ou bien de conception totalement différente

Symboles

*	* L'astérisque indique un parfum disparu, mentionné dans le guide parce qu'il constitue une référence ou bien parce qu'il est encore disponible dans certaines boutiques
♂	♂ Indique un parfum mixte (unisex) à la fois destiné aux femmes et aux hommes
Ⓛ	Ⓛ Indique un parfum en édition limitée

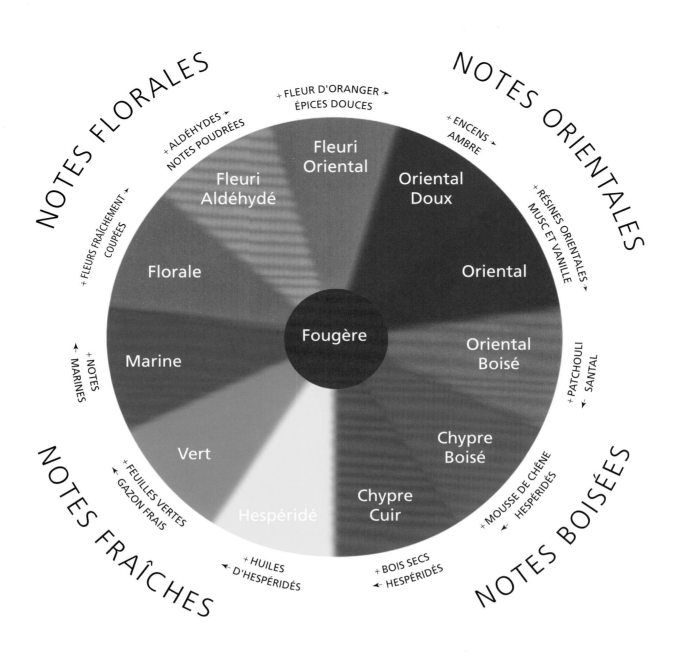

NOTES FLORALES

NOTES ORIENTALES

NOTES FRAÎCHES

NOTES BOISÉES

+ FLEUR D'ORANGER →
ÉPICES DOUCES

+ ALDÉHYDES →
NOTES POUDRÉES

+ ENCENS
AMBRE →

+ FLEURS FRAÎCHEMENT →
COUPÉES

+ RÉSINES ORIENTALES
MUSC ET VANILLE →

Fleuri
Oriental

Fleuri
Aldéhydé

Oriental
Doux

Florale

Oriental

+ NOTES
MARINES

Fougère

Oriental
Boisé

Marine

+ PATCHOULI
SANTAL

Chypre
Boisé

Vert

+ FEUILLES VERTES
GAZON FRAIS

+ MOUSSE DE CHÊNE
HESPÉRIDÉS

Chypre
Cuir

Hespéridé

+ HUILES
D'HESPÉRIDÉS

+ BOIS SECS
HESPÉRIDÉS

Le Cercle des Parfums

Les émotions jouent de façon si importante dans l'odorat, que l'on croit souvent que toute logique est absente du choix d'un parfum.

Pourtant, parmi les parfums que l'on préfère, il y en a toujours au moins deux qui appartiennent à la même « famille ».

Les familles de parfum détiennent la clé des goûts et des rejets de chacun.

Le Cercle des Parfums vous permet de voir en un coup d'œil les rapports entre les différentes familles.

Aux groupes dominants de parfums définis par les parfumeurs - Florale, Oriental, Boisé - s'est ajouté un quatrième : les notes Fraîches.

La parfumerie moderne a transformé ce qui, autrefois, était simplement des eaux de Cologne légères en de véritables parfums hespéridés.

Les vrais parfums Verts et les parfums aux notes Marines font aussi partie des notes Fraîches.

Pour faciliter votre selection précise, le Cercle des Parfums divise les quatre grands groupes en 12 familles distinctes. Chaque famille introduit à la suivante. Les parfums Floraux deviennent des Floraux aldéhydés lorsque on y mélange des aldéhydes piquants mais équilibrés par un fond d'iris doux ou de vanille. Les parfums au ton Fleuri aldéhydé se transforment en parfums au ton Oriental doux si on leur ajoute des senteurs de fleur d'oranger et d'épices douces, telles que la noix de muscade et la cannelle.

Au centre du Cercle des Parfums sont les Fougères aromatiques, une famille de senteurs universelles qui rassemblent des éléments des autres familles :

La fraîcheur de l'Hespéridé
La note Florale de la lavande
La douceur épicée du Fleuri oriental
La profondeur ambrée de l'Oriental
Le Chypre boisé fait des chauds
bois de santal et de mousse de chêne

Son attrait universel fait des masculines Fougères aromatiques le complément parfait de presque chaque parfum féminin.

Nouveautés

Citrus · Hespéridé

AROMATONIC   Lancôme
BULLES DE FRAÎCHEUR   Molinard
CANNELLE ORANGE   L'Occitane ♂
CÉDRAT POMELO   L'Occitane ♂
CHANSON DE VIE   Coty
EAU DE CARON FORTE   Caron ♂
FEUILLE DE VERVEINE   L'Occitane ♂
GOURMANDISE DE RODIER   Rodier
GREEN TEA   Elizabeth Arden
I AM ENERGY   Danica Aromatics
INTENSE DE SCAPA   Scapa of Scotland
ORANGE CAFÉ   Molinard
PAMPLELUNE   Guerlain ♂
PENHALIGON'S CASTILE   Penhaligon's ♂
THÉ VERT   L'Occitane ♂
D&G MASCULINE   Dolce & Gabbana
EAU DU BADIAN   L'Occitane
HAPPY FOR MEN   Clinique
L'EAU PAR KENZO POUR HOMME   Kenzo

Green · Vert

FEUILLE D'HERBE FRAÎCHE HERBACÉE
   L'Occitane
GRAIN DE FOLIE   Grès
HERBA FRESCA   Guerlain ♂
I AM SERENE   Danica Aromatics
MENTHE FROISSÉE   L'Occitane
SONOMA VALLEY   Crabtree & Evelyn

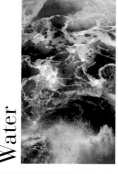

Water · Marine

FLEUR DE LOTUS   L'Occitane
MARE   Creative Universe ♂
WILD WIND   Gabriela Sabatini

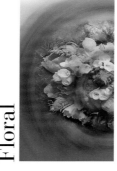

Floral · Florale

57 FOR HER   Chevignon
2000 ET UNE RÔSE ℒ   Lancôme
À LA FRANÇAISE   Marina de Bourbon
ACQUA DI FIORI   De Ruy
ALEGRIA   Adolfo Dominguez
AMOUR D'AMANDIER   Nina Ricci
AMULETI   Mariella Burani
ANDY WARHOL FOR WOMEN   Cofinluxe
APRIL FIELDS   Coty
AROMANTIC   Decléor
ASPHALT FLOWER   MAC
AZZURA   Loris Azzaro
BABY DOLL PARIS   Yves Saint Laurent
BASILIC FLEUR D'ORANGER   Molinard
BENETTON SPORT WOMAN   Benetton
BIRMANE   Van Cleef & Arpels
CALYPSO JASMINE   Calypso
CALYPSO VIOLET   Calypso
CANDIE'S   Liz Claiborne
CASSISSIER   L'Occitane
CE SOIR OU JAMAIS   Annick Goutal
CHAUMET   Chaumet
CHELSEA DREAMS   Old England
CHIEMSEE   Chiemsee
CHRISTIAN LACROIX   Christian Lacroix
CLEAR DAY LIGHT   Etienne Aigner
CONSENT WOMAN   Consent
DARBY ROSE   Sylvie Chantecaille
DUÉ 2 DAY   Lomani
DUÉ 2 NIGHT   Lomani
EAU MARINE   Les Copains
EAU POUR SOI   Roger & Gallet
ÉLÀ NONCHALANCE   Mäurer & Wirtz
ESSENZA DI MEDITERRANEÒ DONNA   Parah
ETERNAL ROSE   Fragrances of Ireland
ÉTHÉRÉ   Vicky Tiel
FIORUCCI   Fiorucci
FLEUR   Floris
FLEURS DE CHIARA BONI   Chiara Boni
FLOWERS   Gilles Cantuel
FRAGILE   Jean Paul Gaultier
FREE WORLD WOMAN   Mäurer & Wirtz
FREEDOM FOR HER   Tommy Hilfiger
FREESIA   Woods of Windsor
GATTINONI À PORTER   Gattinoni
HIGH TECH WOMEN   Lomani
HIRIS   Hermès
I AM PASSION   Danica Aromatics
INÈS DE LA FRESSANGE   Inès de la Fressange
J'ADORE   Christian Dior
KISS & TELL   Fragrance International
LA CHASSE AUX PAPILLONS
   L'Artisan Parfumeur
LACOSTE FOR WOMEN   Lacoste
LAIT SUCRÉ   Comptoir Sud Pacifique
LAVANDE VELOURS   Guerlain ♂
LE BAISER   Lalique
LILY ℒ   Christian Dior
LOVING BOUQUET ℒ   Escada
MARBERT WOMAN RED   Marbert
MCM   MCM
MILLENNIUM HOPE WOMAN   Jivago
MODERN QUARTZ   Molyneux
OFRÉSIA   Diptyque
PEOPLE DONNA   Luciano Soprani

RÉMY FOR WOMAN   Rémy Marquis
ROSA MAGNIFICA   Guerlain
ROSE NÉROLI   L'Occitane
ROSE SANTAL   Molinard
SHEER TIFFANY   Tiffany
SOLO FIORI FREESIA   Solo Soprani
SOLO FIORI JASMINE   Solo Soprani
SOLO FIORI LILY OF THE VALLEY
   Solo Soprani
SOLO FIORI ROSE   Solo Soprani
SOLO FIORI TUBEROSE   Solo Soprani
SOLO FIORI VIOLET   Solo Soprani
THE SPIRIT OF SWITZERLAND   Michel Jordi
U   Natio
U de V POUR ELLE   Ulric de Varens
UNZIPPED SPORT   Perfumer's Workshop
VICE VERSA   Yves Saint Laurent
YIN   Jacques Fath
YLANG & VANILLE   Guerlain

Soft Floral · Fleuri Aldéhyde

AMAZING   Bill Blass
ANNA SUI   Anna Sui
BABYLON   Gilles Cantuel
COUNTRY ROAD WOMAN   Country Road
D&G FEMININE   Dolce & Gabbana
DEAUVILLE   Michel Germain
DI ROMEO GIGLI   Romeo Gigli
DKNY WOMEN   Donna Karan
ENERGIZING FRAGRANCE   Shiseido
EXCITING ARROGANCE   Arrogance
FLEURAGE   Visari
G   Giorgio Beverly Hills
JASMIN MANDARINE   L'Occitane
LE CIRQUE DE POPY MORENI   Popy Moreni
PARESSE DE RODIER   Rodier
SAMBA RED WOMAN   Perfumer's Workshop
TILLEUL CHÈVREFEUILLE   L'Occitane

Floral Oriental · Fleuri Oriental

BETTY BARCLAY WOMAN N° 2
   Mäurer & Wirtz
CHINA ROSE   Floris
DALIMANIA   Salvador Dali
DÉLICE D'ÉPICES   Nina Ricci
ENFANTS DU SOLEIL   Comptoir Sud Pacifique
GLAMOUR   Gale Hayman
GMV DONNA   Gian Marco Venturi
GOLDEN MOMENT   Priscilla Presley
GOOD LIFE WOMAN   Davidoff

HERVÉ LÉGER   Hervé Léger
ORGUEIL DE RODIER   Rodier
POLEMIC!   Succès de Paris
RED PEARL   Red Pearl
RÊVERIE   Gloria Vanderbilt
STYLE   Gale Hayman
SUMATRA RAIN WOMAN   Muelhens
ULTRAVIOLET   Paco Rabanne
UNZIPPED UNIVERSE   Perfumer's Workshop
URVASHI   Gandhi Sugandh

Soft Oriental / Oriental Doux

CARAMEL PAIN D'ÉPICE   Molinard
HYPERSOUK   MAC
THEOREMA ESPRIT D'ÉTÉ   Fendi
TRÈS CHIC   Holzman & Stephanie
VANILLE   L'Occitane ♂

Oriental / Oriental

ADRIENNE VITTADINI   Adrienne Vittadini
AYAKO   Marc de la Morandière
CHOCOLAT MENTHE   Molinard
I AM WILD   Danica Aromatics
JAÏPUR SAPHIR   Boucheron
OZBEK 1001   Rifat Ozbek

Woody Oriental / Oriental Boisé

COLÈRE DE RODIER   Rodier
DESTINY WOMAN   Harley-Davidson
DIESEL ZERO PLUS FEMININE   Diesel
DULCE VANILLA   Coty
FABLE   Hope Diamond Collection
FEUILLE D'HERBE FRAÎCHE EPICÉE
   L'Occitane
FIRE & ICE SMOULDER FOR HER   Revlon
GRAIN DE SOLEIL   Fragonard

GUCCI RUSH   Gucci
GUET-APENS ⓛ   Guerlain
I AM ETERNAL   Danica Aromatics
KIRI   Kiri Te Kanawa
LA PLAGE   Marc de la Moriandière
LAPIS   Napoleon
LELONG POUR FEMME   Lucien Lelong
MANIA   Giorgio Armani
MARQUIS POUR FEMME   Rémy Marquis
NAOMI CAMPBELL   Naomi Campbell
ORGANZA INDÉCENCE   Givenchy
PYTHON   Trussardi
ROCOCO   Joop!
ROUGE   Annabella
ROYAL SECRET II   Royal Secret
SYNTHETIC NIRVANA   MAC
TEMPORE DONNA   Laura Biagiotti
57 FOR HIM   Chevignon
BODY KOUROS   Yves Saint Laurent
CASRAN   Chopard
CASUAL FRIDAY   Escada
CONVICTION MEN   Omar Sharif
DIESEL ZERO PLUS MASCULINE   Diesel
GERANI UOMO   Gerani
JORDAN BY MICHAEL   Bijan
LP N° 9 FOR MEN   Penhaligon's
NEMO   Cacharel
PARADOX FOR MEN   Jacomo
PASSION D'HOMME   Rodier
PEOPLE UOMO   Luciano Soprani
RÉMY   Rémy Marquis
ROCHAS MAN   Rochas
TED   Ted Lapidus
TEMPORE UOMO   Laura Biagiotti
U de V N° 2   Ulric de Varens
VERY VALENTINO POUR HOMME
   Valentino
YANG   Jacques Fath
ZAHAROFF POUR HOMME   Zaharoff
ZIPPED UNIVERSE   Perfumer's Workshop

Mossy Woods / Chypre Boisé

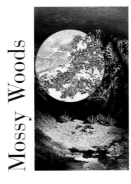

COMME DES GARÇONS 2 ♂
   Comme des Garçons
EASY KRIZIA   Krizia
FEUILLE D'HERBE FLORALE FRUITÉE
   L'Occitane
FLEUR DE FIGUIER   Molinard
POMME CANNELLE   Molinard
TIEMPE PASSATE   Antonia's Flowers
212 MEN   Carolina Herrera
BOURBON HOMME   Marina de Bourbon
CHAMADE POUR HOMME ⓛ   Guerlain
DESTINY   Harley-Davidson
FERRARI BLACK   Ferrari
FIRE & ICE SMOULDER FOR HIM   Revlon
GREEN VALLEY   Creed
HIGH TECH MEN   Lomani
HUGO DARK BLUE   Hugo Boss
SALVATORE FERRAGAMO POUR HOMME
   Salvatore Ferragamo
SAMBA RED MAN   Perfumer's Workshop

Dry Woods / Chypre Cuir

DZING!   L'Artisan Parfumeur
PASSAGE D'ENFER   L'Artisan Parfumeur
CARVEN HOMME   Carven
ESSENZA DI MEDITERRANEÒ UOMO   Parah
OSCAR FOR MEN   Oscar de la Renta
PHEROMONE FOR MEN   Marilyn Miglin
PONTACCIO 21   Gianfranco Ferré
SIESTE   Fragonard
TRUSSARDI UOMO FRESH   Trussardi

Aromatic / Fougère

AQUA RELAX   Biotherm
MERGE   Xan Kim ♂
ADIDAS MOVES   Adidas
ADVENTURE QUASAR   J. Del Pozo
ANDY WARHOL FOR MEN   Cofinluxe
BENETTON SPORT MAN   Benetton
BUGATTI   Ettore Bugatti
CANDIE'S MEN   Liz Claiborne
CONSENT MAN   Consent
COUNTRY ROAD MAN   Country Road
CULTURE by TABAC BLUE   Mäurer & Wirtz
DANIEL HECHTER SPORT   Daniel Hechter
DEAUVILLE POUR HOMME   Michel Germain
DKNY MEN   Donna Karan
DRAKKAR DYNAMIK   Guy Laroche
FREE WORLD MAN   Mäurer & Wirtz
FREEDOM FOR HIM   Tommy Hilfiger
LACOSTE 2000   Lacoste
LANCETTI POUR HOMME   Lancetti
LAVANDE   L'Occitane
LUCIANO   Pavarotti
MARQUIS   Rémy Marquis
MILLENNIUM HOPE MAN   Jivago
NOMAD   Crabtree & Evelyn
PERRY ELLIS PORTFOLIO   Perry Ellis
PRESSURE   Rémy Latour
ROMANCE MEN   Ralph Lauren
RYKIEL HOMME   Sonia Rykiel
SANDER FOR MEN   Jil Sander
SPORT MAXIMUM   Davinci
VERINO POUR HOMME   Roberto Verino
VIKING   Royal Copenhagen
VOLCANO HOMME   Lomani
VUARNET   Vuarnet
WILD WIND FOR MEN   Gabriela Sabatini
WILKES SAN FRANCISCO   Wilkes Bashford
YOHJI HOMME   Yohji Yamamoto
ZIPPED SPORTS   Perfumer's Workshop

New Fragrances 1999-2000

New Fragrances

13

Hespéridé

Citrus

From the zest of lemons, mandarins, bergamot, oranges and grapefruit come the citrus oils that lend these fragrances their distinctive, tangy aroma. Floral, spicy and woody notes transformed the light, refreshing eaux de cologne into real fragrances. A new generation of musk and tea accents adds an interesting dimension to the oldest fragrance family.

C'est du zeste de citron, de la mandarine, de la bergamote, de l'orange, du pamplemousse que proviennent les huiles hespéridées qui communiquent à ces parfums leur arôme pétillant si typique. Les notes florales, épicées et boisées transforment les eaux de Cologne légères et fraîches en de véritables parfums. Une nouvelle génération de tons musqués et de senteurs de thé ajoutent une dimension intéressante à la plus ancienne famille de parfums.

● ➡

Fresh / Frais

AROMATONIC   Lancôme 1999
BULGARI EAU PARFUMÉE   Bulgari 1993 ♂
BULLES DE FRAÎCHEUR   Molinard 1999
CANNELLE ORANGE   L'Occitane 1996/99 ♂
CHANSON DE VIE   Coty 1999
CITRON VERT   Molinard 1993 ♂
cK ONE   Calvin Klein 1994 ♂
CROWN ESS BOUQUET   Crown 1872
DALIMIX   Salvador Dali 1996 ♂
EAU BELLE   Loris Azzaro 1995
EAU D'ORLANE   Orlane 1992
EAU DE VARENS N° 2   Ulric de Varens 1997 ♂
EX'CLA.MA'TION EAU   Coty 1996
EXTASE BODY TALK   Muelhens 1996 ♂
FEUILLE DE VERVEINE   L'Occitane 1999 ♂
FIRE & ICE COOL   Revlon 1996
FRENCH CONNECTION   French Connection 1997
FUJIYAMA   Succès de Paris 1995 ♂
FUSION   Fabergé 1997
GIEFFEFFE   Gianfranco Ferré 1995 ♂
GOLD JEANS FEMME   Roccobarocco 1997
GOURMANDISE DE RODIER   Rodier 1999
GREEN TEA   Elizabeth Arden 1999
I AM ENERGY   Danica Aromatics 1999
ICEBERG TWICE ICE   Iceberg 1998
L'EAU DE KOOKAÏ   Kookaï 1996
NETWORK   Lomani 1996 ♂
O$_2$XYGEN WOMAN   California North 1996
PACO   Paco Rabanne 1996 ♂
QUERCUS   Penhaligon's 1996 ♂
REYNALD KATZ   Reynald Katz 1998 ♂
ROUTE DU THÉ   Barneys New York 1986
SANGUINE MUSKISSIME   Maître Parfumeur et Gantier 1988 ♂
SOLO SOPRANI   Solo Soprani 1995 ♂
SPORT SPIRIT   Escada 1996 ♂
SUMMER SPLASH   Lilian Barony 1998
TÉ   Creative Universe 1996 ♂
THÉ POUR UN ÉTÉ   L'Artisan Parfumeur 1996 ♂
VERY M.C.   MCM 1996 ♂
WEIL EAU DE FRAÎCHEUR   Weil 1961/93 ♂
X LIMITED   Etienne Aigner 1997 ♂
XTC   Davinci 1996 ♂

●● ➡

Crisp / Pétillant

CARRIÈRE   Gendarme 1996
CÉDRAT POMELO   L'Occitane 1999 ♂
CEYLON   Robert Isabell 1996
CRISTALLE   Chanel 1974
DIORELLA   Christian Dior 1972
EAU D'ÉTÉ   Patricia de Nicolaï 1997
EAU DE VARENS N° 3   Ulric de Varens 1997 ♂
EAU DU SUD   Annick Goutal 1995 ♂
EAU FRAÎCHE   Molinard 1992 ♂
EAU VITAMINÉE   Biotherm 1997
EAU VIVE   Carven 1966/95
ESPRIT DU ROI   Penhaligon's 1989 ♂
ESTIVALIA   Puig 1975
ETIQUETTE BLEUE   d'Orsay 1908/95 ♂
FRAÎCHE PASSIFLORE   Maître Parfumeur et Gantier 1988
GRAPEFRUIT   Jo Malone 1992 ♂
KUMQUAT   Comptoir Sud Pacifique 1998 ♂
L'EAU   Laura Ashley 1995
LOVIN' GIRL   Un Monde Nouveau 1995/98
MANDARINE   Comptoir Sud Pacifique 1976 ♂
NATURE SYSTEM   Roger & Gallet 1992 ♂
NOI MISSONI   Missoni 1994
PACO ENERGY   Paco Rabanne 1998 ♂
PAMPLEMOUSSE   Comptoir Sud Pacifique 1985 ♂
SCAPA   Scapa of Scotland 1991
SOUTHERN EXPOSURE   Terry Ellis 1997
SPORTS EXTREME USA   Azurel 1997 ♂
THÉ VERT   L'Occitane 1999 ♂
VOCALISE   Maître Parfumeur et Gantier 1988

Classical / Classique

4711 ORIGINAL   Muelhens 1792 ♂
ACQUA CLASSICA DI BORSARI   Borsari 1880 ♂
ACQUA DI PARMA   Colonia 1916 ♂
ATKINSON GOLD MEDAL   Atkinson 1799 ♂
BOIS DE CÉDRAT   Creed 1875 ♂
CHANSON D'EAU   Coty 1995
CITRUS BIGARRADE   Creed 1901 ♂
CLÉMENTINE   Molinard 1993
COLOGNE SOLOGNE   Patricia de Nicolaï 1989 ♂
CROWN ESTERHAZY   Crown 1874
EAU D'HADRIEN   Annick Goutal 1981 ♂
EAU DE COLOGNE   Penhaligon's 1927 ♂
EAU DE FLEURS DE CÉDRAT   Guerlain 1920 ♂
EAU DE GUERLAIN   Guerlain 1974 ♂
EAU DE LANCASTER   Lancaster 1977
EAU DE MÛRE   Maître Parfumeur et Gantier 1988
EAU DE PATOU   Jean Patou 1976
EAU DE ROCHAS   Rochas 1970
EAU DU COQ   Guerlain 1894 ♂
EAU DU GANTIER   Maître Parfumeur et Gantier 1988 ♂
EAU DYNAMISANTE   Clarins 1987 ♂
EAU FRAÎCHE   Caron 1997 ♂
EAU FRAÎCHE   Christian Tortu 1998
EAU FRAÎCHE   Léonard 1974
EAU FRANCE   Molinard 1949 ♂
EAU IMPÉRIALE   Guerlain 1853 ♂
ENGLISH FINE COLOGNE   Yardley 1984 ♂
GIVRINE (SICILE)   E.Coudray 1950 ♂
JEAN-MARIE FARINA   Roger & Gallet 1806 ♂
L'EAU DE L'ARTISAN   L'Artisan Parfumeur 1993 ♂
MONT ST MICHEL   Mont St Michel 1920 ♂
Ô de LANCÔME   Lancôme 1969
PENHALIGON'S CASTILE   Penhaligon's 1999 ♂
ROGER & GALLET EXTRA-VIEILLE   Roger & Gallet 1991 ♂
SPECIAL N° 127   Floris 1910 ♂
VERBENAS OF PROVENCE   Jo Malone 1995 ♂
VERVEINE   Le Jardin Retrouvé 1978 ♂

Rich / Profond

ALPONA   Caron 1939
BOUQUET IMPÉRIAL   Roger & Gallet 1991 ♂
COLD   Benetton 1997 ♂
EAU D'ORANGE VERTE   Hermès 1979 ♂
EAU DE CARON FORTE   Caron 1999 ♂
EAU DE VARENS N° 4   Ulric de Varens 1998 ♂
EAU DE VERVEINE   Penhaligon's 1949 ♂
EXTRACT OF LIMES   Penhaligon's 1963 ♂
FRAÎCHEUR MUSKISSIME   Maître Parfumeur et Gantier 1988 ♂
FRUITS SAUVAGES   Comptoir Sud Pacifique 1987
INTENSE DE SCAPA   Scapa of Scotland 1999
LIME, BASIL & MANDARIN   Jo Malone 1991 ♂
LIMES   Floris 1832 ♂
MIEL ORANGE   E.Coudray 1995
MÛRE   Molinard 1993
MÛRE ET MUSC   L'Artisan Parfumeur 1978
MÛRE ET MUSC EXTRÊME   L'Artisan Parfumeur 1993
ORANGE CAFÉ   Molinard 1999
PAMPLELUNE   Guerlain 1999 ♂
TRISH McEVOY 1   Trish McEvoy 1997
TURQUOISE   Morabito 1992
ZESTE MANDARINE PAMPLEMOUSSE   Creed 1975 ♂

● ➤ Fresh / Frais

BULGARI EAU PARFUMÉE   Bulgari 1993 ♂
CANNELLE ORANGE   L'Occitane 1996/99 ♂
CITRON VERT   Molinard 1993 ♂
cK ONE   Calvin Klein 1994 ♂
CLAIBORNE FOR MEN*   Liz Claiborne 1989
DALIMIX   Salvador Dali 1996 ♂
EAU DE VARENS N° 2   Ulric de Varens 1997 ♂
EXTASE BODY TALK   Muelhens 1996 ♂
FEUILLE DE VERVEINE   L'Occitane 1999 ♂
FUJIYAMA   Succès de Paris 1995 ♂
GAI MATTIOLO UOMO   Gai Mattiolo-ICR 1998
GIEFFEFFE   Gianfranco Ferré 1995 ♂
HAPPY FOR MEN   Clinique 1999
HILFIGER ATHLETICS   Tommy Hilfiger 1998
NETWORK   Lomani 1996 ♂
NOI UOMINI   Missoni 1997
O₂XYGEN   California North 1994
PACO   Paco Rabanne 1996 ♂
POUR LE JEUNE HOMME   Maître Parfumeur et Gantier 1990
QUERCUS   Penhaligon's 1996 ♂
REBEL   Salle 1997
REYNALD KATZ   Reynald Katz 1998 ♂
SANGUINE MUSKISSIME   Maître Parfumeur et Gantier 1988 ♂
SOLO SOPRANI   Solo Soprani 1995 ♂
SPORT SPIRIT   Escada 1996 ♂
TÉ   Creative Universe 1996 ♂
THÉ POUR UN ÉTÉ   L'Artisan Parfumeur 1996 ♂
TOM TAILOR   Viale! 1995
VERY M.C.   MCM 1996 ♂
WEIL EAU DE FRAÎCHEUR   Weil 1961/93 ♂
X LIMITED   Etienne Aigner 1997 ♂
XTC   Davinci 1996 ♂

●● ➤ Crisp / Pétillant

ADIDAS SPORT   Adidas 1994
BOGNER MAN   Bogner 1985/90
BOOSTER   Lacoste 1996
CAPUCCI POUR HOMME   Roberto Capucci 1965
CÉDRAT POMELO   L'Occitane 1999 ♂
CERRUTI 1881   Cerruti 1990
CHROME   Loris Azzaro 1996
EAU DE VARENS N° 3   Ulric de Varens 1997 ♂
EAU DU BADIAN   L'Occitane 1999
EAU DU SUD   Annick Goutal 1995 ♂
EAU FRAÎCHE   Molinard 1992 ♂
ESPRIT DU ROI   Penhaligon's 1989 ♂
ETIQUETTE BLEUE   d'Orsay 1908/95 ♂
EVASION   Bourjois 1996
GRAPEFRUIT   Jo Malone 1992 ♂
GREEN WATER   Jacques Fath 1947/67/93 ♂
KUMQUAT   Comptoir Sud Pacifique 1998 ♂
L'EAU PAR KENZO POUR HOMME   Kenzo 1999
MANDARINE   Comptoir Sud Pacifique 1976 ♂
NATURE SYSTEM   Roger & Gallet 1992 ♂
PACO ENERGY   Paco Rabanne 1998 ♂
PAMPLEMOUSSE   Comptoir Sud Pacifique 1985 ♂
POUR L'HOMME   Roger & Gallet 1993
QUARTZ POUR HOMME   Molyneux 1996
SÉLECTION VERTE   Creed 1970
SILVER LIGHT   Escada 1997
SPORT DE PACO RABANNE   Paco Rabanne 1986
SPORTS EXTREME USA   Azurel 1997 ♂
THÉ VERT   L'Occitane 1999 ♂
ZIPPED   Perfumer's Workshop 1998

Classical / Classique

4711 ORIGINAL   Muelhens 1792 ♂
ACQUA CLASSICA DI BORSARI   Borsari 1880 ♂
ACQUA DI PARMA   Colonia 1916 ♂
ATKINSON GOLD MEDAL   Atkinson 1799 ♂
BLENHEIM BOUQUET   Penhaligon's 1902
BOIS DE CÉDRAT   Creed 1875 ♂
CITRUS BIGARRADE   Creed 1901 ♂
COLOGNE SOLOGNE   Patricia de Nicolaï 1989 ♂
EAU D'HADRIEN   Annick Goutal 1981 ♂
EAU DE COLOGNE   Penhaligon's 1927 ♂
EAU DE FLEURS DE CÉDRAT   Guerlain 1920 ♂
EAU DE GUERLAIN   Guerlain 1974 ♂
EAU DE QUININE   Crown 1890
EAU DES PRINCES   L.T.Piver 1850
EAU DES TROPIQUES   Comptoir Sud Pacifique 1988
EAU DU COQ   Guerlain 1894 ♂
EAU DU GANTIER   Maître Parfumeur et Gantier 1988 ♂
EAU DYNAMISANTE   Clarins 1987 ♂
EAU FRAÎCHE   Caron 1997 ♂
EAU FRANCE   Molinard 1949 ♂
EAU IMPÉRIALE   Guerlain 1853 ♂
EAU SAUVAGE   Christian Dior 1966
ENGLISH FINE COLOGNE   Yardley 1984 ♂
FERRARI COLOGNE WATER   Ferrari 1998
GIVRINE (SICILE)   E.Coudray 1950 ♂
HUNGARY WATER   Crabtree & Evelyn 1975
JEAN-MARIE FARINA   Roger & Gallet 1806 ♂
L'EAU DE L'ARTISAN   L'Artisan Parfumeur 1993 ♂
MESSIRE   Jean d'Albret 1961/96
MONSIEUR DE GIVENCHY   Givenchy 1959
MONT ST MICHEL   Mont St Michel 1920 ♂
PENHALIGON'S CASTILE   Penhaligon's 1999 ♂
ROGER & GALLET EXTRA-VIEILLE   Roger & Gallet 1991 ♂
SIGNORICCI   Nina Ricci 1975
SPECIAL N° 127   Floris 1910 ♂
VERBENAS OF PROVENCE   Jo Malone 1995 ♂
VERVEINE   Le Jardin Retrouvé 1978 ♂
VERVEINE   Molinard 1949
VORAGO ACTION   California Fragrances 1992

Rich / Profond

ACTION SPORT   Trussardi 1993
ARMANI POUR HOMME   Giorgio Armani 1984
BOUCHERON POUR HOMME   Boucheron 1991
BOUQUET IMPÉRIAL   Roger & Gallet 1991 ♂
CAMP BEVERLY HILLS FOR MEN*   CBH 1988
CHEVALIER D'ORSAY   d'Orsay 1911/95
COLD   Benetton 1997 ♂
CROWN IMPERIAL   Crown 1905
CROWN SPICED LIMES   Crown 1921
D&G MASCULINE   Dolce & Gabbana 1999
EAU D'ORANGE VERTE   Hermès 1979 ♂
EAU DE CARON FORTE   Caron 1999 ♂
EAU DE COLOGNE EXTRA FINE   L'Occitane 1990
EAU DE ROCHAS HOMME   Rochas 1993
EAU DE VARENS N° 4   Ulric de Varens 1998 ♂
EAU DE VERVEINE   Penhaligon's 1949 ♂
EAU POUR HOMME   L.T.Piver 1995
EAU SAUVAGE EXTRÊME   Christian Dior 1984
ELITE   Floris 1980
EXTRACT OF LIMES   Penhaligon's 1963 ♂
FRAÎCHEUR MUSKISSIME   Maître Parfumeur et Gantier 1988 ♂
GENDARME   Gendarme 1991
ICEBERG HOMME   Iceberg 1991
LIME, BASIL & MANDARIN   Jo Malone 1991 ♂
LIMES   Floris 1832 ♂
LORDS   Penhaligon's 1911
MISSONI SPORT   Missoni 1990
MONSIEUR BALMAIN   Pierre Balmain 1964/90
NÉROLI SAUVAGE   Creed 1994
PAMPLELUNE   Guerlain 1999 ♂
PINO SILVESTRE EXTREME   Pino Silvestre-Mavive 1998
SAMBA FOR MEN   Perfumer's Workshop 1990
SANTOS EAU DE SPORT   Cartier 1989
SUMARE   Crown 1925
TED BAKER   Ted Baker 1998
THAT MAN   Revlon 1958/89
TROPHÉE LANCÔME   Lancôme 1982
UNGARO POUR L'HOMME II*   Ungaro 1992
YSL POUR HOMME   Yves Saint Laurent 1971
ZESTE MANDARINE PAMPLEMOUSSE   Creed 1975 ♂

Green

Green fragrances capture the sharp scent of fresh-cut grass and violet leaves. Despite the outdoors imagery, the impact of the classic resinous galbanum accord is so potent that many green fragrances have a formal rather than sporty personality. In recent years, a palette of softer, lighter green notes has given this fragrance family fresh appeal.

Les parfums Verts capturent l'odeur vive du gazon fraîchement coupé et des feuilles de violette. Bien qu'ils évoquent des paysages extérieurs, l'accord de la résine classique (galbanum) résonne en eux avec une telle puissance que beaucoup de parfums verts font plus « habillé » que « sport ». Ces dernières années, une palette de notes vertes plus douces ou légères est venue donner à cette famille de parfums un rafraîchissant renouveau.

Fresh / Frais

ANNABELLA   Annabella 1997
CHÈVREFEUILLE ORIGINAL   Creed 1982 ♂
DALIMIX GOLD   Salvador Dali 1997 ♂
FEUILLE D'HERBE FRAÎCHE HERBACÉE   L'Occitane 1999
MENTHE FROISSÉE   L'Occitane 1999
RICHARDSON BAY   California North 1991 ♂
SONOMA VALLEY   Crabtree & Evelyn 1999
SUNG SPA   Alfred Sung 1992

Crisp / Pétillant

ACTION*   Trussardi 1989
GRAIN DE FOLIE   Grès 1999
HERBA FRESCA   Guerlain 1999 ♂
INDISCRET   Lucien Lelong 1935/97
JONES NEW YORK   Jones New York 1996
VIRGILIO   Diptyque 1990 ♂

CHÈVREFEUILLE ORIGINAL Creed 1982 ♂
DALIMIX GOLD   Salvador Dali 1997 ♂
RICHARDSON BAY   California North 1991 ♂
TIFFANY FOR MEN SPORT   Tiffany 1998

HERBA FRESCA   Guerlain 1999 ♂
Ô POUR HOMME   Lancôme 1996
VIRGILIO   Diptyque 1990 ♂

Classical / Classique

AIRE LOEWE   Loewe 1985
ALIAGE / ALLIAGE   Estée Lauder 1972
DI BORGHESE*   Marcella Borghese 1978
EAU DE CAMPAGNE   Sisley 1974 ♂
I AM SERENE   Danica Aromatics 1999
INOUÏ   Shiseido 1976
VACANCES   Jean Patou 1936
VENT VERT   Pierre Balmain 1947/90
WEIL DE WEIL   Weil 1971

Rich / Profond

CAMÉLIA CHINOIS   Maître Parfumeur et Gantier 1997
JEAN-LOUIS SCHERRER   Jean-Louis Scherrer 1979
PHEROMONE   Marilyn Miglin 1978
PRIVATE COLLECTION   Estée Lauder 1973
SABI   Henry Dunay 1998
SILENCES   Jacomo 1978
WITH PLEASURE   Caron 1949

EAU DE CAMPAGNE   Sisley 1974 ♂
GREEN IRISH TWEED   Creed 1985
HALSTON 1-12   Halston 1976

DEVIN   Aramis 1978
MILA SCHÖN UOMO   Mila Schön 1986
NINO CERRUTI   Cerruti 1979
TACTICS   Shiseido 1979

Water

Marine

Redolent of the scent of soft sea breezes, the marine notes were created in 1990. The early water notes captured the ozonic aroma of wet air after a thunderstorm. Today, the water notes are more often used as an accent to enliven florals, orientals and woody fragrances.

Vivifiées par des senteurs de brise marine, ces notes ont été crées en 1990. Les premières capturaient l'arôme d'ozone de l'air humide et frais après l'orage. Aujourd'hui, les notes marines sont utilisées le plus souvent pour aviver les parfums floraux, orientaux et boisés.

Fresh / Frais

AQUAFLORE   Carolina Herrera 1996
CHARLIE WHITE   Revlon 1994
CYBERSP@CE   Mäurer & Wirtz 1997 ♂
DUENDE   J. del Pozo 1992
EAU PURE   Caron 1996 ♂
GHOST MYST   Coty 1995
INIS   Fragrances of Ireland 1998 ♂
MOTU   Comptoir Sud Pacifique 1992
MUST DE CARTIER II   Cartier 1993
ROOTS UNISCENT   Coty 1996 ♂
SEAWEST   Via Paris 1998
STRADIVARIUS WHITE   Arman 1997
WRAPPINGS   Clinique 1990

Crisp / Pétillant

CARITA   Carita 1996
FLEUR DE LOTUS   L'Occitane 1996/99
FUN WATER WOMAN   De Ruy 1998
L'EAU D'ISSEY   Issey Miyake 1992
L'EAU LILIAN   Lilian Barony 1994
MARE   Creative Universe 1999 ♂
MONSOON EAU   Monsoon 1997
ODEUR 53   Comme des Garçons 1998 ♂
POLO SPORT WOMAN   Ralph Lauren 1996
SAMBA NATURAL   Perfumer's Workshop 1996
SANS ADIEU   Worth 1925/95
SERGIO TACCHINI DONNA   Sergio Tacchini 1998
WILD WIND   Gabriela Sabatini 1999

CYBERSP@CE   Mäurer & Wirtz 1997 ♂
EAU PURE   Caron 1996 ♂
EROLFA   Creed 1992
INIS   Fragrances of Ireland 1998 ♂
KENZO POUR HOMME   Kenzo 1991
NAUTICA   Nautica 1992
ROOTS UNISCENT   Coty 1996 ♂

ACQUA DI GIÒ POUR HOMME   Giorgio Armani 1996
MARE   Creative Universe 1999 ♂
ODEUR 53   Comme des Garçons 1998 ♂
SILVER MOUNTAIN WATER   Creed 1995

Classical / Classique

ASPEN FOR WOMEN   Coty 1990
BEST OF CHEVIGNON   Chevignon 1996 ♂
NEW WEST FOR HER   Aramis 1990
PROFUMO DI MONTECATINI   Marcella Borghese 1993 ♂
SUNFLOWERS   Elizabeth Arden 1993

Rich / Profond

ESCAPE   Calvin Klein 1991
VANILLE MARINE   Molinard 1998

BEST OF CHEVIGNON   Chevignon 1996 ♂
L'EAU D'ISSEY POUR HOMME   Issey Miyake 1994
LATITUDE SPORT   Olivier de Kersauson 1997
MOLINARD HOMME III   Molinard 1996
PROFUMO DI MONTECATINI   Marcella Borghese 1993 ♂

MILLÉSIME IMPÉRIAL   Creed 1995
NAUTILUS AQUA   Nautilus 1998
NEW WEST FOR HIM   Aramis 1988

Floral

Florale

Florals remain the most popular fragrance family. Their repertoire is vast, ranging from concertos on the theme of a single floral note to mighty symphonies of heady mixed bouquets. Headspace technology has given perfumers an avalanche of exciting new floral notes: it allows them to identify and clone the scent of blooms from which no oil can be extracted by traditional methods. Each year, unusual new notes are found, revitalising the traditional floral theme.

Les parfums floraux restent les plus appréciés. Leur répertoire est vaste, allant du concerto sur le thème d'une seule note florale, à la puissante symphonie de bouquets entêtants de fleurs mêlées. La technologie appelée « headspace » a développé pour les parfumeurs une kyrielle de nouvelles notes florales passionnantes: elle leur permet d'identifier et de reproduire la senteur de fleurs trop fragiles pour supporter les procédés d'extraction d'huile et de distillation traditionnels. Ainsi, chaque année apporte de nouvelles notes surprenantes qui régénèrent le thème floral.

Fresh / Frais

Iris

HIRIS   Hermès 1999
INÈS DE LA FRESSANGE   Inès de la Fressange 1999

Lily of the Valley / Muguet

CROWN ALPINE LILY   Crown 1879
DIORISSIMO   Christian Dior 1956
EAU FRAÎCHE   Elizabeth Arden 1986
FLORE   Caroline Herrera 1994
JESSICA McCLINTOCK   Jessica McClintock 1987
LE MUGUET DE ROSINE   Rosine 1996
LILY   ℓ   Christian Dior 1999
LILY OF THE VALLEY   Crabtree & Evelyn 1970
LILY OF THE VALLEY   Floris 1847
LILY OF THE VALLEY   Penhaligon's 1976
LILY OF THE VALLEY   Woods of Windsor 1978
LILY OF THE VALLEY   Yardley 1980/94
MUGUET / LILY OF THE VALLEY   Molinard 1994
MUGUET DES BOIS   Coty 1942
MUGUET DU BONHEUR   Caron 1952
SOLO FIORI LILY OF THE VALLEY   Solo Soprani 1999
WILD MUGUET   Jo Malone 1995

Lime Blossom / Fleur de tilleul

FRENCH LIME BLOSSOM   Jo Malone 1995
TILLEUL   d'Orsay 1955/95 ♂

Crisp / Pétillant

Freesia

ANTONIA'S FLOWERS   Antonia's Flowers 1984
FREESIA   Crabtree & Evelyn 1993
FREESIA   Woods of Windsor 1999
NATURE'S ONE FREESIA   Perlier 1995
SOLO FIORI FREESIA   Solo Soprani 1999

Gardenia / Gardénia

ADIEU SAGESSE   Jean Patou 1925
CLASSIC GARDENIA   Dana 1995
GARDÉNIA   Chanel 1925
GARDENIA   Crabtree & Evelyn 1974
GARDENIA   Floris 1997
GARDENIA   Jo Malone 1995
GARDENIA   Penhaligon's 1976
ISLAND GARDENIA   Jovan 1986
JUNGLE GARDENIA   Tuvaché / Coty 1950/95
NATURE'S ONE GARDENIA   Perlier 1994
TIARÉ   Comptoir Sud Pacifique 1984
TIARÉ   Sylvie Chantecaille 1997

Honeysuckle / Chèvrefeuille

CHÈVREFEUILLE   Le Jardin Retrouvé 1977
CHÈVREFEUILLE   Molinard 1993
HONEYSUCKLE   Woods of Windsor 1974

Lily / Lys

LYS   Le Jardin Retrouvé 1989

Mimosa

CALYPSO MIMOSA   Calypso 1998
FARNESIANA   Caron 1947
LA BASE FOR HER   Magic Helvetia 1994
MIMOSA   Molinard 1994
MIMOSA   Woods of Windsor 1997
MIMOSA POUR MOI   L'Artisan Parfumeur 1992
MIMOSAÏQUE   Patricia de Nicolaï 1992
UN MATIN D'ÉTÉ   Morabito 1997

Rose

AGUA FRESCA DE ROSAS   Adolfo Dominguez 1995
CE SOIR OU JAMAIS   Annick Goutal 1999
ETERNAL ROSE   Fragrances of Ireland 1999
ROSA MAGNIFICA   Guerlain 1999

Sweet Pea / Pois de senteur

FLORET   Antonia's Flowers 1995

Wisteria / Glycine

WISTERIA   Sylvie Chantecaille 1997

Classical / Classique

Boronia

BORONIA   Déco 1976

Jasmine / Jasmin

CALYPSO JASMINE   Calypso 1999
JASMIN   Le Jardin Retrouvé 1977
JASMIN   Maître Parfumeur et Gantier 1988
JASMIN   Molinard 1994
JASMIN DE PROVENCE   Crabtree & Evelyn 1970
JASMINE*   Yardley 1994
NUAGES D'EAU   Marc de la Morandière 1994
OZBEK   Rifat Ozbek 1995
SOLO FIORI JASMINE   Solo Soprani 1999

Lavender / Lavande

AGUA LAVANDA   Puig 1940 ♂
ARÔME 3   d'Orsay 1943/95 ♂
EAU DE LAVANDE   Annick Goutal 1981 ♂
EAU DE LAVANDE   Mont St Michel 1920 ♂
EAU DE PROVENCE   Patricia de Nicolaï 1992 ♂
ENGLISH LAVENDER   Atkinson 1910 ♂
ENGLISH LAVENDER   Yardley 1873
LAVANDA   Myrurgia 1916 ♂
LAVANDE ROYALE   Roger & Gallet 1991
LAVANDE VELOURS   Guerlain 1999 ♂
LAVENDER   Crabtree & Evelyn 1970 ♂
LAVENDER   Floris 1828 ♂
LAVENDER   Woods of Windsor 1974

Rose

2000 ET UNE RÔSE ⓛ   Lancôme 1999
CROWN ROSE   Crown 1873
DARBY ROSE   Sylvie Chantecaille 1999
EAU DE MURANO   Kare 1994
ELISABETHAN ROSE   Penhaligon's 1984
ENGLISH ROSE   Yardley 1997
EVELYN   Crabtree & Evelyn 1993
FLEURS DE BULGARIE   Creed 1845/1980
MARECHALE ORIGINAL   Crown 1669/1994
PARIS   Yves Saint Laurent 1983
PRIMROSE   Penhaligon's 1976
QUELQUES ROSES   Claire 1997
RED ROSES   Jo Malone 1996
ROSE   Caron 1949
ROSE   Molinard 1994
ROSE ABSOLUE   Annick Goutal 1984
ROSE NÉROLI   L'Occitane 1999
ROSE OPULENTE   Maître Parfumeur et Gantier 1988
ROSE-PIVOINE   Patricia de Nicolaï 1998
ROSE SANTAL   Molinard 1999
ROSE THÉ   Le Jardin Retrouvé 1989
ROSES AND MORE   Priscilla Presley 1998
SOIR DE PARIS   Bourjois 1928/91
SOLO FIORI ROSE   Solo Soprani 1999
TEA ROSE   Perfumer's Workshop 1972
WILD ROSE   Woods of Windsor 1974

Ylang-ylang

YLANG & VANILLE   Guerlain 1999

Rich / Profond

Carnation / Œillet

BELLODGIA   Caron 1927
MALMAISON   Floris 1830/1999
NIGHT SCENTED STOCK   Penhaligon's 1976
OEILLET   Molinard 1993

Frangipani / Frangipane

FRANGIPANE   Sylvie Chantecaille 1997

Lavender / Lavande

ARÔME 3 TRADITION   d'Orsay 1998 ♂
LAVANDE   Molinard 1925/96 ♂

Orange Flower / Fleur d'oranger

BASILIC FLEUR D'ORANGER   Molinard 1999
MANDARIN   Robert Isabell 1996
NARCISSE BLANC   Caron 1923
NARCISSE NOIR   Caron 1911
ORANGE BLOSSOM   Penhaligon's 1976
STEPHANOTIS   Floris 1786

Tuberose / Tubéreuse

CAROLINA HERRERA   Carolina Herrera 1988
CHIARA BONI   Chiara Boni 1990
CHLOÉ   Chloé 1975
ENJOLI   Revlon 1978
FRACAS   Robert Piguet 1948
FRAGILE   Jean Paul Gaultier 1999
GARDÉNIA PASSION   Annick Goutal 1989
JONTUE   Revlon 1975
MADELEINE   Madeleine Mono 1978
MICHELLE   Balenciaga 1979
PAVLOVA   Payot 1977
SOLO FIORI TUBEROSE   Solo Soprani 1999
TUBÉREUSE   Annick Goutal 1984
TUBÉREUSE   Le Jardin Retrouvé 1980
TUBÉREUSE   Maître Parfumeur et Gantier 1988
TUBEROSE   Jo Malone 1991
VANILLE FLEURIE   Molinard 1998
VERSACE'S BLONDE   Versace 1995

Violet / Violette

APRIL VIOLETS   Yardley 1913
CALYPSO VIOLET   Calypso 1999
CHARTREUSE DE PARME   Stendhal 1960
QUELQUES VIOLETTES   Claire 1996
SOLO FIORI VIOLET   Solo Soprani 1999
VIOLET   Woods of Windsor 1998
VIOLETTA   Penhaligon's 1976
VIOLETTA DI PARMA   Borsari 1870
VIOLETTE   Molinard 1994
VIOLETTE PRÉCIEUSE   Caron 1918

Fresh / Frais

Bouquet Citrus Fruity / Hespéridé Fruité

100% PURE CHIPIE GREEN   Coty 1998
ADIDAS WOMAN SPORT   Adidas 1997
AMERICA FOR WOMEN   Perry Ellis 1996
AMULETI   Mariella Burani 1999
ANDY WARHOL FOR WOMEN   Cofinluxe 1999
AUBUSSON COULEURS   Aubusson 1997
BABY DOLL PARIS   Yves Saint Laurent 1999
BALANCE   Eddie Bauer 1996
BENETTON SPORT WOMAN   Benetton 1999
BOUTON D'OR   L'Artisan Parfumeur 1994
CALYX   Prescriptives 1986
CHAMPS-ELYSÉES   Guerlain 1904/96/98
CHANSON D'AIR   Coty 1997
CHARLIE SILVER   Revlon 1998
CHARLIE SUNSHINE   Revlon 1997
CHEAP & CHIC   Moschino 1995
CHERISH   Revlon 1996
CLAIRE DE NILANG   Lalique 1997
CLEAR DAY LIGHT   Etienne Aigner 1999
CURVE FOR WOMEN   Liz Claiborne 1996
DUÉ 2 DAY   Lomani 1999
EAU DE CHARLOTTE   Annick Goutal 1982
EAU DE CORIANDRE   Jean Couturier 1996
EAU DE DALI   Salvador Dali 1995
EAU DE DOLCE VITA   Christian Dior 1998
EAU DE FATH   Jacques Fath 1996
EAU DE GIVENCHY   Givenchy 1980
EAU POUR SOI   Roger & Gallet 1999
EAU SVELTE   Christian Dior 1995
ELYSIUM   Clarins 1993
ESCADA EN FLEURS   Escada 1997
ESSENZA DI MEDITERRANEÒ DONNA   Parah 1999
EX'CLA.MA'TION BLUSH   Coty 1996
FABULEUSE   Léonard 1998
FIORI DI KRIZIA   Krizia 1995
FLEUR DE WEIL*   Weil 1995
FLOWERS   Gilles Cantuel 1999
GÉNÉRATION COURRÈGES   Courrèges 1996
GREEN GENERATION HER   Pino Silvestre-Mavive 1998
HAPPY   Clinique 1997
HEAD OVER HEELS   Ultima II 1994
HIGH TECH WOMEN   Lomani 1999
I LOVE YOU   Molyneux 1998
ICEBERG   Iceberg 1989
IL BACIO   Marcella Borghese 1993
ÎLES D'OR   Molinard 1929/93
IN LOVE AGAIN   Ⓛ   Yves Saint Laurent 1998
INCLINATION   L.T.Piver 1998
JOVAN FRESH MUSK   Jovan 1996
L'EAU DE SONIA RYKIEL   Sonia Rykiel 1998
LIBERTÉ ACIDULÉE (LES BELLES DE RICCI)   Nina Ricci 1996
LIZ CLAIBORNE   Liz Claiborne 1986
LYRA 3   Alain Delon 1998
MARBERT WOMAN RED   Marbert 1999
MELODIE D'AMOUR   Marc de la Morandière 1996
MISS ARPELS   Van Cleef & Arpels 1994
MISS HABANITA   Molinard 1994
MODERN QUARTZ   Molyneux 1999
MON BOUQUET   Marina de Bourbon 1998
MUST DE CARTIER (JOUR)*   Cartier 1981
Ô OUI   Lancôme 1998
OMBRE ROSE FRAÎCHE   Jean-Charles Brosseau 1997
PASSION FLOWER   Crabtree & Evelyn 1996
PASTEL DE CABOTINE   Grès 1996
PETITE CHÉRIE   Annick Goutal 1998
PLUMES   Pupa 1997
PURE   Alfred Sung 1997
QUARTZ   Molyneux 1977

Crisp / Pétillant

Bouquet Citrus Fruity / Hespéridé Fruité

57 FOR HER   Chevignon 1999
360° FOR WOMEN   Perry Ellis 1993
À LA FRANÇAISE   Marina de Bourbon 1999
ALEGRIA   Adolfo Dominguez 1999
AMAZONE   Hermès 1974/89
AMOUR D'AMANDIER   Nina Ricci 1999
ARIA MISSONI   Missoni 1987
ARROGANCE POUR FEMME   Arrogance 1982
AZZURA   Loris Azzaro 1999
BAMBOU   Weil 1984/91
BAYWATCH WOMAN   Baywatch 1996
BE BOP   Kesling 1991
BEAUTIFUL   Estée Lauder 1985
BIRMANE   Van Cleef & Arpels 1999
BLUE DREAM   Loreste 1997
BOLERO   Gabriela Sabatini 1997
BYBLOS   Byblos 1990
C'EST MAGIQUE   Kesling 1997
CELEBRATE   Coty 1996
CERRUTI 1881 POUR FEMME   Cerruti 1995
CHARLIE RED   Revlon 1993
CHELSEA DREAMS   Old England 1999
CHERRY MUSK   Un Monde Nouveau 1993/98
CLARTÉ   L.T.Piver 1998
CLEAR DAY   Etienne Aigner 1997
COURRÈGES 2020   Courrèges 1997
CRÉATURE D'ANGES   Gilles Cantuel 1997
DALISSIME   Salvador Dali 1994
DAZZLING GOLD   Estée Lauder 1998
DE BERCHELAI   Edgar de Berchelai 1997
DUÉ 2 NIGHT   Lomani 1999
DV8 FOR WOMEN   Davinci 1997
EAU D'INFINITIF   Infinitif 1996
EAU DE MOOVING   Gilles Cantuel 1996
EAU LES COEURS   Molinard 1995
FANTASIA   Fendi 1996
FASCINATION   Holzman & Stephanie 1990
FIORILU EN FLEURS   Pupa 1996
FIORUCCI   Fiorucci 1999
FLEUR D'AMOUR   Victoria Chalon 1994
FOLIE DOUCE   Grès 1997
FOU D'ELLE   Ted Lapidus 1997
GATTINONI A PORTER   Gattinoni 1999
GENNY   Genny 1987/98
GIORGIO HOLIDAY   Ⓛ   Giorgio Beverly Hills 1998
I EX'CLA.MA'TION   Coty 1998
JAÏPUR   Boucheron 1994
KENZO   Kenzo 1988
KITON DONNA   Palladio 1997
KOOKAÏ OUI-NON   Kookaï 1993
L de LOEWE   Loewe 1972/88
L'EAU DE SUCCÈS   Succès de Paris 1997
L'INSAISISSABLE   Stéphanie de Monaco 1991
LE BAISER   Lalique 1999
LAIT SUCRÉ   Comptoir Sud Pacifique 1999
LASTING   Revlon 1995
LAUREN   Ralph Lauren 1978
LIGHT HER   Trussardi 1997
MADLY   Ultima II 1996
MCM   MCM 1999
MCM BLUE PARADISE*   MCM 1989
MILLENNIUM HOPE WOMAN   Jivago 1999
MISS BALAHÉ   Léonard 1996
MON PARFUM   Bourjois 1925/95
MONTAIGNE   Caron 1986
MYSTIC   Marilyn Miglin 1998
ON AIR FEMME   Morabito 1998
PATOU FOR EVER   Jean Patou 1998

Classical / Classique

Bouquet

273 FOR WOMEN   Fred Hayman 1989
BARYSHNIKOV POUR FEMME   Mikhail Baryshnikov 1995
BELLE DE RAUCH   Madeleine de Rauch 1998
BEST LADY   Succès de Paris 1995
BULGARI POUR FEMME   Bulgari 1994
CANDIE'S   Liz Claiborne 1999
CAPRICCI   Nina Ricci 1961
CHANEL N° 22   Chanel 1922
CROWN STEPHANOTIS   Crown 1921
FLEURS DE ROCAILLE   Caron 1933
GIANFRANCO FERRÉ 20   Gianfranco Ferré 1998
JASMIN IMPÉRATRICE EUGÉNIE   Creed 1870/1989
JOY   Jean Patou 1930
L'AIR DU TEMPS   Nina Ricci 1948
LE DE   Givenchy 1957
N'AIMEZ QUE MOI   Caron 1916
OMAR SHARIF   Omar Sharif 1989
ORCHID*   Yardley 1995
ORVAL   Molinard 1900/93
QUELQUES FLEURS   Houbigant / Claire 1912/87
ROMANCE   Ralph Lauren 1998
ROSE VANILLE   Comptoir Sud Pacifique 1989
SISSI   Marc de la Morandière 1991
SORENZA   Fragonard 1996
WHITE SHOULDERS   Evyan 1945
WIND SONG   Prince Matchabelli 1953
ZEN   Shiseido 1964

Rich / Profond

Bouquet

1000   Jean Patou 1972
AMOUR AMOUR   Jean Patou 1925
ASPHALT FLOWER   MAC 1999
AZZARO 9   Loris Azzaro 1984
BILL BLASS   Bill Blass 1978
BLACK JEANS FEMME   Roccobarocco 1998
BLUE GRASS   Elizabeth Arden 1934/89
CAESARS WOMAN   Caesars World 1988
COURRÈGES IN BLUE   Courrèges 1983
CRUISER FOR WOMEN   Lomani 1998
DILYS   Laura Ashley 1991
ÉCOUTE-MOI   Molinard 1997
ESP STAFAST   Yardley 1982/88
ESTÉE   Estée Lauder 1968
EXPERIENCES   Priscilla Presley 1993
FABERGÉ IMPERIAL   Fabergé 1996
FANTASIA DE FLEURS   Creed 1862/1983
FOLIE DE CRÉATURE   Gilles Cantuel 1992
FREEZIA D'OR   Maître Parfumeur et Gantier 1988
GIÒ   Giorgio Armani 1992
IVANA   Ivana Trump 1995
JARDINS DE BAGATELLE   Guerlain 1983
JESS   Jessica McClintock 1995
JIVAGO 24k WOMEN   Jivago 1994
L'EAU DE MONTEIL   Monteil 1995
LA PRAIRIE   La Prairie 1993
MADAME CARVEN*   Carven 1979
MISS BE BOP   Kesling 1993
MISS WORTH   Worth 1977
MOMENT SUPRÊME   Jean Patou 1929
MOONDROPS   Revlon 1970
OMBRE BLEUE*   Jean-Charles Brosseau 1987
PARAH   Parah 1996
RED DOOR   Elizabeth Arden 1989
ROMANCE   Royal Secret 1990
SAND & SABLE   Coty 1983
SENSES   Les Floralies 1994
TATIANA   Diana von Furstenberg 1975
TIFFANY   Tiffany 1987
TWEED   Lenthéric / FFC 1924/92
VICKY TIEL ORIGINALÉ   Vicky Tiel 1990
VICTORIAN POSY   Penhaligon's 1979
VIVID   Liz Claiborne 1993
WINGS   Giorgio Beverly Hills 1992

Fresh / Frais

Bouquet Citrus Fruity / Hespéridé Fruité

ROSE MUSKISSIME   Maître Parfumeur et Gantier 1988
SHAHI AQUA   Chypron 1998
SILVER JEANS FEMME   Roccobarocco 1995
SO DE LA RENTA   Oscar de la Renta 1997
SO…? INSPIRED   Yardley / Bond Street 1997
SPRING FLOWER   Creed 1996
S.T.DUPONT FEMME   S.T.Dupont 1998
SUNSHINE   Chiara Boni 1998
TALISMAN EAU TRANSPARENTE   Balenciaga 1996
U   Natio 1999
UNE TOUCHE DE NAF NAF   Naf Naf 1991
UNZIPPED SPORT   Perfumer's Workshop 1999
V/S   Versace 1998
WHITE CHANTILLY   Dana 1995
YELLOW JEANS   Versace 1996

Bouquet Green / Vert

5th AVENUE   Elizabeth Arden 1996
ADIDAS WOMAN   Adidas 1988/97
ANOUCK   Puig 1989
APRIL FIELDS   Coty 1999
AROMANTIC   Decléor 1999
ASPEN SENSATION   Coty 1998
BLUEBELL   Penhaligon's 1978
BOBBI   Bobbi Brown 1998
CASCAYA SUMMER   Gabriela Sabatini 1998
CASSISSIER   L'Occitane 1999
CATALYST   Halston 1993
CHAUMET   Chaumet 1999
EAU DE CAMILLE   Annick Goutal 1983
ÉTHÉRÉ   Vicky Tiel 1999
EXTRAVAGANCE D'AMARIGE   Givenchy 1998
FACE À FACE FEMME   Façonnable 1996
FEELING FREE   Escada 1996
FIDJI   Guy Laroche 1966
FLEUR   Floris 2000
FLORE AUBUSSON   Aubusson 1998
FREE WORLD WOMAN   Mäurer & Wirtz 1999
I AM PASSION   Danica Aromatics 1999
LE MONDE EST BEAU   Kenzo 1997
LE TEMPS D'UNE FÊTE   Patricia de Nicolaï 1989
LACOSTE FOR WOMEN   Lacoste 1999
LIZSPORT   Liz Claiborne 1997
LONG AGO / WISTFUL   Amway 1997
LOVING BOUQUET Ⓛ   Escada 1999
MORGANE LE FAY   Morgane Le Fay 1997
MV   Madeleine Vionnet 1998
OFRÉSIA   Diptyque 1999
PARFUM D'ÉTÉ   Kenzo 1993
PEOPLE DONNA   Luciano Soprani 1999
PIAZZA DI SPAGNA   Roccobarocco 1997
PLEASURES   Estée Lauder 1995
RELAXING FRAGRANCE   Shiseido 1997
ROOTS FOR HER   Coty 1998

Crisp / Pétillant

Bouquet Citrus Fruity / Hespéridé Fruité

PERSUASION   J Fragrances 1997
PRIVATE NUMBER FOR WOMEN*   Etienne Aigner 1991
REALITIES*   Liz Claiborne 1990
RED JEANS   Versace 1994
RÉMY FOR WOMAN   Rémy Marquis 1999
ROCCOBAROCCO TRE   Roccobarocco 1994
ROMEO   Romeo Gigli 1989
SALVATORE FERRAGAMO   Salvatore Ferragamo 1998
SAMBA   Perfumer's Workshop 1987
SCAASI   Scaasi 1989
SCARF TAORMINA   Marbert 1996
SCHÖN   Mila Schön 1997
SENSO   Ungaro 1987/92
SHADES BY NAVY   Dana 1998
SHE*   Revlon 1997
SPRING FEVER   Origins 1995
SUGGESTION EAU D'OR   Montana 1994
SUN SPIRIT*   Marbert 1995
TOCADILLY   Rochas 1997
TRÈS JOURDAN*   Charles Jourdan 1992
TRIANGLE*   Myrurgia 1996
TRIBÙ   Benetton 1993
U de V POUR ELLE   Ulric de Varens 1999
VALENTINO   Valentino 1977/86
VICE VERSA Ⓛ   Yves Saint Laurent 1999
WHITE LAVENDER   Yardley 1995
YIN   Jacques Fath 1999
ZOA   Régine's 1992

Bouquet Green / Vert

CABOTINE DE GRÈS   Grès 1990
CHARLIE   Revlon 1973
CHRISTIAN LACROIX   Christian Lacroix 1999
CROWN BOUQUET   Crown 1936
DIVINA   Diana de Silva 1996
EAU DU CIEL   Annick Goutal 1985
FASHION FAIR N° 1   Fashion Fair 1977
FLEUR DE ROCAILLE   Caron 1993
FLIRT   Prescriptives 1998
GEOFFREY BEENE   Geoffrey Beene 1998
GFF DONNA   Gianfranco Ferré 1997
L'EFFLEUR   Coty 1990
L'OMBRE DANS L'EAU   Diptyque 1983
LANCETTI EAU DE JOIE   Lancetti 1997
MARJOLAINE   Jean Couturier 1997
MOLINARD DE MOLINARD   Molinard 1979
MONSOON   Monsoon 1994
MOODS   Krizia 1989
NORELL   Norell 1968
POPY MORENI DE FÊTE   Popy Moreni 1998
ROYAL PAVILLON   Etro 1989
SARCANTHUS   Crown 1931
SAVANNA   Robert Isabell 1996
SI FLEURI   Rémy Latour 1994
SOLEIL   Fragonard 1995
TENDRE POISON   Christian Dior 1994
TOUCH FOR WOMEN   Fred Hayman 1993
VALERIA   Valeria Mazza 1998

 **Classical / Classique**

 **Rich / Profond**

Fresh / Frais

Bouquet Green / Vert

ROSE D'ÉTÉ   Rosine 1997
SERINGA   Floris 1993
SPRING RAIN   Crabtree & Evelyn 1979
SUNWATER   Lancaster 1997
THE SPIRIT OF SWITZERLAND   Michel Jordi 1999
TOMMY GIRL   Tommy Hilfiger 1996
TRISH McEVOY 2   Trish McEvoy 1997
UN AMOUR DE PATOU   Jean Patou 1998

Bouquet Water / Marine

ACQUA DI FIORI   De Ruy 1999
ACQUA DI GIÒ   Giorgio Armani 1995
BETTY BARCLAY WOMAN   Mäurer & Wirtz 1998
CHIEMSEE   Chiemsee 1999
CONSENT WOMAN   Consent 2000
"DELICIOUS" FEELINGS   Gale Hayman 1996
DIAMONDS & SAPPHIRES*   Elizabeth Taylor 1993
DREAMS BY TABU   Dana 1996
EAU D'EDEN   Cacharel 1996
EAU DE RÉVILLON   Révillon 1998
EAU DE VERINO   Roberto Verino 1995
EAU MARINE   Les Copains 1999
ESENCIA DE DUENDE   J. del Pozo 1995
FEMINA   Alberta Ferretti 1993
FETISH   Dana 1997
FLEUR D'EAU   Rochas 1996
FLEUR D'INTERDIT   Givenchy 1994
FLEUR DE DIVA   Ungaro 1997
FOREVER   Alfred Sung 1995
GALA DE DIA   Loewe 1996
ICEBERG TWICE   Iceberg 1994
INDIVIDUELLE   Charles Jourdan 1996
L'EAU PAR KENZO   Kenzo 1996
LAURA   Laura Biagiotti 1994
MISS MORABITO   Morabito 1996
OCEAN DREAM   Giorgio Beverly Hills 1996
SONG DE CHINE   Crabtree & Evelyn 1997
THAÏS   Puig 1996
TRIBÙ ACQUA FRESCA   Benetton 1995
TRISH McEVOY 3   Trish McEvoy 1998
WATT   Cofinluxe 1993

Bouquet White Flowers / Fleurs Blanches

ACACIOSA   Caron 1924
ANAÏS ANAÏS   Cacharel 1978
ARROGANCE ME   Arrogance 1997
CASUAL   Paul Sebastian 1995
CHLOÉ INNOCENCE*   Chloé 1996
DESTINY   Marilyn Miglin 1990
EAU DE GUCCI*   Gucci 1982/93
EDWARDIAN BOUQUET   Floris 1901/84
EMOZIONI FOR WOMAN   Fila 1997
ENVY   Gucci 1997
ETERNITY   Calvin Klein 1988
EX'CLA.MA'TION DARE   Coty 1996
FLEUR   Morabito 1998
FLEURISSIMO   Creed 1972
FLEURS D'ORLANE   Orlane 1983
FLEURS DE CHIARA BONI   Chiara Boni 1999
FREEDOM FOR HER   Tommy Hilfiger 1999
J'ADORE   Christian Dior 1999
GIANFRANCO FERRÉ   Gianfranco Ferré 1984
INDRA   Jacques Saint Près 1983
JACINTHE ROSE (ROMANTICA)   E.Coudray 1983
JONTUE MOONLIGHT*   Revlon 1996
KISS & TELL   Fragrance International 1999

Crisp / Pétillant

Bouquet Water / Marine

AV   Adrienne Vittadini 1994
COOL WATER WOMAN   Davidoff 1996
EXTASE EXOTIC NATURE   Muelhens 1997
FERRARI DONNA   Ferrari 1995
HALLOWEEN   J. del Pozo 1997
HAVANA POUR ELLE   Aramis 1995
HUGO WOMAN   Hugo Boss 1997
MISS JAGUAR   Jaguar 1993
SUGGESTION EAU D'ARGENT   Montana 1994
WEEKEND FOR WOMEN   Burberry 1997

Bouquet White Flowers / Fleurs Blanches

24, FAUBOURG   Hermès 1995
BLU BLUMARINE   Blumarine 1995
DÉCADENCE*   Parlux 1985
DIAMONDS & EMERALDS*   Elizabeth Taylor 1993
ÉLÀ NONCHALANCE   Mäurer & Wirtz 1999
GIORGIO   Giorgio Beverly Hills 1981
HONEYSUCKLE & JASMINE   Jo Malone 1996
INDIANA   Creed 1980
JARDIN BLANC   Maître Parfumeur et Gantier 1988
LA CHASSE AUX PAPILLONS   L'Artisan Parfumeur 1999
MEA CULPA   Rosine 1994
MON CLASSIQUE   Morabito 1987
NO REGRETS   Alexandra de Markoff 1994
NUMBER ONE   Patricia de Nicolaï 1989
OLÈNE   Diptyque 1988
PASSION   Annick Goutal 1983
SHANGRI-LA   Imperiale 1989
SPIRIT OF ZEN   Shiseido 1986

Classical / Classique

Rich / Profond

Florale

Fresh / Frais

Crisp / Pétillant

Bouquet White Flowers / Fleurs Blanches

LE JARDIN   Max Factor / H&BF 1983
LAILA   Geir Ness 1995
LILLIE RUBIN   Lillie Rubin 1992
LUCKY BRAND WOMEN'S   Lucky Brand 1997
LUMIÈRE   Rochas 1984
NAUTICA WOMAN   Nautica 1997
NICOLE   Nicole Miller 1998
ODALISQUE   Patricia de Nicolaï 1989
POUR UNE FEMME   Roger & Gallet 1993
SHEER TIFFANY   Tiffany 1999
SPLENDOR   Elizabeth Arden 1998
SUMMER HILL   Crabtree & Evelyn 1988
SUNG   Alfred Sung 1986
WHITE CAMELLIA   St John 1998
WHITE SPELL   Un Monde Nouveau 1993/98
XS POUR ELLE   Paco Rabanne 1994
ZINNIA   Floris 1990

TILLEUL   d'Orsay 1955/95 ♂

INSENSÉ   Givenchy 1993
JARDIN DU NIL   Maître Parfumeur et Gantier 1988

Classical / Classique

Rich / Profond

AGUA LAVANDA   Puig 1940 ♂
ARÔME 3   d'Orsay 1943/95 ♂
EAU DE LAVANDE   Annick Goutal 1981 ♂
EAU DE LAVANDE   Mont St Michel 1920 ♂
EAU DE PROVENCE   Patricia de Nicolaï 1992 ♂
ENGLISH LAVENDER   Atkinson 1910 ♂
LAVANDA   Myrurgia 1916 ♂
LAVANDE VELOURS   Guerlain 1999 ♂
LAVENDER   Crabtree & Evelyn 1970 ♂
LAVENDER   Floris 1828 ♂
ROYAL SCOTTISH LAVENDER   Creed 1856

ARÔME 3 TRADITION   d'Orsay 1998 ♂
LAVANDE   Molinard 1925/96 ♂
LAVANDE DES PRINCES   L.T.Piver 1991
POUR UN HOMME   Caron 1934
TÉNÉRÉ   Paco Rabanne 1988

Soft Floral

The marriage of sparkling aldehydes and delicate flowers creates a family of soft, often powdery, abstract florals. Aldehydes are found naturally in rose and citrus oils, but in such minute amounts that they have to be re-created in the laboratory. Their natural scent is not pleasant: some have a sharp, metallic fragrance, others the burnt, waxy aroma of a just-snuffed candle. Add them to flowers, however, and their subtle magic makes the blossoms sing. Their soprano notes are muted by the powdery accents of iris and vanilla to create a fragrance that is both soft and flowery.

Le mariage des aldéhydes pétillants avec des fleurs délicates crée une famille de parfums floraux tendres et souvent poudrés et abstraits. Les aldéhydes se trouvent naturellement dans les extraits de rose et d'agrumes, mais en quantité infime et il faut donc en faire la synthèse en laboratoire. Leur senteur naturelle n'est pas agréable: parfois tranchante et métallique, parfois à l'odeur de brûlé et de cire de chandelle que l'on vient de souffler. Cependant, ajoutez-les aux fleurs, et leur magie subtile fera chanter un parfum épanoui. Leur registre de soprano est modéré par des tons poudrés d'iris et de vanille pour créer un parfum à la fois tendre et fleuri.

Fresh / Frais

Citrus Fruity / Hespéridé Fruité

212   Carolina Herrera 1997
CAMÉLIA IRIS (BLEU)   E.Coudray 1946
COLORS   Alexander Julian 1993
DESIGN   Paul Sebastian 1985
DKNY WOMEN   Donna Karan 1999
G   Giorgio Beverly Hills 1999
G GIGLI*   Romeo Gigli 1994
GIORGIO AIRE*   Giorgio Beverly Hills 1996
HANAE MORI HAUTE COUTURE   Hanae Mori 1998
IMPLICITE   Sea World 1998
JOOP! BERLIN   Joop! 1991
LAURA ASHLEY N° 1   Laura Ashley 1989
OMBRE D'OR*   Jean-Charles Brosseau 1994
PARESSE DE RODIER   Rodier 1999
TRUESTE   Tiffany 1995
VENEZIA PASTELLO*   Laura Biagiotti 1995
WHITE LINEN BREEZE   Estée Lauder 1996

Green / Vert

ALABASTER   Mary McFadden 1996
CHANEL N° 19   Chanel 1971
CIALENGA   Balenciaga 1973
EXCITING ARROGANCE   Arrogance 1999
HEURE EXQUISE   Annick Goutal 1984
IVOIRE   Pierre Balmain 1980
JIL SANDER WOMAN PURE*   Jil Sander 1980
JOSEPH DE JOUR   Joseph 1997
LÉONARD DE LÉONARD*   Léonard 1989
MURASAKI   Shiseido 1980
NUDE   Bill Blass 1990
SAFARI   Ralph Lauren 1990
SI TENDRE   Rémy Latour 1989
SO PRETTY   Cartier 1995

Water / Marine

CHARLIE WHITE MUSK   Revlon 1997
LE CIRQUE DE POPY MORENI   Popy Moreni 1999
OH! DE MOSCHINO   Moschino 1996

White Flowers / Fleurs Blanches

ANNE KLEIN*   Parlux 1984
FLEUR DE FLEURS   Nina Ricci 1980/82
FLEURS DE PÊCHER   Comptoir Sud Pacifique 1976
GUIRLANDES*   Carven 1982
MÉTAL   Paco Rabanne 1979
TILLEUL CHÈVREFEUILLE   L'Occitane 1999
TRUE LOVE   Elizabeth Arden 1994

Crisp / Pétillant

Citrus Fruity / Hespéridé Fruité

ANNA SUI   Anna Sui 1999
BLUMARINE   Blumarine 1988
CAFÉ-CAFÉ   Cofinluxe 1996
CHIARA BONI LIGHT   Chiara Boni 1997
COUNTRY ROAD WOMAN   Country Road 1999
FIRENZE   Enrico Coveri 1993
FLEUR DE DÉSIRADE   Aubusson 1995
FOLAVRIL   Annick Goutal 1981
K de KRIZIA   Krizia 1981
LE CHIC*   Molyneux 1932/95
MARIELLA BURANI   Mariella Burani 1992
NINA   Nina Ricci 1987
PALACE   Régine's 1995
ROUGE FORMIDABLE   Kesling 1998
ROYALISSIME   Henri d'Orléans 1997
SAMBA RED WOMAN   Perfumer's Workshop 1999
SOCIETY*   Burberry 1991
SWEET COURRÈGES   Courrèges 1993
WOMENSWEAR   Alexander Julian 1992

Green / Vert

CALANDRE   Paco Rabanne 1969
CÂLINE   Jean Patou 1964
DAZZLING SILVER   Estée Lauder 1998
DRÔLE DE ROSE   L'Artisan Parfumeur 1996
ENERGIZING FRAGRANCE   Shiseido 1999
FAROUCHE   Nina Ricci 1974
FLEURAGE   Visari 1999
FLORISSA   Floris 1978
GUCCI N° 1*   Gucci 1975
PANACHE   Lenthéric / FFC 1979
RIVE GAUCHE   Yves Saint Laurent 1971
ROSEBERRY   Rosine 1997
TAMANGO   Léonard 1977
VIVRE   Molyneux 1971

Water / Marine

ACTE 2   Escada 1995
EAU DE BIARRITZ   Comptoir Sud Pacifique 1995
V   Gloria Vanderbilt 1994

White Flowers / Fleurs Blanches

AMAZING   Bill Blass 1999
CAMP BEVERLY HILLS*   CBH 1986
DAMASK ROSE   Crabtree & Evelyn 1976/91
DEAUVILLE   Michel Germain 1999
INTRIGUE*   Carven 1986
LA PARISIENNE   Holzman & Stephanie 1989
PERRY ELLIS FOR WOMEN   Perry Ellis 1985/96
REALLY PARAH   Parah 1998
ROSE*   Yardley 1970/94
WHITE DIAMONDS   Elizabeth Taylor 1991
WHITE LINEN   Estée Lauder 1978
WHITE SATIN   Yardley / FFC 1985

TABAC ORIGINAL (EdC)   Mäurer & Wirtz 1959

Classical / Classique

CHANEL N° 5   Chanel 1921
COEUR JOIE   Nina Ricci 1946
ÉCUSSON   Jean d'Albret 1947
EMBRACE*   Mark Cross 1997
FERRÉ BY FERRÉ   Gianfranco Ferré 1991
FLEUR D'IRIS   Maître Parfumeur et Gantier 1988
FORGET ME NOT   Woods of Windsor 1982
GALANOS   Galanos 1979/96
JASMIN MANDARINE   L'Occitane 1999
JOVAN EVENING MUSK*   Jovan 1985
L'AIMANT   Coty 1927
L'INTERDIT   Givenchy 1957
LANCETTI   Lancetti 1998
LIÙ   Guerlain 1929
LOVE'S BABY SOFT   Mem / Dana 1974
MUSK   Bettina Barty 1990
NONCHALANCE   Mäurer & Wirtz 1960
OPHÉLIE   Pierre Cardin 1995
PARCE QUE!*   Roberto Capucci 1963
TURQUOISE   Comptoir Sud Pacifique 1991

Rich / Profond

AIMEZ-MOI   Caron 1996
ALYSSA ASHLEY MUSK   Alyssa Ashley 1992
AMOUAGE   Amouage 1983
ARPÈGE   Lanvin 1927/93
BABYLON   Gilles Cantuel 1999
BLASÉ   Max Factor / H&BF 1975
CALIFORNIA   Jaclyn Smith 1989
CLIMAT   Lancôme 1967
D&G FEMININE   Dolce & Gabbana 1999
"DELICIOUS"   Gale Hayman 1993
DEMI-JOUR*   Houbigant 1988
DETCHÉMA   Révillon 1953/94
DI ROMEO GIGLI   Romeo Gigli 1999
DNA   Bijan 1993
DOLCE & GABBANA   Dolce & Gabbana 1992
EAU DE COUTURE   Philippe Venet 1998
FIRST   Van Cleef & Arpels 1976
GRAND AMOUR   Annick Goutal 1996
HOPE   Frances Denney 1952
INFINI   Caron 1912/70
JE REVIENS   Worth 1932
JOVAN MUSK   Jovan 1972
JUSTINE   Louis Frères 1966
LA ROSE DE ROSINE   Rosine 1991
LE DIX   Balenciaga 1947
LADY STETSON   Coty 1986
MADAME ROCHAS   Rochas 1960/89
NOA   Cacharel 1998
NOCTURNES   Caron 1981
NUAGE D'OR   Marc de la Morandière 1994
RÊVE D'OR   L.T.Piver 1889/1926
SOIR DE PARIS ORIGINAL   Bourjois 1928
SOLILOQUY   Amway 1997
SORTILÈGE*   Le Galion 1937
TOSCA   Muelhens 1921
TOVA   Tova Borgnine 1989
YENDI*   Roberto Capucci 1974

AMOUAGE HOMME   Amouage 1983
JOVAN MUSK FOR MEN   Jovan 1973

Floral Oriental

Soft, spicy orange flower notes meld with piquant aldehydes and sweet spices to create the heart of a Floral Oriental fragrance. Born in the 1900s, Floral Orientals came back to life again in the 1970s. In the past decade, lively, fruity interpretations dominated the Floral Oriental category, but recent fragrances have developed a more subtle, muted personality.

Les notes tendres et corsées de fleur d'oranger se fondent bien avec les aldéhydes piquants et les épices douces pour créer le cœur d'un parfum Fleuri oriental. Découvert à la Belle Époque, le Fleuri oriental est réapparu dans les années 70. Durant la dernière décade, les interprétations vives et fruitées dominaient, mais récemment, une personnalité plus subtile, plus retenue, a été développée pour ces parfums.

Fresh / Frais

Citrus Fruity / Hespéridé Fruité

ALLURE   Chanel 1996
ALVIERO MARTINI DONNA   Atkinson 1997
ANTHRACITE   Jacomo 1991
AURA LOEWE   Loewe 1994
BELLA FIRENZE   Tosca-Muelhens 1998
BERNINI WOMEN   Bernini 1996
BLACK PEARLS*   Elizabeth Taylor 1996
BURBERRY FOR WOMEN   Burberry 1995
CHARLIE GOLD   Revlon 1995
CHIPIE   Coty 1995
COLORS OF BENETTON   Benetton 1987/93
CONTRADICTION   Calvin Klein 1997
CONVICTION   Omar Sharif 1998
ELYSEOS FEMME   Elysios 1997
GAI MATTIOLO   Gai Mattiolo-ICR 1997
GOLDEN MOMENT   Priscilla Presley 1999
GOODLIFE WOMAN   Davidoff 1999
HOT   Benetton 1997
INDIAN SUMMER   Priscilla Presley 1996
INSPIRATION   Charles Jourdan 1998
JIL SANDER N° 4   Jil Sander 1990
JUNGLE: LE TIGRE   Kenzo 1997
KASHÂYA   Kenzo 1994
L'ÉTÉ DE VENTILO   Ventilo 1998
LES COPAINS   Les Copains 1988/97
LAGUNA   Salvador Dali 1991
LONGING   Coty 1994
MAGNETIC   Gabriela Sabatini 1992
ORGUEIL DE RODIER   Rodier 1999
PATTI LaBELLE   Flori Roberts 1996
PERHAPS   Bob Mackie 1997
POLEMIC!   Succès de Paris 1999
RED 2*   Giorgio Beverly Hills 1996
RUBIS D'OR   Kristal Saint Martin 1996
SÉXUAL   Michel Germain 1994
SINAÏ   Kesling 1997
SUMATRA RAIN WOMAN   Muelhens 1999
SUN MOON STARS   Lagerfeld 1994
ULTRAVIOLET   Paco Rabanne 1999
UNZIPPED UNIVERSE   Perfumer's Workshop 1999
VERANDA   Crabtree & Evelyn 1990
VOCALISE   Shiseido 1997
ZAHAROFF   Zaharoff 1997
ZOE   Les Floralies 1995

Green / Vert

C'EST LA VIE*   Christian Lacroix 1990
LP N° 9   Penhaligon's 1998
MAXIM'S DE PARIS   Maxim's 1984
STYLE   Gale Hayman 1999

Crisp / Pétillant

Citrus Fruity / Hespéridé Fruité

ALCHIMIE   Rochas 1998
AMARIGE   Givenchy 1991
ANIMALE ANIMALE   Parlux 1993
ARSENAL FOR WOMAN   Gilles Cantuel 1998
ATREVIDA   De Ruy 1998
BAROQUE   Yardley 1996
BONJOUR   Bonjour 1994
CASCAYA   Gabriela Sabatini 1994
CHLOÉ NARCISSE   Chloé 1992
CIARA FEMME FATALE*   Revlon 1995
DALIMANIA   Salvador Dali 1999
DÉSIRADE   Aubusson 1990
DIAMANT D'OR   Kristel Saint Martin 1996
DONNA BORSALINO   Borsalino 1995
DOULTON   Royal Doulton 1998
DREAMING PRINCESS   Succès de Paris 1994
ENFANTS DU SOLEIL   Comptoir Sud Pacifique 1999
ERUPTION WOMAN   Mäurer & Wirtz 1997
ESSENTIALLY JAGUAR   Jaguar 1998
EX'CLA.MA'TION   Coty 1988
FANTASME   Ted Lapidus 1992
FASHION   Léonard 1970/93
GALICE   Paris Bleu 1995
GENNY SHINE*   Genny 1993
ICI   Coty 1995
INCOGNITO   Cover Girl / Dana 1992
JEAN PAUL GAULTIER   Jean Paul Gaultier 1993
JIN ABE   Jin Abe 1998
JIVAGO 7 NOTES   Jivago 1998
L'ELUE   Rémy Latour 1998
LA COUPE D'OR   Rosine 1993
LALIQUE   Lalique 1992
LORESTE FEMME   Loreste 1993
MACKIE   Bob Mackie 1985/91
NICOLE MILLER   Nicole Miller 1993
NOA NOA*   Otto Kern 1990
NOKOMIS   Coty 1997
PANTHÈRE   Cartier 1987
RED PEARL   Red Pearl 1999
REVOLUTION À VERSAILLES*   Jean Desprez 1989
SHIMÓ   Monsoon 1996
SIRÈNE   Vicky Tiel 1994
SOLYTIS   Lomani 1996
STARDUST   Llewelyn 1998
TRÉSOR   Lancôme 1990
URVASHI   Gandh Sugandh 1999
VAN CLEEF   Van Cleef & Arpels 1993
VENTILO   Ventilo 1997
VERSUS DONNA   Versace 1991
VOLUPTÉ   Oscar de la Renta 1992
ZAHRA   Fashion Fair 1993

Green / Vert

CHAMADE   Guerlain 1969
GALA LOEWE   Loewe 1991
GMV DONNA   Gian Marco Venturi 1999
NANTUCKET BRIAR   Crabtree & Evelyn 1985
VERINO   Roberto Verino 1992
XI'A XI'ANG*   Revlon 1987

Classical / Classique

BAL À VERSAILLES   Jean Desprez 1962/95
BALAHÉ   Léonard 1983
BOUCHERON   Boucheron 1988
BOUDOIR   Vivienne Westwood 1998
BOUVARDIA*   Floris 1996
CHALDÉE   Jean Patou 1927
CORNUBIA   Penhaligon's 1991
DANIEL DE FASSON   Daniel de Fasson 1990
DÉLICE D'ÉPICES   Nina Ricci 1999
DIVINE FOLIE   Jean Patou 1933
EMOTIONS   Victoria Chalon 1993
EMPORIO ARMANI SHE / ELLE   Giorgio Armani 1998
ESCADA   Escada-Margaretha Ley 1990
FABULOUS   Jan Moran 1996
FERENTINA   Caesars World 1994
FÉTICHE   E.Coudray 1998
FOREVER KRYSTLE   Revlon-Carrington 1984
FORMIDABLE   Kesling 1994
GALORÉ   Monteil / Royal Secret 1964
GLAMOUR   Gale Hayman 1999
HELIOTROPE   Etro 1989
HERVÉ LÉGER   Hervé Léger 1999
ICEBERG UNIVERSE FEMME   Iceberg 1997
INITIATION*   Molyneux 1990
JE T'AIME   Holzman & Stephanie 1987
JIL SANDER SUN   Jil Sander 1989
L'HEURE BLEUE   Guerlain 1912
L'ORIGAN*   Coty 1905
MADELEINE VIONNET   Madeleine Vionnet 1925/96
MAROUSSIA   Slava Zaïtsev 1992
MCM 1900*   MCM 1991
OR ET NOIR   Caron 1949
OSCAR DE LA RENTA   Oscar de la Renta 1977
PARFUM SACRÉ   Caron 1990
POÊME   Lancôme 1995
RAFFINÉE   Houbigant / Dana 1982
RAVELLO   Ravello 1997
RÊVERIE   Gloria Vanderbilt 1999
SACREBLEU!   Patricia de Nicolaï 1993
SHAHI GOLDEN SUN   Chypron 1997
SPAZIO KRIZIA DONNA   Krizia 1998
SPELLBOUND   Estée Lauder 1991
SUGGESTION EAU CUIVRÉE   Montana 1994
TANGLEWOOD BOUQUET   Crown 1932
THIARA   Marc de la Morandière 1994
TIGRESS*   Fabergé 1938
TOCADE   Rochas 1994
TRULY LACE   Coty 1992
VALLÉE DES ROIS   Mira Takla 1990
VANDERBILT   Gloria Vanderbilt 1982
VENET   Philippe Venet 1965/96
VÉNUS DE L'AMOUR   Vicky Tiel 1997
VIVA DI TOSCA   Muelhens 1997
VOICE BY BETTY BARCLAY   Mäurer & Wirtz 1995

Rich / Profond

CHINA ROSE   Floris 2000
DARK VANILLA   Coty 1998
EN AVION   Caron 1930
JOOP! LE BAIN   Joop! 1988
LE JARDIN D'AMOUR   Max Factor / HB&F 1987
LOVE STORY   Louis Féraud 1997
LUTÈCE   Parquet / Dana 1984
NAHÉMA   Guerlain 1979
NAVY   Cover Girl / Dana 1990
OMBRE ROSE   Jean-Charles Brosseau 1981
ONLY CRAZY   Julio Iglesias 1994
POISON   Christian Dior 1985
ST JOHN   St John 1994
UNINHIBITED*   Cher 1989
UNRULY   Prince Matchabelli 1997

Fresh / Frais

Crisp / Pétillant

Water / Marine

AUTHENTIC MAROUSSIA   Slava Zaïtsev 1996
DIESEL PLUS PLUS FEMININE   Diesel 1997
EDEN   Cacharel 1994
NILANG   Lalique 1995
PARADOX   Jacomo 1998
SCULPTURE   Nikos 1994
SHEER HALSTON   Halston 1998
VICOLO FIORI   Etro 1996

White Flowers / Fleurs Blanches

ACCENTI   Gucci 1995
APRÈS L'ONDÉE   Guerlain 1906
BETTY BARCLAY WOMAN N° 2   Mäurer & Wirtz 1999
BYZANTINE   Rochas 1995
FRIDAY!   Bonne Bell 1989
VANILLA   Crabtree & Evelyn 1994

White Flowers / Fleurs Blanches

ANTICIPATE / SULTRY   Amway 1998
BETTY BARCLAY*   Mäurer & Wirtz 1992
BYZANCE   Rochas 1987
FOREVER*   Yardley 1991
FRENCH CANCAN   Caron 1936
GABRIELA SABATINI   Gabriela Sabatini 1989
LOULOU BLUE*   Cacharel 1995
MATSUKITA   Crown 1929
PHANTOM OF THE OPERA*   Parlux 1988
SCHERRER 2   Jean-Louis Scherrer 1986
SUNSET BOULEVARD   Gale Hayman 1998

Classical / Classique

Rich / Profond

Oriental Doux

Soft Oriental

Incense adds sensual overtones to fragrant flowers, spices and amber to create a softer style of Oriental. The base notes of a modern Soft Oriental are not as sweet or as heavy as a true Oriental and the result - a mélange of flowers and spices - is distinctly softer.

L'encens libère des accents sensuels dans les fleurs parfumées, les épices et l'ambre pour créer un style Oriental fait de douceur. Les notes fondamentales d'un Oriental doux, aujourd'hui, ne sont ni aussi suaves ni aussi fortes que le vrai Oriental. Le résultat est un mélange de fleurs et d'épices, nettement plus tendre.

Fresh / Frais

Citrus Fruity / Hespéridé Fruité

KL Lagerfeld 1982
ROYAL BAIN DE CHAMPAGNE Caron 1941 ♂

Green / Vert

REALM WOMEN Erox / HPS 1993
TRÈS CHIC Holzman & Stephanie 2000

Water / Marine

MARIELLA Mariella Burani 1996
PERLE DE SILENCES Jacomo 1996

White Flowers / Fleurs Blanches

CRISTAL DE MUSC Comptoir Sud Pacifique 1986
JOVAN WHITE MUSK Jovan 1992

Crisp / Pétillant

Citrus Fruity / Hespéridé Fruité

CARAMEL PAIN D'ÉPICE Molinard 1999
L'EAU Diptyque 1968 ♂
LE ROY SOLEIL Salvador Dali 1997
OH LA LA Loris Azzaro 1993
ORANGE-CANNELLE Molinard 1993
THEOREMA ESPRIT D'ÉTÉ Fendi 1999

Green / Vert

COTONNADE Comptoir Sud Pacifique 1988 ♂
PARFUM D'HERMÈS Hermès 1984

JIL SANDER FEELING MAN Jil Sander 1989
PIERRE CARDIN POUR MONSIEUR Pierre Cardin 1972
ROYAL BAIN DE CHAMPAGNE Caron 1941 ♂
SAMOURAÏ Alain Delon 1995
SCOTT McCLINTOCK Jessica McClintock 1992

COTONNADE Comptoir Sud Pacifique 1988 ♂
JOVAN EVENING MUSK FOR MEN* Jovan 1985
L'EAU Diptyque 1968 ♂
M de M Marc de la Morandière 1998
MONSIEUR CARVEN* Carven 1978

●●● ➜ Classical / Classique

ALEXANDRA   Alexandra de Markoff 1979
AMBRE CANNELLE   Creed 1949
ANNE PLISKA   Anne Pliska 1987
ASJA   Fendi 1992
CAFÉ   Cofinluxe 1978
CALLA   Robert Isabell 1996
CINNABAR   Estée Lauder 1978
COCO   Chanel 1984
CRÉATURE   Gilles Cantuel 1985
CROWN OF GOLD   Crown 1910
DIORESSENCE   Christian Dior 1969/79
ENJOLI MIDNIGHT   Revlon 1984
ENRICO COVERI   Enrico Coveri 1987
ÉVÉ   Pierre Réne 1981
FELCE AZZURRA   Paglieri 1920
GALANOS DE SERENE   Galanos 1979
HYPERSOUK   MAC 1999
JACQUI   Pierre Réne 1980
J'AI OSÉ   Guy Laroche / J'Ai Osé 1977
JUNGLE: L'ÉLÉPHANT   Kenzo 1996
MAJA   Myrurgia 1921
MULBERRY   Mulberry 1997
NOHIBA (TULIPE NOIRE)   E.Coudray 1922
NORMANDIE   Jean Patou 1935
OPIUM   Yves Saint Laurent 1977
ORIENT   Déco 1981
POIS DE SENTEUR   Caron 1927
PRÉLUDE*   Balenciaga 1982
SALVADOR DALI   Salvador Dali 1983
SUBLIME   Jean Patou 1992
TEATRO ALLA SCALA*   Krizia 1986
THEOREMA   Fendi 1998
VANILLE   L'Occitane 1999 ♂
YOU'RE THE FIRE FOR WOMEN   Yardley 1973
YOUTH-DEW   Estée Lauder 1953

●●●● ➜ Rich / Profond

BLEU DE CHINE   Marc de la Morandière 1987/94
LOULOU   Cacharel 1987
POIVRE   Caron 1954
ROYAL DELIGHT   Creed 1993 ♂
SHAAL NUR   Etro 1997 ♂

GRABAZZI   Gendarme 1995
J.H.L.   Aramis 1982
OLD SPICE   Shulton / P&G 1937
PS   Paul Sebastian 1979
VANILLE   L'Occitane 1999 ♂

ROYAL COPENHAGEN MUSK   Royal Copenhagen 1976
ROYAL DELIGHT   Creed 1993 ♂
SHAAL NUR   Etro 1997 ♂

Oriental

Orientals are the exotic queens of perfumery. Sensual, often heavy, blends of oriental resins, opulent flowers, sweet vanilla and musks are introduced by refreshing citrus, green or fruity top notes. The new 'sheer' Orientals gained some ground in the late 1990s, but the appeal of the full-bodied, take-no-prisoners Orientals endures.

Les notes orientales sont les reines exotiques de la parfumerie. Sensuels et souvent lourds, des mélanges de résines orientales, de fleurs opulentes, de vanille douce et de musc sont introduits par les notes tenues et qui rafraîchissent de l'hespéridé, du vert ou du fruité. Les nouveaux parfums Orientaux « purs » ont gagné du terrain à la fin de la Belle Époque, mais l'attrait pour le faste des parfums Orientaux « sans merci » reste...

Fresh / Frais

Citrus Fruity / Hespéridé Fruité

ADRIENNE VITTADINI   Adrienne Vittadini 1999
BOND   James Bond 1997
EXCEPTION   Renaud de Lustrac 1989
I AM WILD   Danica Aromatics 1999
MAGOT   Etro 1996
OBSESSION   Calvin Klein 1985
OZBEK 1001   Rifat Ozbek 1999
VANILLE ABRICOT   Comptoir Sud Pacifique 1994
VANILLE AMANDE   Comptoir Sud Pacifique 1994
VANILLE CERISE   Comptoir Sud Pacifique 1997

Green / Vert

ANNE KLEIN II*   Parlux 1986
AYAKO   Marc de la Morandière 1999
DIONNE   Dionne Warwick 1986
MCM OBELISK*   MCM 1985
MUST DE CARTIER   Cartier 1981
VERY VALENTINO   Valentino 1997

White Flowers / Fleurs Blanches

LANCASTER BODY & BATH   Lancaster 1987
VANILIA   L'Artisan Parfumeur 1978
VANILLE TIARÉ   Comptoir Sud Pacifique 1989

Crisp / Pétillant

Citrus Fruity / Hespéridé Fruité

AMOUR DE CACAO   Comptoir Sud Pacifique 1993
CHOCOLAT MENTHE   Molinard 1999
EAU DE CARON   Caron 1980
FATH DE FATH   Jacques Fath 1953/93
FIRE & ICE   Revlon 1994
KRAZY KRIZIA*   Krizia 1991
VANILLE FRAÎCHEUR   Molinard 1998
VANILLE FRUITÉE   Molinard 1998
YOHJI   Yohji Yamamoto 1996

Green / Vert

JAÏPUR SAPHIR   Boucheron 1999
ROMA   Laura Biagiotti 1988

White Flowers / Fleurs Blanches

JACQUELINE   Jean-Jacques Diener 1998
VANILLE   Comptoir Sud Pacifique 1978

EAU DE RUSSE   Crown 1911
VERSAILLES   Jean Desprez 1980

Classical / Classique

AMBRE   Molinard 1993
ANGÉLIQUE ENCENS   Creed 1933
CHANTILLY   Houbigant / Dana 1941
CRUISE FOR WOMEN   Carnival 1996
EAU LENTE   Diptyque 1986 ♂
ÉMERAUDE   Coty 1921
EXTASE MUSK WOMAN   Muelhens 1976
INTERLUDE   Frances Denney 1965
L'EAU D'AMBRE   L'Artisan Parfumeur 1978
LYRA   Alain Delon 1993
MALABAR   Crown 1919
MARBERT WOMAN   Marbert 1987
MISUKI   Holzman & Stephanie 1987
MOSCHINO   Moschino 1987
NUITS INDIENNES   Jean-Louis Scherrer 1994
OR DES INDES   Maître Parfumeur et Gantier 1988
ROYAL SECRET   Monteil / Royal Secret 1958
SHALIMAR   Guerlain 1925
SHOCKING   Schiaparelli 1937/97
VANILLE   Molinard 1993
VANILLE CAFÉ   Comptoir Sud Pacifique 1987 ♂
VANILLE CANNELLE   E.Coudray 1935
VANILLE-TONKA   Patricia de Nicolaï 1997
VANISIA   Creed 1987

Rich / Profond

AMBRE PRÉCIEUX   Maître Parfumeur et Gantier 1988 ♂
ATTAR   Robert Isabell 1996
CIARA   Revlon 1973
KÉORA   Jean Couturier 1983
MOLTO MISSONI   Missoni 1990
SECRETE DATURA   Maître Parfumeur et Gantier 1992
TABU   Dana 1932
TOUJOURS MOI   Corday / Dana 1921
UNTAMED MUSK   Déco 1994
WILD MUSK   Coty 1973

EAU LENTE   Diptyque 1986 ♂
HABIT ROUGE   Guerlain 1965
KL HOMME*   Lagerfeld 1986
VANILLE CAFÉ   Comptoir Sud Pacifique 1987 ♂

AMBRE PRÉCIEUX   Maître Parfumeur et Gantier 1988 ♂
EXTASE MUSK MAN   Muelhens 1985
MONSIEUR MUSK   Parquet / Dana 1973

Woody Oriental

The liaison of rich Oriental notes and the potent scents of patchouli and sandalwood produced some of the most original perfumes of the 1990s. This family emphasises the woody character of Floral Orientals. The key difference is that their flowers and spices play second string to the dominant sandalwood and/or patchouli notes. The Oriental influence is more noticeable, too, and balances the deep wood notes.

La liaison de riches notes orientales avec les puissantes senteurs du patchouli et du bois de santal a donné certains des parfums les plus originaux des années 90. Cette famille met en valeur le caractère boisé des parfums Fleuris orientaux. La différence essentielle est que les fleurs et les épices jouent en sourdine tandis que les notes de santal et/ou de patchouli dominent. L'influence orientale est plus nette aussi, elle crée un équilibre avec les notes boisées profondes.

Fresh / Frais

Citrus Fruity / Hespéridé Fruité

100% PURE CHIPIE PURPLE Coty 1998
ALL ABOUT EVE Joop! 1996
ALYSSA ASHLEY VANILLA Alyssa Ashley 1996
ANGEL Thierry Mugler 1992
ANGEL INNOCENT Thierry Mugler 1998
CHRISTOS WOMAN Christopher Chronis 1998
COLÈRE DE RODIER Rodier 1999
CRISTOBAL Balenciaga 1998
DESTINY WOMAN Harley-Davidson 1999
DIESEL ZERO PLUS FEMININE Diesel 1999
DULCE VANILLA Coty 1999
ESCADA COLLECTION Escada 1997
FIRE & ICE SMOULDER FOR HER Revlon 1999
GATTINONI COUTURE Gattinoni 1998
GOLD Mary McFadden 1996
GOSSIP Cindy Adams 1997
GUET-APENS ⓛ Guerlain 1999
LOLITA LEMPICKA Lolita Lempicka 1997
MARINA DE BOURBON Marina de Bourbon 1994
MYSTERY AUSTRALIA WOMAN Globe 1998
NIRMALA* Molinard 1955/93
PLEINE LUNE Ulric de Varens 1995
POPY MORENI Popy Moreni 1996
PRINCESSE CHIPIE Coty 1997
RODIER Rodier 1998
SONIA RYKIEL Sonia Rykiel 1997
SOPRANI 2 Luciano Soprani 1994
TODD OLDHAM* Todd Oldham 1995
UNZIPPED Perfumer's Workshop 1998
VANILLE COCO E.Coudray 1990
WISH Chopard 1997
WITH LOVE* Fred Hayman 1991
ZUT Schiaparelli 1937/97

Green / Vert

EXTASE DEVOTION WOMAN Muelhens 1994
JIL Jil Sander 1997
TUSCANY PER DONNA Aramis / Estée Lauder 1992
UN AIR DE SAMSARA Guerlain 1995

Water / Marine

DUNE Christian Dior 1991
LA PLAGE Marc de la Moriandière 1999

White Flowers / Fleurs Blanches

25 Aubusson 1994
BEVERLY HILLS Gale Hayman 1990
BIBI Jean Barthet 1988
BLACK TIE Oleg Cassini 1998
COEUR D'OR Paris Bleu 1998
CYANE* Ulric de Varens 1986
ENCHANTÉ Déco 1987
E.N.C.O.R.E Alfred Sung 1990
GERANI Gerani 1998
GILDA Pierre Wulff 1985
LUNE D'ÉTÉ Rémy Latour 1993
MARQUIS POUR FEMME Rémy Marquis 1999
MONDI PURSENSE Mondi 1991
NINO CERRUTI* Cerruti 1987
ROUGE Annabella 1999
VENDETTA* Valentino 1991
YSATIS Givenchy 1984

Crisp / Pétillant

Citrus Fruity / Hespéridé Fruité

AMBUSH Dana 1955/97
CASMIR Chopard 1991
CHAOS* Donna Karan 1996
DOLCE VITA Christian Dior 1995
FRENCH VANILLA Dana 1994
HANAE MORI Hanae Mori 1968/95
HOLLYWOOD FOR WOMEN Fred Hayman 1998
HONEYMOON Gloria Vanderbilt 1996
JUST ME Montana 1997
L'INSOLENT* Charles Jourdan 1995
LE PARFUM Sonia Rykiel 1993
MIRA BAÏ Chopard 1998
SCARF Marbert 1993
SKARLETT SECRETS Mäurer & Wirtz 1996
TEMPORE DONNA Laura Biagiotti 1999
YPNO* Otto Kern 1994

Green / Vert

GUCCI RUSH Gucci 1999
JOLIE MADAME Pierre Balmain 1953/92
LAPIS Napoleon 1999
MAGIE NOIRE Lancôme 1978
MYSTÈRE Rochas 1978
NUTMEG & GINGER Jo Malone 1990 ♂
ORGANZA Givenchy 1996
ORMOLU Penhaligon's 1977
ROYAL SECRET II Royal Secret 1999
SAVAGE VANILLA Un Monde Nouveau 1993
SYNTHETIC NIRVANA MAC 1999
VOL DE NUIT Guerlain 1933

White Flowers / Fleurs Blanches

CAPUCCI DE CAPUCCI Roberto Capucci 1987
GRAFFITI VANILLA Naf Naf 1995
GUESS* Georges Marciano 1990
JUSTE UN RÊVE Patricia de Nicolaï 1996
LYRA 2 Alain Delon 1995
OTTOMANE Ulric de Varens 1992
VANILLA FIELDS Coty 1993

Classical / Classique

AMBER & LAVENDER   Jo Malone 1995 ♂
BIJAN   Bijan 1987
BOIS DES ÎLES   Chanel 1926
BY WOMAN   Dolce & Gabbana 1997
CROWN HELIOTROPE   Crown 1939
DIAMONDS & RUBIES*   Elizabeth Taylor 1993
ENIGMA   Alexandra de Markoff 1972
EUNECE   Fashion Fair 1985
FABLE   Hope Diamond Collection 1999
FEMINITÉ DU BOIS   Shiseido 1992
GRAIN DE SOLEIL   Fragonard 1999
I AM ETERNAL   Danica Aromatics 1999
INTOXICATION D'AMOUR   d'Orsay 1997
JOOP! NUIT D'ÉTÉ   Joop! 1990
KIRI   Kiri Te Kanawa 1999
L'HEURE ATTENDUE   Jean Patou 1946
LE FEU D'ISSEY   Issey Miyake 1998
LELONG POUR FEMME   Lucien Lelong 1999
MANIA   Giorgio Armani 1999
MING   Imperiale 1983
MOMENTS   Priscilla Presley 1990
MUSC   Molinard 1995
NUBIADE   Omar Sharif 1994
NUIT DE NOËL   Caron 1922
ONLY   Julio Iglesias 1989
PAIN D'ÉPICES   Comptoir Sud Pacifique 1986
PASSION   Elizabeth Taylor 1987
PATCHOULY   Etro 1989 ♂
PYTHON   Trussardi 1999
RÉGINE'S   Régine's 1989
ROCOCO   Joop! 1999
SAMSARA   Guerlain 1989
SANDALWOOD   Yardley 1996 ♂
SANTAL IMPÉRIAL   Creed 1850 ♂
SECRET DE VÉNUS   Weil 1933/96
SKARLETT   Mäurer & Wirtz 1994
SMALTO DONNA*   Francesco Smalto 1993
SO...?   Yardley / Bond Street 1994
SOLEIL LEVANT   Comptoir Sud Pacifique 1975
SOTTO VOCE   Laura Biagiotti 1996
STÉPHANIE   Stéphanie de Monaco 1989
TENTATIONS   Paloma Picasso 1996
THÉ   Comptoir Sud Pacifique 1997 ♂
VANILLA MUSK   Coty 1994
VANILLE PATCHOULI   Molinard 1998
VENEZIA   Laura Biagiotti 1992
WOMAN*   Jovan 1976
WOODHUE*   Fabergé 1944

Rich / Profond

FENDI   Fendi 1985
FEUILLE D'HERBE FRAÎCHE EPICÉE   L'Occitane 1999
GEM   Van Cleef & Arpels 1987
HABANITA   Molinard 1921
HYPNOTIC POISON   Christian Dior 1998
JOOP!   Joop! 1987
NAOMI CAMPBELL   Naomi Campbell 1999
ORGANZA INDÉCENCE   Givenchy 1999
SHAHI   Chypron 1995
UNFORGETTABLE   Revlon 1990
UNGARO   Ungaro 1977/90

Woody Oriental

Fresh / Frais

57 FOR HIM   Chevignon 1999
ALLURE HOMME   Chanel 1998
ANIMALE ANIMALE FOR MEN   Parlux 1994
ARSENAL   Gilles Cantuel 1996
BEST MAN   Succès de Paris 1995
BLEU MARINE   Pierre Cardin 1965/98
BODY KOUROS   Yves Saint Laurent 2000
CASRAN   Chopard 1999
CASUAL FRIDAY   Escada 1999
COLORS FOR MEN   Benetton 1988
CONTRADICTION FOR MEN   Calvin Klein 1998
DIESEL PLUS PLUS MASCULINE   Diesel 1997
DUNE POUR HOMME   Christian Dior 1997
ENVY FOR MEN   Gucci 1998
FERRARI   Ferrari 1996
GENGIS KHAN   Marc de la Morandière 1989
GERANI UOMO   Gerani 1999
H.M.   Hanae Mori 1997
ICEBERG UNIVERSE HOMME   Iceberg 1997
JORDAN BY MICHAEL   Bijan 1999
JOVAN WHITE MUSK FOR MEN   Jovan 1992
KITON NAPOLI   Palladio 1998
LAND   Lacoste 1991
LIGHT HIM   Trussardi 1997
MOLINARD HOMME II   Molinard 1996
OBSESSION FOR MEN   Calvin Klein 1986
OURAGAN   Bourjois 1997
PARADOX FOR MEN   Jacomo 1999
PEOPLE UOMO   Luciano Soprani 1999
PERIPHERY / OPPORTUNE   Amway 1998
RAW VANILLA   Coty 1996
RÉGINE'S FOR MEN   Régine's 1993
REPLAY   Replay 1996
SANTA FE FOR MEN   Tsumura 1988
SÉXUAL POUR HOMME   Michel Germain 1996
TEMPORE UOMO   Laura Biagiotti 1999
ULYSSE   Vicky Tiel 1998
UOMO? MOSCHINO   Moschino 1997
VERSUS UOMO   Versace 1990
X   Mäurer & Wirtz 1998
XXL   Daniel Hechter 1997
YANG   Jacques Fath 1999

Crisp / Pétillant

AGUIRRE   Bourjois 1991
A*MEN / ANGEL MEN   Thierry Mugler 1996
BACKGROUND   Jil Sander 1993
BLACK JEANS HOMME   Roccobarroco 1998
BLUE JEANS   Versace 1994
BOSS   Hugo Boss 1998
BY MAN   Dolce & Gabbana 1998
CATALYST FOR MEN   Halston 1994
CENTAURE CUIR AMBRE   Pierre Cardin 1996
CHRISTOS MAN   Christopher Chronis 1998
CIGAR   Rémy Latour 1996
CONVICTION MEN   Omar Sharif 1999
DNA FOR MEN   Bijan 1993
ERUPTION MAN   Mäurer & Wirtz 1997
ESCADA POUR HOMME   Escada 1993
FORCE MAJEURE   Jacques Bogart 1998
GIGLI PER UOMO   Romeo Gigli 1991
GINSENG N.R.G   Jovan 1998
GRAVITY   Coty 1992
HÉRITAGE   Guerlain 1992
HÉROS   Didier Calvo-Uomo 1995
HERRERA FOR MEN   Carolina Herrera 1991
JACOMO DE JACOMO   Jacomo 1980
JAGUAR MARK II   Jaguar 1995
JAÏPUR HOMME   Boucheron 1997
JAKO   Lagerfeld 1997
JIMMY'Z   Régines 1991
JIVAGO 7 ELEMENTS   Jivago 1998
JOHNNY LAMBS   Schiapparelli Pikenz 1995
JUNGLE POUR HOMME   Kenzo 1998
KIPLING   Weil 1986
LE MÂLE   Jean Paul Gaultier 1995
LALIQUE POUR HOMME   Lalique 1997
MANÈS   Rémy Latour 1990
MINOTAURE   Paloma Picasso 1992
MONTANA POUR HOMME   Montana 1989
NAUTICA COMPETITION   Nautica 1997
NEMO   Cacharel 1999
NEW YORK   Patricia de Nicolaï 1989
NICOLE MILLER FOR MEN   Nicole Miller 1994
NUTMEG & GINGER   Jo Malone 1990 ♂
OPIUM POUR HOMME   Yves Saint Laurent 1995
PASSION D'HOMME   Rodier 1999
PATCHOULI   Crabtree & Evelyn 1970
POUR L'HOMME   Jacques Fath 1998
REALM MEN   Erox / HPS 1993
RELAX   Davidoff 1990
RÉMY   Rémy Marquis 1999
RICCI-CLUB   Nina Ricci 1989
ROCHAS MAN   Rochas 1999
ROMA UOMO   Laura Biagiotti 1994
SABLES   Annick Goutal 1985
SAFRANIER   Comptoir Sud Pacifique 1996
SALVADOR DALI POUR HOMME   Salvador Dali 1987
SAMBA NOVA HOMME   Perfumer's Workshop 1993
SCULPTURE HOMME   Nikos 1995
SUMATRA RAIN WOOD   Muelhens 1998
SYBARIS   Puig 1988
TED   Ted Lapidus 1999
THE DREAMER   Versace 1996
TYCOON   Marbert 1997
U de V N° 2   Ulric de Varens 1999
UNGARO POUR L'HOMME I*   Ungaro 1991
VENEZIA UOMO   Laura Biagiotti 1995
VERY VALENTINO POUR HOMME   Valentino 1999
WITNESS*   Jacques Bogart 1992
XERYUS ROUGE   Givenchy 1995
ZIPPED UNIVERSE   Perfumer's Workshop 1999

Classical / Classique

π   Givenchy 1998
AMBER & LAVENDER   Jo Malone 1995 ♂
AMBRO DE JACOMO   Jacomo 1996
BAIE DE GENIÈVRE   Creed 1982
CHAPS   Ralph Lauren 1979
CHAPS MUSK   Ralph Lauren 1985
DERRICK   Orlane 1978/80
DIESEL   Diesel 1996
DIESEL ZERO PLUS MASCULINE   Diesel 1999
EAU DE SANDALWOOD   Le Jardin Retrouvé 1977
ÉGOÏSTE / L'ÉGOÏSTE   Chanel 1990
EXTASE MAGMA MAN   Muelhens 1993
FERRÉ FOR MAN   Gianfranco Ferré 1986
HAMMAM BOUQUET   Penhaligon's 1872
JOOP! HOMME   Joop! 1989
KANØN   Scannon 1966
LAGERFELD   Lagerfeld 1978
LP N° 9 FOR MEN   Penhaligon's 1999
MCM 24 EVENING*   MCM 1993
MOODS UOMO   Krizia 1989
MUSK FOR MEN   Coty 1974
PASSION FOR MEN   Elizabeth Taylor 1989
PATCHOULY   Etro 1989 ♂
PATOU POUR HOMME   Jean Patou 1980
ROI SANTAL   Comptoir Sud Pacifique 1988
ROYAL COPENHAGEN   Royal Copenhagen 1970
SANDALWOOD   Crabtree & Evelyn 1970
SANDALWOOD   Yardley 1996 ♂
SANDRINGHAM   Crown 1873
SANTAL IMPÉRIAL   Creed 1850 ♂
SEX APPEAL FOR MEN*   Jovan 1976
STETSON   Coty 1981
THÉ   Comptoir Sud Pacifique 1997 ♂
TIFFANY FOR MEN   Tiffany 1989
VERDI 800   Pol 1995
VERSACE L'HOMME   Versace 1984
ZIZANIE*   Fragonard 1932

Rich / Profond

BALENCIAGA POUR HOMME   Balenciaga 1990
BOIS DU PORTUGAL   Creed 1987
FURYO*   Jacques Bogart 1988
M de MORABITO   Morabito 1989
MAN DE RAUCH   Madeleine de Rauch 1998
MAXIM'S POUR HOMME   Maxim's 1988
SANDALO   Etro 1989
ZAHAROFF POUR HOMME   Zaharoff 1999
ZINO DAVIDOFF   Davidoff 1986

Woody Oriental

Mossy Woods

Perfumers call these forest notes of oakmoss, woods and citrus Chypre fragrances. The family takes its name from the first significant mossy-woody fragrance, Chypre de Coty, created by François Coty in 1917. Chypre is the French name for the island of Cyprus, birthplace of Venus, the legendary goddess of love. From Cyprus, too, comes the oakmoss that is at the heart of all Chypre fragrances.

Les parfumeurs appellent ces notes sylvestres de mousse de chêne, de bois et d'hespéridé, parfums de Chypre. Le nom de cette famille vient du premier parfum important moussu-boisé, Chypre de Coty, créé par François Coty en 1917. Chypre est l'île où serait née Vénus, déesse légendaire de l'amour. De Chypre vient aussi la mousse de chêne qui est au cœur des parfums chyprés.

Fresh / Frais

Citrus Fruity / Hespéridé Fruité

CHOC   Pierre Cardin 1981
FEUILLE D'HERBE FLORALE FRUITÉE   L'Occitane 1999
FLEUR DE FIGUIER   Molinard 1999
HALSTON   Halston 1975
MAGIC   Céline 1996
NIKI DE SAINT PHALLE   Niki de St Phalle 1982
PHILOSYKOS   Diptyque 1996 ♂
PREMIER FIGUIER   L'Artisan Parfumeur 1994
YVRESSE (CHAMPAGNE)   Yves Saint Laurent 1993

Green / Vert

ARMANI   Giorgio Armani 1982
BALMAIN   Pierre Balmain 1998
CIELO   Napa Valley 1998
COCKTAIL   Jean Patou 1930
COMME DES GARÇONS 2   Comme des Garçons 1999 ♂
DENEUVE*   Catherine Deneuve 1986
GAULOISE*   Molyneux 1980
GIVENCHY III   Givenchy 1970
GRAIN DE PLAISIR   Maître Parfumeur et Gantier 1998 ♂
INTIMATE*   Revlon 1955
MISS DIOR   Christian Dior 1947
U II SHEER SCENT   Ultima II 1990
Y   Yves Saint Laurent 1964

Water / Marine

EASY KRIZIA   Krizia 1999
MONTANA PARFUM D'ELLE*   Montana 1990

White Flowers / Fleurs Blanches

CONSIDERATIONS / CONFIDENT   Amway 1998
CRÉATION   Ted Lapidus 1984
LACE   Yardley / FFC 1984
SAMBA NOVA   Perfumer's Workshop 1992

Crisp / Pétillant

Citrus Fruity / Hespéridé Fruité

ANOUCHKA   Révillon 1994
CASSINI   Oleg Cassini 1990
CHAPEAU BLEU   DC Design 1994
COLONY   Jean Patou 1938
DECI DELÀ   Nina Ricci 1994
FLEURS DES COMORES   Maître Parfumeur et Gantier 1988
IO   La Perla 1995
IQUITA*   Alain Delon 1996
JARDIN SECRET   Patricia de Nicolaï 1992
PARFUM D'OR   Kristel Saint Martin 1995
PAVAROTTI DONNA   Pavarotti 1995
POMME CANNELLE   Molinard 1999
RACINE   Maître Parfumeur et Gantier 1988 ♂
RED   Giorgio Beverly Hills 1989
RUE PEROGLÈSE   Ulric de Varens 1996
TALISMAN   Balenciaga 1994
VARENSIA   Ulric de Varens 1994
V'E VERSACE   Versace 1989
VETYVER HAITI   Comptoir Sud Pacifique 1977 ♂
YOHJI ESSENTIAL   Yohji Yamamoto 1998

Green / Vert

APHRODISIA*   Fabergé 1938
CHANT D'ARÔMES   Guerlain 1962
FLORAMYE   L.T.Piver 1905/91
MA GRIFFE   Carven 1946
VETYVER   Jo Malone 1995 ♂

White Flowers / Fleurs Blanches

EXPLOSIVE*   Etienne Aigner 1986
GUCCI N° 3*   Gucci 1985
JIL SANDER WOMAN II*   Jil Sander 1982

Classical / Classique

ANTILOPE   Weil 1945
APOGÉE   Les Senteurs 1991
AUDACE   Fabergé 1983
AZZARO   Loris Azzaro 1975
CALÈCHE   Hermès 1961/92
CHYPRE DE COTY*   Coty 1917
DIORAMA   Christian Dior 1949
DONNA TRUSSARDI   Trussardi 1993
EAU DE CHEVERNY   Patricia de Nicolaï 1992 ♂
EAU DU SOIR   Sisley 1990
EAU FRAÎCHE   Christian Dior 1953
EXC'LA.MA'TION NOIR   Coty 1998
FEMME   Rochas 1944/89
FILLE D'EVE   Nina Ricci 1952
FLEURS DE LA FORÊT   Jo Malone 1995
GUÉPARD   Guépard 1997
HISTOIRE D'AMOUR   Aubusson 1984
IMPERIAL VETYVER   Yardley 1996 ♂
INFINITIF   Infinitif 1994
INSTINCT D'ANIMALE   Parlux 1997
JIL SANDER BATH & BEAUTY   Jil Sander 1981
KNOWING   Estée Lauder 1988
L'ARTE DI GUCCI*   Gucci 1991
LE TEMPS D'AIMER*   Alain Delon 1981
LANCETTI MADAME   Lancetti 1995
MARECHALE 90   Crown 1994
MILA SCHÖN   Mila Schön 1981
MITSOUKO   Guerlain 1919
PALOMA PICASSO   Paloma Picasso 1984
PARFUM PRIVÉ   La Perla 1998
PARURE   Guerlain 1975
PATCHOULI   Molinard 1993 ♂
PURE SILK*   Yardley 1982
QUADRILLE   Balenciaga 1955
QUE SAIS-JE?   Jean Patou 1925
RÉPLIQUE*   Raphaël 1947
ROSE CARDIN   Pierre Cardin 1990
SOIR D'ÉTÉ   Morabito 1995
TIEMPE PASSATE   Antonia's Flowers 1999
UBAR   Amouage 1995
WHITE JEANS   Versace 1997
ZIBELINE   Weil 1928

Rich / Profond

ANIMALE   Parlux 1987
CHIQUE   Yardley / FFC 1976
COMME DES GARÇONS   Comme des Garçons 1994 ♂
CORIANDRE   Jean Couturier 1973
DIVA   Ungaro 1983
GIANNI VERSACE   Versace 1982
MAROC*   Revlon 1985
MISHA   Mikhail Baryshnikov 1989
MISSONI   Missoni 1981
TURBULENCES   Révillon 1981

Mossy Woods

Fresh / Frais

212 MEN   Carolina Herrera 1999
CHAMADE POUR HOMME ⓛ   Guerlain 1999
COMME DES GARÇONS 2   Comme des Garçons 1999 ♂
EAU DE GREY FLANNEL   Geoffrey Beene 1996
EAU GRISE   Comptoir Sud Pacifique 1976
FAHRENHEIT   Christian Dior 1988
GRAIN DE PLAISIR   Maître Parfumeur et Gantier 1998 ♂
GREEN VALLEY   Creed 1999
GREY FLANNEL   Geoffrey Beene 1976
HUGO DARK BLUE   Hugo Boss 1999
IRIS BLEU GRIS   Maître Parfumeur et Gantier 1988
KITON MEN   Palladio 1996
MARBERT MAN PURE   Marbert 1989
PHILOSYKOS   Diptyque 1996 ♂
R   Révillon 1995
SALVATORE FERRAGAMO POUR HOMME   Ferragamo 1999
VOYAGEUR   Jean Patou 1995

Crisp / Pétillant

AQUA VELVA ICE BLUE   Williams 1935
AUBUSSON HOMME   Aubusson 1992
CENTAURE CUIR BLANC   Pierre Cardin 1996
CHEVIGNON   Chevignon 1992
CORIOLAN   Guerlain 1998
CRUISE FOR MEN   Carnival 1996
EAU DE VÉTYVER   Le Jardin Retrouvé 1977
EMPORIO ARMANI HE / LUI   Giorgio Armani 1998
FERRARI BLACK   Ferrari 1999
FIRE & ICE SMOULDER FOR HIM   Revlon 1999
FRAÎCHE BADIANE   Maître Parfumeur et Gantier 1994
GUÉPARD HOMME   Guépard 1998
HALSTON Z   Halston 1998
HALSTON Z-14   Halston 1976
HIGH TECH MEN   Lomani 1999
IMPLICITE HOMME   Sea World 1998
LE ROY SOLEIL HOMME   Salvador Dali 1998
LES COPAINS L'HOMME   Les Copains 1998
LIFE ESSENCE   Fendi 1996
MADRIGAL   Molinard 1935/93
MARBERT GENTLEMAN*   Marbert 1986
METROPOLIS   Estée Lauder 1987
MOUSTACHE   Rochas 1948
PRIVATE NUMBER FOR MEN*   Etienne Aigner 1992
RACINE   Maître Parfumeur et Gantier 1988 ♂
SAMBA RED MAN   Perfumer's Workshop 1999
SIENNA   Crabtree & Evelyn 1990
SIR IRISH MOSS   Muelhens 1969
SMALTO   Francesco Smalto 1987/98
STETSON COUNTRY   Coty 1998
TOWN & COUNTRY   Crown 1925
VERSION HOMME*   Ulric de Varens 1995
VETYVER   Jo Malone 1995 ♂
VETYVER HAITI   Comptoir Sud Pacifique 1977 ♂
VETIVER HOMBRE   Adolfo Dominguez 1998
WEEKEND FOR MEN   Burberry 1997

Classical / Classique

ACQUA DI SELVA   Victor 1949
AGUA BRAVA   Puig 1968
AGUA FRESCA   Adolfo Dominguez 1996
CHANEL POUR MONSIEUR   Chanel 1955
CLASSIC   Yardley / Parfums Bleu 1985
DESTINY   Harley-Davidson 1999
EAU DE CHEVERNY   Patricia de Nicolaï 1992 ♂
EAU DE MONSIEUR   Annick Goutal 1981
FOR GENTLEMEN   Woods of Windsor 1981
IMPERIAL VETYVER   Yardley 1996 ♂
PATCHOULI   Molinard 1993 ♂
PINO SILVESTRE ORIGINAL   Pino Silvestre-Mavive 1955
ROUTE DU VÉTIVER   Maître Parfumeur et Gantier 1988
SILVESTRE   Victor 1946
VÉTIVER   Carven 1957
VETIVER   Creed 1948
VETIVER   Guerlain 1959
VÉTYVER   L.T.Piver 1991
VETYVER   Molinard 1984
VÉTYVER   Roger & Gallet 1974/91
YARDLEY CLASSIC   Yardley 1985

Rich / Profond

ACIER ALUMINIUM   Creed 1973
BOIS PRÉCIEUX   Molinard 1995
BOURBON HOMME   Marina de Bourbon 1999
COMME DES GARÇONS   Comme des Garçons 1994 ♂
GIORGIO MEN*   Giorgio Beverly Hills 1984
GIVENCHY GENTLEMAN   Givenchy 1974
IQUITOS*   Alain Delon 1987
MCM SUCCESS*   MCM 1986
SANTAL NOBLE   Maître Parfumeur et Gantier 1988

Dry Woods

A mossy-woody fragrance takes on a drier character with the addition of cedar, tobacco and burnt wood notes. The Dry Woods family is often called Leather, after the dry, smoky scent of Russian leather. Fresh citrus notes play an important role in most Dry Woods fragrances, lightening the deep, almost animalic heart notes.

Une senteur moussue-boisée prend un caractère plus sec si l'on y additionne de notes de cèdre, de tabac et de bois brûlé. Souvent, on appelle « cuir » cette famille de Bois secs, à cause de sa senteur sèche et fumée de cuir russe. Les notes fraîches hespéridées jouent un rôle important dans la plupart des parfums Chypre cuir, en allégeant et éclaircissant les notes profondes, presque animales, au cœur du parfum.

Chypre Cuir

Fresh / Frais

Crisp / Pétillant

Citrus Fruity / Hespéridé Fruité

BULGARI BLACK   Bulgari 1998 ♂
FIORA   Parour 1997
JITROIS   Jean-Claude Jitrois 1989
RUMBA   Balenciaga 1988
SOIE ROUGE   Maître Parfumeur et Gantier 1988

Green / Vert

AROMATICS ELIXIR   Clinique 1971
EAU DE CÈDRE   Comptoir Sud Pacifique 1975 ♂
GENNY* (Original)   Genny 1987
VOLEUR DE ROSES   L'Artisan Parfumeur 1993 ♂

Green / Vert

COEUR DE PARFUM*   Jacomo 1985
JIL SANDER WOMAN III   Jil Sander 1986
L'EAU TROIS   Diptyque 1975 ♂

White Flowers / Fleurs Blanches

CASHMERE MIST   Donna Karan 1994

White Flowers / Fleurs Blanches

PASSAGE D'ENFER   L'Artisan Parfumeur 1999

273 FOR MEN   Fred Hayman 1990
ACTEUR   Loris Azzaro 1989
ADIDAS CLASSIC   Adidas 1986
BASILE UOMO   Basile 1987
BOSS SPIRIT*   Hugo Boss 1989
BULGARI BLACK   Bulgari 1998 ♂
CARACTÈRE   Daniel Hechter 1989
CARLO CORINTO   Carlo Corinto 1984
CARVEN HOMME   Carven 1999
CROWN PARK ROYAL   Crown 1929
DK MEN*   Donna Karan 1994
EAU DE CUIR DE RUSSIE   Le Jardin Retrouvé 1977
ENGLISH LEATHER   Mem / Dana 1949
ESENCIA LOEWE   Loewe 1987
L'EAU TROIS   Diptyque 1975 ♂
L'HOMME   Comptoir Sud Pacifique 1993
LEGENDARY   Harley-Davidson 1994
LORD*   Molyneux 1988
MARBERT HOMME*   Marbert 1988
MARK BIRLEY FOR MEN   Mark Birley 1996
MOSCHINO POUR HOMME   Moschino 1991
MULBERRY FOR MEN   Mulberry 1966
NIAGARA   Courrèges 1995
OSCAR DE LA RENTA POUR LUI   Oscar de la Renta 1980
OSCAR FOR MEN   Oscar de la Renta 1999
PHEROMONE FOR MEN   Marilyn Miglin 1999
POLO   Ralph Lauren 1978
POLO CREST   Ralph Lauren 1991
POLO SPORT EXTREME   Ralph Lauren 1998
PONTACCIO 21   Gianfranco Ferré 1999
QUORUM   Puig 1982
TRUSSARDI UOMO FRESH   Trussardi 1999
VENDETTA POUR HOMME*   Valentino 1991

ARAMIS 900   Aramis 1973
BE BOP MAN   Kesling 1995
DÉCLARATION   Cartier 1998
DK MEN UNLEADED*   Donna Karan 1995
EAU DE CÈDRE   Comptoir Sud Pacifique 1975 ♂
ESSENZA DI MEDITERRANEÒ UOMO   Parah 1999
LE DANDY   d'Orsay 1923/98
SPAZIO KRIZIA UOMO   Krizia 1993
SPRINGFIELD   Puig 1993
VETIVER   L'Artisan Parfumeur 1978
VOLEUR DE ROSES   L'Artisan Parfumeur 1993 ♂

Classical / Classique

AZURÉE   Estée Lauder 1969
BANDIT   Robert Piguet 1944
CABOCHARD   Grès 1959
CACHET* (Original)   Prince Matchabelli 1970
CUIR DE RUSSIE   Chanel 1924
CUIR DE RUSSIE   L.T.Piver 1939 ♂
DIORLING   Christian Dior 1963
DONNA KARAN   Donna Karan 1992
EAU D'HERMÈS   Hermès 1951 ♂
EMPREINTE   Courrèges 1971/92
IMPRÉVU   Coty 1966
LA PERLA   La Perla 1987
MISS BALMAIN   Pierre Balmain 1967
POMPEÏA   L.T.Piver 1907
TABAC BLOND   Caron 1919
TRUSSARDI   Trussardi 1982

ARAMIS   Aramis 1965
ARAMIS GOLD   Aramis 1998
ATMAN   Atman 1998
BALADIN   Patricia de Nicolaï 1994
BARBIER DES ISLES   Comptoir Sud Pacifique 1978
CENTAURE CUIR ÉTALON   Pierre Cardin 1996
ᶜN   California North 1995
CRABTREE & EVELYN FOR MEN   Crabtree & Evelyn 1984
CUIR DE RUSSIE   L.T.Piver 1939 ♂
DUNHILL   Dunhill 1934
EAU D'HERMÈS   Hermès 1951 ♂
ETIENNE AIGNER N° 1*   Etienne Aigner 1975
IGNIS   Omar Sharif 1994
IMPERIAL LEATHER   Cussons 1976
KNIZE TEN   Knize 1924
LANCETTI MONSIEUR   Lancetti 1995
LUCIANO PAVAROTTI   Pavarotti 1994
MISSONI UOMO   Missoni 1983
PERRY ELLIS FOR MEN   Perry Ellis 1985/96
PIROGUIER   Comptoir Sud Pacifique 1990
PORTOS*   Balenciaga 1980
ROYAL ENGLISH LEATHER   Creed 1781
SANTAL   L'Artisan Parfumeur 1978
SIESTE   Fragonard 1999
TECK   Molinard 1989
VÉTIVER   Annick Goutal 1985
VETIVER   Etro 1989
YOU'RE THE FIRE FOR MEN   Yardley 1989

Rich / Profond

DZING!   L'Artisan Parfumeur 1999
L'AUTRE   Diptyque 1973 ♂
LA NUIT   Paco Rabanne 1985
MONTANA PARFUM DE PEAU   Montana 1986
PALAIS JAMAIS   Etro 1989 ♂

ANTAEUS   Chanel 1981
BEL AMI   Hermès 1986
CIGARILLO   Rémy Latour 1996
DAVIDOFF   Davidoff 1984
DAVINCI CLASSICO   Davinci 1991
DEEP FOREST   Bogner 1995
DERBY   Guerlain 1985
EAU DES ÎLES   Maître Parfumeur et Gantier 1988
EAU DU NAVIGATEUR   L'Artisan Parfumeur 1982
ELYSEOS HOMME   Elysios 1997
FENDI UOMO   Fendi 1988
HO HANG CLUB*   Balenciaga 1986
HOMME DE GRÈS   Grès 1996
JIL SANDER MAN PURE   Jil Sander 1981
KRIZIA UOMO   Krizia 1984
L'AUTRE   Diptyque 1973 ♂
L'HOMME DE VENTILO   Ventilo 1998
LA BASE FOR HIM   Magic Helvetia 1994
LÉONARD POUR HOMME*   Léonard 1980
MACASSAR   Rochas 1980
MÉCHANT LOUP   L'Artisan Parfumeur 1997
MONSIEUR JOVAN*   Jovan 1975
ONE MAN SHOW   Jacques Bogart 1980
PALAIS JAMAIS   Etro 1989 ♂
PARFUM D'HABIT   Maître Parfumeur et Gantier 1988
ROCABAR   Hermès 1998
S.T.DUPONT HOMME   S.T.Dupont 1998
TABAROME   Creed 1875/1999
VAN CLEEF & ARPELS POUR HOMME   Van Cleef & Arpels 1978
VANITECK   Molinard 1996
YATAGAN   Caron 1976

Aromatic

This is the universal fragrance family, with sexy cool-warm notes of citrus and lavender, sweet spices and oriental woods. It takes its name from a fragrance long since discontinued: Fougère Royale, introduced by Houbigant in 1882. Men grew up on Fougères. Most of the key men's fragrances developed since the mid-1960s have come from this family; their zesty, masculine character makes men feel comfortable. Most women, too, find the blend of Fresh, Floral, Oriental and Woody notes appealing. It is a winning combination.

Voici une famille de parfums universels, avec ses notes « sexy » qui créent une sorte de chaud-et-froid à partir de l'hespéridé et de la lavande, des épices douces et des bois orientaux. Son nom vient d'un parfum disparu depuis longtemps : Fougère Royale, introduit par Houbigant en 1882. Devenir un homme voulait aussi dire porter des senteurs de Fougère. La plupart des parfums masculins développés depuis le milieu des années 60 proviennent de cette famille. Son zeste et son caractère nettement masculin conviennent bien aux hommes. Beaucoup de femmes trouvent aussi la combinaison Frais, Floral, Oriental et Boisé séduisante. C'est une formule qui a beaucoup de succès.

Fougère

Fresh / Frais

AQUA RELAX   Biotherm 1999
cK BE   Calvin Klein 1996 ♂
ESPRIT DE LAVANDE   Penhaligon's 1976 ♂
LEMON SORBET   Etro 1989 ♂
MERGE   Xan Kim 1999 ♂

Crisp / Pétillant

BLACK SILVER   MCM 1998 ♂
COUNTRY WEEKEND   Escada 1996 ♂
EAU SANS PAREIL   Penhaligon's 1992 ♂
GREEN GENERATION   Pino Silvestre-Mavive 1996 ♂
ORANGE SPICE   Creed 1950 ♂
VERTIGO FOR WOMEN   Paul Djirkali 1998

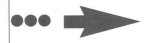

Classical / Classique

CROWN COURT BOUQUET   Crown 1882
EAU D'ÉLIDE   Diptyque 1988 ♂
ENGLISH FERN   Penhaligon's 1911 ♂
GINGHAM   Innoxa 1970
HEAVEN SENT   Mem / Dana 1941
JEAN NATÉ   Ritz 1935
JICKY   Guerlain 1889 ♂
MA LIBERTÉ*   Jean Patou 1987
MOOVING   Gilles Cantuel 1994
OPOPONAX   Comptoir Sud Pacifique 1992

Rich / Profond

Aromatic

Fougère

Fresh / Frais

Aromatic / Aromatique

ADVENTURE QUASAR   J. del Pozo 1999
ANDY WARHOL FOR MEN   Cofinluxe 1999
AVATAR   Coty 1997
AZZARO POUR HOMME   Loris Azzaro 1978
CASSINI FOR MEN   Oleg Cassini 1995
CENTAURE CUIR FOUGÈRE   Pierre Cardin 1996
CHAPEAU   Borsalino 1997
CONSENT MAN   Consent 2000
CURVE FOR MEN   Liz Claiborne 1996
DALI   Salvador Dali 1996
DANIEL HECHTER SPORT   Daniel Hechter 1999
DEAUVILLE POUR HOMME   Michel Germain 1999
DISCOVERY   Conroy 1992
ÉGOÏSTE PLATINUM   Chanel 1993
ELEMENTS   Hugo Boss 1993
ESPRIT DE LAVANDE   Penhaligon's 1976 ♂
GFF UOMO   Gianfranco Ferré 1997
GOLD   Yardley / Parfums Bleu 1983
GREEN GENERATION HIM   Pino Silvestre-Mavive 1998
GRIGIO PERLA   La Perla 1991
ICEBERG TWICE HOMME   Iceberg 1995
INSATIABLE   Pierre Cardin 1995
JAZZ   Yves Saint Laurent 1988
JIVAGO 24k MEN   Jivago 1995
L'UOMO TRUSSARDI   Trussardi 1995
LANVIN L'HOMME   Lanvin 1997
MATCH PLAY   Golf Elegance 1990
MICHAEL JORDAN   Bijan 1996
MOLTO SMALTO*   Francesco Smalto 1992
ON AIR HOMME   Morabito 1998
PERRY ELLIS PORTFOLIO   Perry Ellis 1999
PREFERRED STOCK   Coty 1990
R de CAPUCCI   Roberto Capucci 1985
ROUTE 66 COLORADO RAIN   Coty 1997
SAFARI FOR MEN   Ralph Lauren 1992
SECRET MÉLANGE   Maître Parfumeur et Gantier 1988
SERGIO TACCHINI   Sergio Tacchini 1987
SILVER JEANS HOMME   Roccobarocco 1995
SPORT 2000   Davinci 1997
STATEMENT FOR MEN   Etienne Aigner 1994
STETSON SIERRA   Coty 1993
TABAC EXTREME   Mäurer & Wirtz 1991
TSAR   Van Cleef & Arpels 1989
TUSCANY PER UOMO   Aramis 1984
UNGARO POUR L'HOMME III   Ungaro 1993
UNIVERSO   Coty 1994
XS POUR HOMME   Paco Rabanne 1993
YARDLEY GOLD   Yardley 1983

Crisp / Pétillant

Aromatic / Aromatique

ADIDAS ACTIVE BODIES   Adidas 1990
ADIDAS ADVENTURE   Adidas 1992
ARROGANCE UOMO   Arrogance 1987
BARYSHNIKOV   Mikhail Baryshnikov 1991
BAYWATCH MAN   Baywatch 1996
BE BOP POUR HOMME   Kesling 1992
BIJAN FOR MEN   Bijan 1981
BLACK JEANS   Versace 1997
BLACK SILVER   MCM 1998 ♂
BOGNER MAN II   Bogner 1988
BOSS NUMBER ONE   Hugo Boss 1985
BOSS SPORT*   Hugo Boss 1987
BOSTON MAN   Puig 1989
BOWLING GREEN   Geoffrey Beene 1987
BRISTOL BLUE   Applewoods 1996
BRUT INSTINCT   Fabergé 1997
BUCKINGHAM   Crown 1880
BURBERRY FOR MEN   Burberry 1992/95
CAESARS MAN   Caesars World 1988
CALIFORNIA FOR MEN   Jaclyn Smith 1990
CALVIN   Calvin Klein 1981
CAPTAIN*   Molyneux 1975
CENTAURE DIAMANT NOIR   Pierre Cardin 1998
CENTAURE TÊTE D'OR   Pierre Cardin 1998
C'EST MAGIQUE HOMME   Kesling 1997
CRUISER FOR MEN   Lomani 1998
DISCOVER   Juvena 1994
DRAKKAR NOIR   Guy Laroche 1982
DUC DE VERVINS   Houbigant / Claire 1991
EAU SANS PAREIL   Penhaligon's 1992 ♂
EL PASO   Lomani 1993
ENGLISH BLAZER   Yardley / Parfums Bleu 1989
EXTASE EXOTIC NATURE MAN   Muelhens 1997
GARRIGUE   Maître Parfumeur et Gantier 1988
HOLLYWOOD FOR MEN   Fred Hayman 1998
INSTINCT   Les Floralies 1993
JIL SANDER MAN III*   Jil Sander 1987
L'HOMME   Roger & Gallet 1980
LATITUDE   Olivier de Kersauson 1992
LOMANI   Lomani 1987
LORESTE   Loreste 1987
MANDATE   Shulton / H&BF 1976
MASERATI   Italart 1989
MR J   Fashion Fair 1975
NICKI LAUDA   Florbath 1978
OLD SPICE WHITEWATER   Shulton / P&G 1997
PACO RABANNE POUR HOMME   Paco Rabanne 1973
PARFUM D'HOMME   Kristel Saint Martin 1995
PASHA   Cartier 1992
RAFALE   Molinard 1977/94
RAPPORT   Shulton / H&BF 1988
RED FOR MEN   Giorgio Beverly Hills 1990
ROUTE 66   Coty 1995
SALVADOR   Salvador Dali 1992
SANDER FOR MEN   Jil Sander 1999
SANTOS   Cartier 1981
SCAPA POUR HOMME   Scapa of Scotland 1994
SERGIO TACCHINI UOMO   Sergio Tacchini 1996
SUNG HOMME   Alfred Sung 1988
TRIESTE   Conroy 1993
VERINO POUR HOMME   Roberto Verino 1999
VORAGO   California Fragrances 1987
WATT FOR MEN   Cofinluxe 1991
WORTH POUR HOMME   Worth 1981
XERYUS   Givenchy 1986
ZEGNA   Ermenegildo Zegna 1992

Classical / Classique

BRITISH STERLING   Mem / Dana 1965
BRUT   Fabergé 1964
CANOÉ   Dana 1936
CENTAURE   Maître Parfumeur et Gantier 1991
CROWN FOUGÈRE   Crown 1885
DOLCE & GABBANA POUR HOMME   Dolce & Gabbana 1994
EAU D'ÉLIDE   Diptyque 1988 ♂
EAU DU CONTADOUR   L'Occitane 1994
ENGLISH FERN   Penhaligon's 1911 ♂
EQUATEUR   Bourjois 1993
FOUGÈRE ROYALE*   Houbigant 1882
JADE EAST   Swank / Regency 1964
JICKY   Guerlain 1889 ♂
MENNEN SKIN BRACER   Mennen 1931
MONSIEUR ROCHAS   Rochas 1969
MOUCHOIR DE MONSIEUR   Guerlain 1904
N° 89   Floris 1950
ONLY FOR MEN   Julio Iglesias 1991
PATOU POUR HOMME PRIVÉ   Jean Patou 1994
POLICE   Police 1998
PUB   Revlon 1965
RACQUETS FORMULA   Penhaligon's 1989
SILVER   Mem / Dana 1989
THE BARON   Evyan / LTL 1965/96
TOUCH FOR MEN*   Fred Hayman 1995

Rich / Profond

ARIOS   Parour 1994
BASALA   Shiseido 1993
CIGAR AFICIONADO   Cigar Aficionado 1997
ÉQUIPAGE   Hermès 1970
ETIENNE AIGNER N° 2   Etienne Aigner 1976
GUESS FOR MEN*   Georges Marciano 1991
HAVANA   Aramis 1994
JAGUAR   Jaguar 1988
JULES   Christian Dior 1980
KOUROS   Yves Saint Laurent 1981
LAPIDUS POUR HOMME   Ted Lapidus 1987
LAVANDE   L'Occitane 1999
MONSIEUR LÉONARD   Léonard 1992
PIERRE CARDIN MUSK   Pierre Cardin 1987
ROCCOBAROCCO*   Roccobarocco 1989
ROYAL WATER   Creed 1997
TENAZ   Daniel de Fasson 1994
THIRD MAN / 3ᵉ HOMME   Caron 1985
VAN GILS   Van Gils 1988
YOHJI HOMME   Yohji Yamamoto 1999

Fresh / Frais

Citrus / Hespéridé

ASPEN FOR MEN   Coty 1989
BENETTON SPORT MAN   Benetton 1999
BUGATTI   Ettore Bugatti 1992/99
BULGARI POUR HOMME   Bulgari 1995
CANDIE'S MEN   Liz Claiborne 1999
cK BE   Calvin Klein 1996 ♂
CLEAR DAY FOR MEN   Etienne Aigner 1998
DKNY MEN   Donna Karan 2000
DV8 FOR MEN   Davinci 1997
EAU DES 4 VOLEURS   L'Occitane 1991
EAU FRESH   Jacques Bogart 1993
FREE WORLD MAN   Mäurer & Wirtz 1999
FUN WATER FOR MEN   De Ruy 1996
GREEN JEANS   Versace 1996
HÉROS SPORT   Didier Calvo-Uomo 1997
HORIZON   Guy Laroche 1993
LACOSTE 2000   Lacoste 1999
LEMON SORBET   Etro 1989 ♂
M pour MONSIEUR   Marc de la Morandière 1992
MANÈS ICE   Rémy Latour 1997
MERGE   Xan Kim 1999 ♂
NAVIGATOR   Dana 1996
OLYMPIOS   Missoni 1994
ROLAND GARROS   Coty 1992
SUMATRA RAIN FRESH   Muelhens 1997
TOMMY   Tommy Hilfiger 1995
VUARNET   Vuarnet 1999
WILD WIND FOR MEN   Gabriela Sabatini 1999
WILKES SAN FRANCISCO   Wilkes Bashford 1999

Fruity / Fruité

360° FOR MEN   Perry Ellis 1995
ACTION UOMO*   Trussardi 1990
ADIDAS MOVES   Adidas 1999
ADOLFO DOMINGUEZ   Adolfo Dominguez 1991
AMERICA FOR MEN   Perry Ellis 1996
ANIMALE FOR MEN   Parlux 1993
BARYSHNIKOV SPORT   Mikhail Baryshnikov 1996
BROOKS BROS   Brooks Bros 1998
CARRÉ D'AS   Patricia de Nicolaï 1995
CELSIUS   Celsius 1989
CHEMISTRY   Clinique 1995
COOL WATER   Davidoff 1988
CYCLE*   Otto Kern 1991
D   Dunhill 1996
DEEP BLUE   Lomani 1994
DESIGN FOR MEN   Paul Sebastian 1995
EAU DU TSAR   Van Cleef & Arpels 1998
ETERNITY FOR MEN   Calvin Klein 1989
FIRE & ICE FOR MEN   Revlon 1994
GMV UOMO   Gian Marco Venturi 1997
GRANITE BLUE   Granite 1996
IMAGE   Cerruti 1998
J.F.   Floris 1993
KYRIAZ   Rémy Latour 1994
LUCKY BRAND MEN'S   Lucky Brand 1997
MACKIE FOR MEN   Bob Mackie 1992
MARBERT MAN TOO   Marbert 1998
MARQUIS   Crown 1928
MARQUIS   Rémy Marquis 1999
MCM 24 MORNING*   MCM 1993
MYSTERY AUSTRALIA MAN   Globe 1998
NAVY FOR MEN   Cover Girl / Dana 1996
NIGHTFLIGHT   Joop! 1992
NIKE   Nike Cosmetics 1991
NOMAD   Crabtree & Evelyn 1999
PERRY ELLIS RESERVE   Perry Ellis 1997

Crisp / Pétillant

Citrus / Hespéridé

BAD BOYS   Viale! 1997
BOGART   Jacques Bogart 1975
BYBLOS UOMO   Byblos 1993
EAU DE SPORT*   Alain Delon 1997
EAU POUR HOMME   Le Jardin Retrouvé 1980
ÉBÈNE   Pierre Balmain 1983
FORMIDABLE HOMME   Kesling 1995
FREEDOM FOR HIM   Tommy Hilfiger 1999
GALILEO DE VIENTO   Muelhens 1995
GREEN GENERATION   Pino Silvestre-Mavive 1996 ♂
HEAVEN   Chopard 1994
KOUROS FRAÎCHEUR   Yves Saint Laurent 1993
LACOSTE   Lacoste 1984
LANCETTI POUR HOMME   Lancetti 1999
LAUDER FOR MEN   Estée Lauder 1987
PHOTO   Lagerfeld 1990
RÄKS   André Barnwell 1998
TABAC ORIGINAL (Aftershave)   Mäurer & Wirtz 1959

Fruity / Fruité

GLOBE*   Rochas 1990
GOODLIFE   Davidoff 1998
JOSEPH ABBOUD   EuroItalia 1993
OMAR SHARIF POUR HOMME   Omar Sharif 1992
ORPHÉE   Maxim's 1998
PUMA CHALLENGE   Muelhens 1998
SOPRANI ACTIVE MAN   Luciano Soprani 1994
VÉTIVER DRY   Carven 1988

Classical / Classique

Rich / Profond

Fougère

Fresh / Frais

Fruity / Fruité

PHAROS   Alain Delon 1997
PLEASURES FOR MEN   Estée Lauder 1997
REBEL ... JAMES DEAN   Kraft International 1998
ROMANCE MEN   Ralph Lauren 1999
ROYAL GREEN   Seve Ballesteros 1992
SPORTIF   Pierre Cardin 1996
STREET GAMES   Karl Moran 1997
U de V   Ulric de Varens 1993
VERTIGO FOR MEN   Paul Djirkali 1995
VIKING   Royal Copenhagen 1999
WINGS FOR MEN   Giorgio Beverly Hills 1994
YARDLEY ORIGINAL   Yardley 1992

Green / Vert

ADIDAS ACTION   Adidas 1998
ALVIERO MARTINI UOMO   Atkinson 1997
BLUE STRATOS   Shulton / Parfums Bleu 1975
CAFÉ-CAFÉ POUR HOMME   Cofinluxe 1996
CHIARA BONI UOMO   Chiara Boni 1997
COUNTRY ROAD MAN   Country Road 1999
CROSSROADS   Amway 1997
DRAKKAR DYNAMIK   Guy Laroche 1999
HUGO   Hugo Boss 1995
LUCIANO   Pavarotti 1999
SPORT MAXIMUM   Davinci 1999
SWISS ARMY   Precise International 1996
WHAT ABOUT ADAM   Joop! 1997
ZIPPED SPORTS   Perfumer's Workshop 1999

Water / Marine

ADIDAS DYNAMIC   Adidas 1997
AQUA QUORUM   Puig 1994
BLUE   Parfums Bleu 1997
BRUT ACTIF BLUE   Fabergé 1994
CLAIBORNE SPORT   Liz Claiborne 1997
CULTURE by TABAC BLUE   Mäurer & Wirtz 1999
ESCAPE FOR MEN   Calvin Klein 1993
FACE À FACE HOMME   Façonnable 1996
FAÇONNABLE   Façonnable 1994
GALILEO 21st CENTURY   Muelhens 1997
GMV ENERGY   Gian Marco Venturi 1998
GRANITE ORIGINAL   Granite 1992
ICE WATER*   Pino Silvestre-Mavive 1992
INSENSÉ ULTRAMARINE   Givenchy 1994
JAGUAR SPECIAL EDITION   Jaguar 1998
LIVE JAZZ   Yves Saint Laurent 1998
MILLENNIUM HOPE MAN   Jivago 1999
MONSIEUR MORABITO   Morabito 1994
NK   Nike Cosmetics 1997
POLO SPORT   Ralph Lauren 1994
PUMA INDEPENDENCE   Muelhens 1997
QUASAR   J. del Pozo 1994
ROYAL COPENHAGEN SPORT*   Royal Copenhagen 1996
SAMBA NATURAL MAN   Perfumer's Workshop 1997
SO ... FOR HIM   Yardley / Bond Street 1998

Spicy / Epicé

BLEU FORMIDABLE   Kesling 1998
EMOZIONI FOR MAN   Fila 1997
PEN DUICK   Eric Tabarly 1998
PIAZZA DI SPAGNA UOMO   Roccobarroco 1998
RYKIEL HOMME   Sonia Rykiel 1999
SERGIO TACCHINI SPORT EXTREME   Sergio Tacchini 1993
SUD EST   Romeo Gigli 1995
VOLCANO HOMME   Lomani 1999

Crisp / Pétillant

Green / Vert

ACIER   Bourjois 1988
CENTAURE CUIR CASAQUE   Pierre Cardin 1996
COUNTRY WEEKEND   Escada 1996 ♂
GUCCI NOBILE*   Gucci 1988
MOLINARD HOMME I   Molinard 1996
SUMATRA RAIN   Muelhens 1993

Spicy / Epicé

ANTHRACITE POUR L'HOMME   Jacomo 1991
ARROGANCE YOU   Arrogance 1997
BORSALINO   Borsalino 1984
CACHAREL POUR L'HOMME   Cacharel 1981
CULTURE by TABAC   Mäurer & Wirtz 1996
DUNHILL EDITION   Dunhill 1985
ELEMENTS AQUA   Hugo Boss 1996
ENIGME   Pierre Cardin 1992
EPICÉA   Creed 1965
GALE HAYMAN MAN   Gale Hayman 1997
GOLD JEANS HOMME   Roccobarocco 1997
HO HANG   Balenciaga 1971
LOEWE POUR HOMME   Loewe 1974
M de BOURBON   Marina de Bourbon 1997
MARBERT MAN   Marbert 1977
OPEN   Roger & Gallet 1985
ORANGE SPICE   Creed 1950 ♂
PRESSURE   Rémy Latour 1999
WEIL POUR HOMME   Weil 1980/97

 **Classical / Classique**

 **Rich / Profond**

5th AVENUE *Floral / Florale 34* ●
24, FAUBOURG *Floral / Florale 36* ●●
25 *Woody Oriental / Oriental Boisé 60* ●
57 FOR HER *Floral / Florale 32* ●●
100% PURE CHIPIE GREEN *Floral / Florale 32* ●
100% PURE CHIPIE PURPLE *Woody Oriental / Oriental Boisé 60* ●
212 *Soft Floral / Fleuri Aldéhydé 42* ●
273 FOR WOMEN *Floral / Florale 33* ●●●
360° FOR WOMEN *Floral / Florale 32* ●●
1000 *Floral / Florale 33* ●●●●
2000 ET UNE RÔSE Ⓛ *Floral / Florale 31* ●●●
2020 → COURRÈGES 2020
4711 ORIGINAL ♂ *Citrus / Hespéridé 17* ●●●

A

À LA FRANÇAISE *Floral / Florale 32* ●●
ACACIOSA *Floral / Florale 36* ●
ACCENTI *Floral Oriental / Fleuri Oriental 48* ●
ACQUA CLASSICA DI BORSARI ♂ *Citrus / Hespéridé 17* ●●●
ACQUA DI FIORI *Floral / Florale 36* ●
ACQUA DI GIÒ *Floral / Florale 36* ●
ACQUA DI PARMA ♂ *Citrus / Hespéridé 17* ●●●
ACTE 2 *Soft Floral / Fleuri Aldéhydé 42* ●●
ACTION Trussardi* *Green / Vert 22* ●●
ADIDAS WOMAN *Floral / Florale 34* ●
ADIDAS WOMAN SPORT *Floral / Florale 32* ●
ADIEU SAGESSE *Floral / Florale 30* ●●
ADRIENNE VITTADINI *Oriental / Oriental 56* ●
AGUA FRESCA DE ROSAS *Floral / Florale 30* ●●
AGUA LAVANDA ♂ *Floral / Florale 31* ●●●
AIMEZ-MOI *Soft Floral / Fleuri Aldéhydé 43* ●●●●
AIR DE SAMSARA → UN AIR DE SAMSARA
AIRE → GIORGIO AIRE*
AIRE LOEWE *Green / Vert 23* ●●●
ALABASTER *Soft Floral / Fleuri Aldéhydé 42* ●
ALCHIMIE *Floral Oriental / Fleuri Oriental 46* ●●
ALEGRIA *Floral / Florale 32* ●●
ALEXANDRA *Soft Oriental / Oriental Doux 53* ●●●
ALIAGE / ALLIAGE *Green / Vert 23* ●●●
ALL ABOUT EVE *Woody Oriental / Oriental Boisé 60* ●
ALLURE *Floral Oriental / Fleuri Oriental 46* ●
ALPONA *Citrus / Hespéridé 17* ●●●●
ALVIERO MARTINI DONNA *Floral Oriental / Fleuri Oriental 46* ●
ALYSSA ASHLEY MUSK *Soft Floral / Fleuri Aldéhydé 43* ●●●●
ALYSSA ASHLEY VANILLA *Woody Oriental / Oriental Boisé 60* ●
AMARIGE *Floral Oriental / Fleuri Oriental 46* ●●
AMAZING *Soft Floral / Fleuri Aldéhydé 42* ●●
AMAZONE *Floral / Florale 32* ●●
AMBER & LAVENDER ♂ *Woody Oriental / Oriental Boisé 61* ●●●
AMBRE *Oriental / Oriental 57* ●●●
AMBRE CANNELLE *Soft Oriental / Oriental Doux 53* ●●●
AMBRE PRÉCIEUX ♂ *Oriental / Oriental 57* ●●●●
AMBUSH *Woody Oriental / Oriental Boisé 60* ●●
AMERICA FOR WOMEN *Floral / Florale 32* ●
AMOUAGE *Soft Floral / Fleuri Aldéhydé 43* ●●●●
AMOUR D'AMANDIER *Floral / Florale 32* ●●
AMOUR DE CACAO *Oriental / Oriental 56* ●●
AMOUR DE PATOU → UN AMOUR DE PATOU
AMOUR AMOUR *Floral / Florale 33* ●●●●
AMULETI *Floral / Florale 32* ●
ANAÏS ANAÏS *Floral / Florale 36* ●
ANDY WARHOL FOR WOMEN *Floral / Florale 32* ●
ANGEL *Woody Oriental / Oriental Boisé 60* ●
ANGEL INNOCENT *Woody Oriental / Oriental Boisé 60* ●
ANGÉLIQUE ENCENS *Oriental / Oriental 57* ●●●
ANIMALE *Mossy Woods / Chypre Boisé 67* ●●●●
ANIMALE ANIMALE *Floral Oriental / Fleuri Oriental 46* ●●
ANNA SUI *Soft Floral / Fleuri Aldéhydé 42* ●●
ANNABELLA *Green / Vert 22* ●
ANNE KLEIN* *Soft Floral / Fleuri Aldéhydé 42* ●
ANNE KLEIN II* *Oriental / Oriental 56* ●
ANNE PLISKA *Soft Oriental / Oriental Doux 53* ●●●
ANOUCHKA *Mossy Woods / Chypre Boisé 66* ●●
ANOUCK *Floral / Florale 34* ●
ANTHRACITE *Floral Oriental / Fleuri Oriental 46* ●

ANTICIPATE / SULTRY *Floral Oriental / Fleuri Oriental 48* ●●
ANTILOPE *Mossy Woods / Chypre Boisé 67* ●●●
ANTONIA'S FLOWERS *Floral / Florale 30* ●●
APHRODISIA* *Mossy Woods / Chypre Boisé 66* ●●
APOGÉE *Mossy Woods / Chypre Boisé 67* ●●●
APRÈS L'ONDÉE *Floral Oriental / Fleuri Oriental 48* ●
APRIL FIELDS *Floral / Florale 34* ●
APRIL VIOLETS *Floral / Florale 31* ●●●●
AQUA RELAX *Aromatic / Fougère 76* ●
AQUAFLORE *Water / Marine 26* ●
ARIA MISSONI *Floral / Florale 32* ●●
ARMANI *Mossy Woods / Chypre Boisé 66* ●
AROMANTIC *Floral / Florale 34* ●
AROMATICS ELIXIR *Dry Woods / Chypre Cuir 72* ●
AROMATONIC *Citrus / Hespéridé 16* ●
ARÔME 3 ♂ *Floral / Florale 31* ●●●
ARÔME 3 TRADITION ♂ *Floral / Florale 31* ●●●●
ARPÈGE *Soft Floral / Fleuri Aldéhydé 43* ●●●●
ARROGANCE ME *Floral / Florale 36* ●
ARROGANCE POUR FEMME *Floral / Florale 32* ●●
ARSENAL FOR WOMAN *Floral Oriental / Fleuri Oriental 46* ●●
ASJA *Soft Oriental / Oriental Doux 53* ●●●
ASPEN FOR WOMEN *Water / Marine 27* ●●●
ASPEN SENSATION *Floral / Florale 34* ●
ASPHALT FLOWER *Floral / Florale 33* ●●●●
ATKINSON GOLD MEDAL ♂ *Citrus / Hespéridé 17* ●●●
ATREVIDA *Floral Oriental / Fleuri Oriental 46* ●●
ATTAR *Oriental / Oriental 57* ●●●●
AUBUSSON COULEURS *Floral / Florale 32* ●
AUDACE *Mossy Woods / Chypre Boisé 67* ●●●
AURA LOEWE *Floral Oriental / Fleuri Oriental 46* ●
AUTHENTIC MAROUSSIA *Floral Oriental / Fleuri Oriental 48* ●
AV *Floral / Florale 36* ●●
AYAKO *Oriental / Oriental 56* ●
AZURÉE *Dry Woods / Chypre Cuir 73* ●●●
AZZARO *Mossy Woods / Chypre Boisé 67* ●●●
AZZARO 9 *Floral / Florale 33* ●●●●
AZZURA *Floral / Florale 32* ●●

B

BABY DOLL PARIS *Floral / Florale 32* ●
BABYLON *Soft Floral / Fleuri Aldéhydé 43* ●●●●
BAL À VERSAILLES *Floral Oriental / Fleuri Oriental 47* ●●●
BALAHÉ *Floral Oriental / Fleuri Oriental 47* ●●●
BALANCE *Floral / Florale 32* ●
BALMAIN *Mossy Woods / Chypre Boisé 66* ●
BAMBOU *Floral / Florale 32* ●●
BANDIT *Dry Woods / Chypre Cuir 73* ●●●
BAROQUE *Floral Oriental / Fleuri Oriental 46* ●●
BARYSHNIKOV POUR FEMME *Floral / Florale 33* ●●●
BASILIC FLEUR D'ORANGER *Floral / Florale 31* ●●●●
BAYWATCH WOMAN *Floral / Florale 32* ●●
BE BOP *Floral / Florale 32* ●●
BEAUTIFUL *Floral / Florale 32* ●●
BELLA FIRENZE *Floral Oriental / Fleuri Oriental 46* ●
BELLE DE RAUCH *Floral / Florale 33* ●●●
BELLODGIA *Floral / Florale 31* ●●●●
BENETTON SPORT WOMAN *Floral / Florale 32* ●
BERNINI WOMEN *Floral Oriental / Fleuri Oriental 46* ●
BEST LADY *Floral / Florale 33* ●●●
BEST OF CHEVIGNON ♂ *Water / Marine 27* ●●●
BETTY BARCLAY* *Floral Oriental / Fleuri Oriental 48* ●●
BETTY BARCLAY WOMAN *Floral / Florale 36* ●
BETTY BARCLAY WOMAN N° 2 *Floral Oriental / Fleuri Oriental 48* ●
BEVERLY HILLS *Woody Oriental / Oriental Boisé 60* ●
BIBI *Woody Oriental / Oriental Boisé 60* ●
BIJAN *Woody Oriental / Oriental Boisé 61* ●●●
BILL BLASS *Floral / Florale 33* ●●●●
BIRMANE *Floral / Florale 32* ●●
BLACK JEANS FEMME *Floral / Florale 33* ●●●●
BLACK PEARLS* *Floral Oriental / Fleuri Oriental 46* ●
BLACK SILVER ♂ *Aromatic / Fougère 76* ●●
BLACK TIE *Woody Oriental / Oriental Boisé 60* ●
BLASÉ *Soft Floral / Fleuri Aldéhydé 43* ●●●●
BLEU DE CHINE *Soft Oriental / Oriental Doux 53* ●●●●

BLONDE → VERSACE'S BLONDE
BLU BLUMARINE *Floral / Florale* 36 ●●
BLUEBELL Penhaligon's *Floral / Florale* 34 ●
BLUE DREAM *Floral / Florale* 32 ●●
BLUE GRASS *Floral / Florale* 33 ●●●●
BLUMARINE *Soft Floral / Fleuri Aldéhydé* 42 ●●
BOB MACKIE → MACKIE
BOBBI *Floral / Florale* 34 ●
BOIS DE CÉDRAT ♂ *Citrus / Hespéridé* 17 ●●●
BOIS DES ÎLES *Woody Oriental / Oriental Boisé* 61 ●●●
BOLERO *Floral / Florale* 32 ●●
BOND *Oriental / Oriental* 56 ●
BONJOUR *Floral Oriental / Fleuri Oriental* 46 ●●
BORONIA *Floral / Florale* 31 ●●●
BORSALINO DONNA → DONNA BORSALINO
BOUCHERON *Floral Oriental / Fleuri Oriental* 47 ●●●
BOUDOIR *Floral Oriental / Fleuri Oriental* 47 ●●●
BOUQUET IMPÉRIAL ♂ *Citrus / Hespéridé* 17 ●●●●
BOUTON D'OR *Floral / Florale* 32 ●
BOUVARDIA* *Floral Oriental / Fleuri Oriental* 47 ●●●
BULGARI BLACK ♂ *Dry Woods / Chypre Cuir* 72 ●●
BULGARI POUR FEMME *Floral / Florale* 33 ●●●
BULGARI EAU PARFUMÉE ♂ *Citrus / Hespéridé* 16 ●
BULLES DE FRAÎCHEUR *Citrus / Hespéridé* 16 ●
BURBERRY FOR WOMEN *Floral Oriental / Fleuri Oriental* 46 ●
BY WOMAN *Woody Oriental / Oriental Boisé* 61 ●●●
BYBLOS *Floral / Florale* 32 ●●
BYZANCE *Floral Oriental / Fleuri Oriental* 48 ●●
BYZANTINE *Floral Oriental / Fleuri Oriental* 48 ●

C

CABOCHARD *Dry Woods / Chypre Cuir* 73 ●●●
CABOTINE DE GRÈS *Floral / Florale* 34 ●●
CACHET* (Original) *Dry Woods / Chypre Cuir* 73 ●●●
CAESARS WOMAN *Floral / Florale* 33 ●●●●
CAFÉ *Soft Oriental / Oriental Doux* 53 ●●●
CAFÉ-CAFÉ *Soft Floral / Fleuri Aldéhydé* 42 ●●
CALANDRE *Soft Floral / Fleuri Aldéhydé* 42 ●●
CALÈCHE *Mossy Woods / Chypre Boisé* 67 ●●●
CALIFORNIA *Soft Floral / Fleuri Aldéhydé* 43 ●●●●
CÂLINE *Soft Floral / Fleuri Aldéhydé* 42 ●●
CALLA *Soft Oriental / Oriental Doux* 53 ●●●
CALYPSO JASMINE *Floral / Florale* 31 ●●●
CALYPSO MIMOSA *Floral / Florale* 30 ●●
CALYPSO VIOLET *Floral / Florale* 31 ●●●●
CALYX *Floral / Florale* 32 ●
CAMÉLIA CHINOIS *Green / Vert* 23 ●●●●
CAMÉLIA IRIS (BLEU) *Soft Floral / Fleuri Aldéhydé* 42 ●
CAMP BEVERLY HILLS* *Soft Floral / Fleuri Aldéhydé* 42 ●●
CANDIE'S *Floral / Florale* 33 ●●●
CANNELLE ORANGE ♂ *Citrus / Hespéridé* 16 ●
CAPRICCI *Floral / Florale* 33 ●●●
CAPUCCI DE CAPUCCI *Woody Oriental / Oriental Boisé* 60 ●●
CARAMEL PAIN D'ÉPICE *Soft Oriental / Oriental Doux* 52 ●●
CARITA *Water / Marine* 26 ●●
CAROLINA HERRERA *Floral / Florale* 31 ●●●●
CARRIÈRE *Citrus / Hespéridé* 16 ●●
CASCAYA *Floral Oriental / Fleuri Oriental* 46 ●●
CASCAYA SUMMER *Floral / Florale* 34 ●
CASHMERE MIST *Dry Woods / Chypre Cuir* 72 ●
CASMIR *Woody Oriental / Oriental Boisé* 60 ●●
CASSINI *Mossy Woods / Chypre Boisé* 66 ●●
CASSISSIER *Floral / Florale* 34 ●
CASUAL *Floral / Florale* 36 ●
CATALYST *Floral / Florale* 34 ●
C'EST LA VIE* *Floral Oriental / Fleuri Oriental* 46 ●
C'EST MAGIQUE *Floral / Florale* 32 ●●
CE SOIR OU JAMAIS *Floral / Florale* 30 ●●
CÉDRAT POMELO ♂ *Citrus / Hespéridé* 16 ●●
CELEBRATE *Floral / Florale* 32 ●●
CERRUTI 1881 POUR FEMME *Floral / Florale* 32 ●●
CEYLON *Citrus / Hespéridé* 16 ●●
CHALDÉE *Floral Oriental / Fleuri Oriental* 47 ●●●
CHAMADE *Floral Oriental / Fleuri Oriental* 46 ●●
CHAMPAGNE → YVRESSE

CHAMPS-ELYSÉES *Floral / Florale* 32 ●
CHANEL N° 5 *Soft Floral / Fleuri Aldéhydé* 43 ●●●
CHANEL N° 19 *Soft Floral / Fleuri Aldéhydé* 42 ●
CHANEL N° 22 *Floral / Florale* 33 ●●●
CHANSON D'AIR *Floral / Florale* 32 ●
CHANSON D'EAU *Citrus / Hespéridé* 17 ●●●
CHANSON DE VIE *Citrus / Hespéridé* 16 ●
CHANT D'ARÔMES *Mossy Woods / Chypre Boisé* 66 ●●
CHANTILLY *Oriental / Oriental* 57 ●●●
CHAOS* *Woody Oriental / Oriental Boisé* 60 ●●
CHAPEAU BLEU *Mossy Woods / Chypre Boisé* 66 ●●
CHARLIE *Floral / Florale* 34 ●●
CHARLIE GOLD *Floral Oriental / Fleuri Oriental* 46 ●
CHARLIE RED *Floral / Florale* 32 ●●
CHARLIE SILVER *Floral / Florale* 32 ●
CHARLIE SUNSHINE *Floral / Florale* 32 ●
CHARLIE WHITE *Water / Marine* 26 ●
CHARLIE WHITE MUSK *Soft Floral / Fleuri Aldéhydé* 42 ●
CHARTREUSE DE PARME *Floral / Florale* 31 ●●●●
CHAUMET *Floral / Florale* 34 ●
CHEAP & CHIC *Floral / Florale* 32 ●
CHELSEA DREAMS *Floral / Florale* 32 ●●
CHERISH *Floral / Florale* 32 ●
CHERRY MUSK *Floral / Florale* 32 ●●
CHÈVREFEUILLE Le Jardin Retrouvé *Floral / Florale* 30 ●●
CHÈVREFEUILLE Molinard *Floral / Florale* 30 ●●
CHÈVREFEUILLE ORIGINAL Creed ♂ *Green / Vert* 22 ●
CHIARA BONI *Floral / Florale* 31 ●●●●
CHIARA BONI LIGHT *Soft Floral / Fleuri Aldéhydé* 42 ●●
CHIEMSEE *Floral / Florale* 36 ●
CHINA ROSE *Floral Oriental / Fleuri Oriental* 47 ●●●●
CHIQUE *Mossy Woods / Chypre Boisé* 67 ●●●●
CHIPIE *Floral Oriental / Fleuri Oriental* 46 ●
CHOC *Mossy Woods / Chypre Boisé* 66 ●
CHOCOLAT MENTHE *Oriental / Oriental* 56 ●●
CHLOÉ *Floral / Florale* 31 ●●●●
CHLOÉ INNOCENCE* *Floral / Florale* 36 ●
CHLOÉ NARCISSE *Floral Oriental / Fleuri Oriental* 46 ●●
CHRISTIAN LACROIX *Floral / Florale* 34 ●●
CHRISTOS WOMAN *Woody Oriental / Oriental Boisé* 60 ●
CHYPRE DE COTY* *Mossy Woods / Chypre Boisé* 67 ●●●
CIALENGA *Soft Floral / Fleuri Aldéhydé* 42 ●
CIARA *Oriental / Oriental* 57 ●●●●
CIARA FEMME FATALE* *Floral Oriental / Fleuri Oriental* 46 ●●
CIELO *Mossy Woods / Chypre Boisé* 66 ●
CINNABAR *Soft Oriental / Oriental Doux* 53 ●●●
CITRON VERT ♂ *Citrus / Hespéridé* 16 ●
CITRUS BIGARRADE ♂ *Citrus / Hespéridé* 17 ●●●
cK BE ♂ *Aromatic / Fougère* 76 ●
cK ONE ♂ *Citrus / Hespéridé* 16 ●
CLAIRE DE NILANG *Floral / Florale* 32 ●
CLARTÉ *Floral / Florale* 32 ●●
CLASSIC GARDENIA *Floral / Florale* 30 ●●
CLEAR DAY *Floral / Florale* 32 ●●
CLEAR DAY LIGHT *Floral / Florale* 32 ●
CLÉMENTINE *Citrus / Hespéridé* 17 ●●●
CLIMAT *Soft Floral / Fleuri Aldéhydé* 43 ●●●●
COCKTAIL *Mossy Woods / Chypre Boisé* 66 ●
COCO *Soft Oriental / Oriental Doux* 53 ●●●
COEUR DE PARFUM* *Dry Woods / Chypre Cuir* 72 ●●
COEUR D'OR *Woody Oriental / Oriental Boisé* 60 ●
COEUR JOIE *Soft Floral / Fleuri Aldéhydé* 43 ●●●
COLD ♂ *Citrus / Hespéridé* 17 ●●●●
COLÈRE DE RODIER *Woody Oriental / Oriental Boisé* 60 ●
COLOGNE SOLOGNE ♂ *Citrus / Hespéridé* 17 ●●●
COLONY *Mossy Woods / Chypre Boisé* 66 ●●
COLORS Alexander Julian *Soft Floral / Fleuri Aldéhydé* 42 ●
COLORS OF BENETTON *Floral Oriental / Fleuri Oriental* 46 ●
COMME DES GARÇONS ♂ *Mossy Woods / Chypre Boisé* 67 ●●●●
COMME DES GARÇONS 2 ♂ *Mossy Woods / Chypre Boisé* 66 ●
CONFIDENT / CONSIDERATIONS *Mossy Woods / Chypre Boisé* 66 ●
CONSENT WOMAN *Floral / Florale* 36 ●
CONSIDERATIONS / CONFIDENT *Mossy Woods / Chypre Boisé* 66 ●
CONTRADICTION *Floral Oriental / Fleuri Oriental* 46 ●
CONVICTION *Floral Oriental / Fleuri Oriental* 46 ●
COOL WATER WOMAN *Floral / Florale* 36 ●●
CORIANDRE *Mossy Woods / Chypre Boisé* 67 ●●●●

CORNUBIA *Floral Oriental / Fleuri Oriental* 47 ●●●
COTONNADE ♂ *Soft Oriental / Oriental Doux* 52 ●●
COUNTRY ROAD WOMAN *Soft Floral / Fleuri Aldéhydé* 42 ●●
COUNTRY WEEKEND ♂ *Aromatic / Fougère* 76 ●●
COURRÈGES 2020 *Floral / Florale* 32 ●●
COURRÈGES IN BLUE *Floral / Florale* 33 ●●●●
CRÉATION *Mossy Woods / Chypre Boisé* 66 ●
CRÉATURE *Soft Oriental / Oriental Doux* 53 ●●●
CRÉATURE D'ANGES *Floral / Florale* 32 ●●
CRISTAL DE MUSC *Soft Oriental / Oriental Doux* 52 ●
CRISTALLE *Citrus / Hespéridé* 16 ●●
CRISTOBAL *Woody Oriental / Oriental Boisé* 60 ●
CROWN ALPINE LILY *Floral / Florale* 30 ●
CROWN BOUQUET *Floral / Florale* 34 ●●
CROWN COURT BOUQUET *Aromatic / Fougère* 77 ●●●
CROWN ESS BOUQUET *Citrus / Hespéridé* 16 ●
CROWN ESTERHAZY *Citrus / Hespéridé* 17 ●●●
CROWN HELIOTROPE *Woody Oriental / Oriental Boisé* 61 ●●●
CROWN OF GOLD *Soft Oriental / Oriental Doux* 53 ●●●
CROWN ROSE *Floral / Florale* 31 ●●●
CROWN STEPHANOTIS *Floral / Florale* 33 ●●●
CRUISE FOR WOMEN *Oriental / Oriental* 57 ●●●
CRUISER FOR WOMEN *Floral / Florale* 33 ●●●●
CUIR DE RUSSIE Chanel *Dry Woods / Chypre Cuir* 73 ●●●
CUIR DE RUSSIE L.T. Piver ♂ *Dry Woods / Chypre Cuir* 73 ●●●
CURVE FOR WOMEN *Floral / Florale* 32 ●
CYANE* *Woody Oriental / Oriental Boisé* 60 ●
CYBERSP@CE ♂ *Water / Marine* 26 ●

D

D&G FEMININE *Soft Floral / Fleuri Aldéhydé* 43 ●●●●
DALIMANIA *Floral Oriental / Fleuri Oriental* 46 ●●
DALIMIX ♂ *Citrus / Hespéridé* 16 ●
DALIMIX GOLD ♂ *Green / Vert* 22 ●
DALISSIME *Floral / Florale* 32 ●●
DAMASK ROSE *Soft Floral / Fleuri Aldéhydé* 42 ●●
DANIEL DE FASSON *Floral Oriental / Fleuri Oriental* 47 ●●●
DARBY ROSE *Floral / Florale* 31 ●●●
DARK VANILLA *Floral Oriental / Fleuri Oriental* 47 ●●●●
DAZZLING GOLD *Floral / Florale* 32 ●●
DAZZLING SILVER *Soft Floral / Fleuri Aldéhydé* 42 ●●
DE BERCHELAI *Floral / Florale* 32 ●●
DEAUVILLE *Soft Floral / Fleuri Aldéhydé* 42 ●●
DÉCADENCE* *Floral / Florale* 36 ●●
DECI DELÀ *Mossy Woods / Chypre Boisé* 66 ●●
DÉLICE D'ÉPICES *Floral Oriental / Fleuri Oriental* 47 ●●●
"DELICIOUS" *Soft Floral / Fleuri Aldéhydé* 43 ●●●●
"DELICIOUS" FEELINGS *Floral / Florale* 36 ●
DEMI-JOUR* *Soft Floral / Fleuri Aldéhydé* 43 ●●●●
DENEUVE* *Mossy Woods / Chypre Boisé* 66 ●
DÉSIRADE *Floral Oriental / Fleuri Oriental* 46 ●●
DESIGN *Soft Floral / Fleuri Aldéhydé* 42 ●
DESTINY *Floral / Florale* 36 ●
DESTINY WOMAN *Woody Oriental / Oriental Boisé* 60 ●
DETCHÉMA *Soft Floral / Fleuri Aldéhydé* 43 ●●●●
DI BORGHESE* *Green / Vert* 23 ●●●
DI ROMEO GIGLI *Soft Floral / Fleuri Aldéhydé* 43 ●●●●
DIAMANT D'OR *Floral Oriental / Fleuri Oriental* 46 ●●
DIAMONDS & EMERALDS* *Floral / Florale* 36 ●●
DIAMONDS & RUBIES* *Woody Oriental / Oriental Boisé* 61 ●●●
DIAMONDS & SAPPHIRES* *Floral / Florale* 36 ●
DIESEL PLUS PLUS FEMININE *Floral Oriental / Fleuri Oriental* 48 ●
DIESEL ZERO PLUS FEMININE *Woody Oriental / Oriental Boisé* 60 ●
DILYS *Floral / Florale* 33 ●●●●
DIONNE *Oriental / Oriental* 56 ●
DIORAMA *Mossy Woods / Chypre Boisé* 67 ●●●
DIORELLA *Citrus / Hespéridé* 16 ●●
DIORESSENCE *Soft Oriental / Oriental Doux* 53 ●●●
DIORISSIMO *Floral / Florale* 30 ●
DIORLING *Dry Woods / Chypre Cuir* 73 ●●●
DIVA *Mossy Woods / Chypre Boisé* 67 ●●●●
DIVINA *Floral / Florale* 34 ●●
DIVINE FOLIE *Floral Oriental / Fleuri Oriental* 47 ●●●
DKNY WOMEN *Soft Floral / Fleuri Aldéhydé* 42 ●
DNA *Soft Floral / Fleuri Aldéhydé* 43 ●●●●

DOLCE & GABBANA *Soft Floral / Fleuri Aldéhydé* 43 ●●●●
DOLCE VITA *Woody Oriental / Oriental Boisé* 60 ●●
DOLCE VITA, EAU DE *Floral / Florale* 32 ●
DONNA BORSALINO *Floral Oriental / Fleuri Oriental* 46 ●●
DONNA KARAN *Dry Woods / Chypre Cuir* 73 ●●●
DONNA TRUSSARDI *Mossy Woods / Chypre Boisé* 67 ●●●
DOULTON *Floral Oriental / Fleuri Oriental* 46 ●●
DREAMING PRINCESS *Floral Oriental / Fleuri Oriental* 46 ●●
DREAMS BY TABU *Floral / Florale* 36 ●
DRÔLE DE ROSE *Soft Floral / Fleuri Aldéhydé* 42 ●●
DUÉ 2 DAY *Floral / Florale* 32 ●
DUÉ 2 NIGHT *Floral / Florale* 32 ●●
DUENDE *Water / Marine* 26 ●
DULCE VANILLA *Woody Oriental / Oriental Boisé* 60 ●
DUNE *Woody Oriental / Oriental Boisé* 60 ●
DV8 FOR WOMEN *Floral / Florale* 32 ●●
DZING! *Dry Woods / Chypre Cuir* 73 ●●●●

E

EASY KRIZIA *Mossy Woods / Chypre Boisé* 66 ●
EAU BELLE *Citrus / Hespéridé* 16 ●
EAU D'EDEN *Floral / Florale* 36 ●
EAU D'ÉLIDE ♂ *Aromatic / Fougère* 77 ●●●
EAU D'ÉTÉ *Citrus / Hespéridé* 16 ●●
EAU D'HADRIEN ♂ *Citrus / Hespéridé* 17 ●●●
EAU D'HERMÈS ♂ *Dry Woods / Chypre Cuir* 73 ●●●
EAU D'INFINITIF *Floral / Florale* 32 ●●
EAU D'ORANGE VERTE ♂ *Citrus / Hespéridé* 17 ●●●●
EAU D'ORLANE *Citrus / Hespéridé* 16 ●
EAU DE BIARRITZ *Soft Floral / Fleuri Aldéhydé* 42 ●●
EAU DE CAMILLE *Floral / Florale* 34 ●
EAU DE CAMPAGNE ♂ *Green / Vert* 23 ●●●
EAU DE CARON *Oriental / Oriental* 56 ●●
EAU DE CARON FORTE ♂ *Citrus / Hespéridé* 17 ●●●●
EAU DE CÈDRE ♂ *Dry Woods / Chypre Cuir* 72 ●
EAU DE CHARLOTTE *Floral / Florale* 32 ●
EAU DE CHEVERNY ♂ *Mossy Woods / Chypre Boisé* 67 ●●●
EAU DE COLOGNE Penhaligon's ♂ *Citrus / Hespéridé* 17 ●●●
EAU DE CORIANDRE *Floral / Florale* 32 ●
EAU DE COUTURE *Soft Floral / Fleuri Aldéhydé* 43 ●●●●
EAU DE DALI *Floral / Florale* 32 ●
EAU DE DOLCE VITA *Floral / Florale* 32 ●
EAU DE FATH *Floral / Florale* 32 ●
EAU DE FLEURS DE CÉDRAT ♂ *Citrus / Hespéridé* 17 ●●●
EAU DE GIVENCHY *Floral / Florale* 32 ●
EAU DE GUCCI* *Floral / Florale* 36 ●
EAU DE GUERLAIN ♂ *Citrus / Hespéridé* 17 ●●●
EAU DE LANCASTER *Citrus / Hespéridé* 17 ●●●
EAU DE LAVANDE Annick Goutal ♂ *Floral / Florale* 31 ●●●
EAU DE LAVANDE Mont St Michel ♂ *Floral / Florale* 31 ●●●
EAU DE MOOVING *Floral / Florale* 32 ●●
EAU DE MURANO *Floral / Florale* 31 ●●●
EAU DE MÛRE *Citrus / Hespéridé* 17 ●●●
EAU DE PATOU *Citrus / Hespéridé* 17 ●●●
EAU DE PROVENCE ♂ *Floral / Florale* 31 ●●●
EAU DE RÉVILLON *Floral / Florale* 36 ●
EAU DE ROCHAS *Citrus / Hespéridé* 17 ●●●
EAU DE VARENS N° 2 ♂ *Citrus / Hespéridé* 16 ●
EAU DE VARENS N° 3 ♂ *Citrus / Hespéridé* 16 ●●
EAU DE VARENS N° 4 ♂ *Citrus / Hespéridé* 17 ●●●●
EAU DE VERINO *Floral / Florale* 36 ●
EAU DE VERVEINE Penhaligon's ♂ *Citrus / Hespéridé* 17 ●●●●
EAU DU CIEL *Floral / Florale* 34 ●●
EAU DU COQ ♂ *Citrus / Hespéridé* 17 ●●●
EAU DU GANTIER ♂ *Citrus / Hespéridé* 17 ●●●
EAU DU SOIR *Mossy Woods / Chypre Boisé* 67 ●●●
EAU DU SUD ♂ *Citrus / Hespéridé* 16 ●●
EAU DYNAMISANTE ♂ *Citrus / Hespéridé* 17 ●●●
EAU FRAÎCHE Caron ♂ *Citrus / Hespéridé* 17 ●●●
EAU FRAÎCHE Christian Dior *Mossy Woods / Chypre Boisé* 67 ●●●
EAU FRAÎCHE Christian Tortu ♂ *Citrus / Hespéridé* 17 ●●●
EAU FRAÎCHE Elizabeth Arden *Floral / Florale* 30 ●
EAU FRAÎCHE Léonard *Citrus / Hespéridé* 17 ●●●
EAU FRAÎCHE Molinard ♂ *Citrus / Hespéridé* 16 ●●
EAU FRANCE ♂ *Citrus / Hespéridé* 17 ●●●

EAU IMPÉRIALE ♂ *Citrus / Hespéridé* 17 ●●●
EAU LENTE ♂ *Oriental / Oriental* 57 ●●●
EAU LES COEURS *Floral / Florale* 32 ●●
EAU MARINE *Floral / Florale* 36 ●
EAU POUR SOI *Floral / Florale* 32 ●
EAU PURE ♂ *Water / Marine* 26 ●
EAU SANS PAREIL ♂ *Aromatic / Fougère* 76 ●●
EAU SVELTE *Floral / Florale* 32 ●
EAU VITAMINÉE *Citrus / Hespéridé* 16 ●●
EAU VIVE *Citrus / Hespéridé* 16 ●●
ÉCOUTE-MOI *Floral / Florale* 33 ●●●●
ÉCUSSON *Soft Floral / Fleuri Aldéhydé* 43 ●●●
EDEN *Floral Oriental / Fleuri Oriental* 48 ●
EDWARDIAN BOUQUET *Floral / Florale* 36 ●
ÉLÀ NONCHALANCE *Floral / Florale* 36 ●●
ELISABETHAN ROSE *Floral / Florale* 31 ●●●
ELYSEOS FEMME *Floral Oriental / Fleuri Oriental* 46 ●
ELYSIUM *Floral / Florale* 32 ●
EMBRACE* *Soft Floral / Fleuri Aldéhydé* 43 ●●●
ÉMERAUDE *Oriental / Oriental* 57 ●●●
EMOTIONS *Floral Oriental / Fleuri Oriental* 47 ●●●
EMOZIONI FOR WOMAN *Floral / Florale* 36 ●
EMPORIO ARMANI SHE / ELLE *Floral Oriental / Fleuri Oriental* 47 ●●●
EMPREINTE *Dry Woods / Chypre Cuir* 73 ●●●
EN AVION *Floral Oriental / Fleuri Oriental* 47 ●●●●
ENCHANTÉ *Woody Oriental / Oriental Boisé* 60 ●
E.N.C.O.R.E *Woody Oriental / Oriental Boisé* 60 ●
ENERGIZING FRAGRANCE *Soft Floral / Fleuri Aldéhydé* 42 ●●
ENFANTS DU SOLEIL *Floral Oriental / Fleuri Oriental* 46 ●●
ENGLISH FERN ♂ *Aromatic / Fougère* 77 ●●●
ENGLISH FINE COLOGNE ♂ *Citrus / Hespéridé* 17 ●●●
ENGLISH LAVENDER Atkinson ♂ *Floral / Florale* 31 ●●●
ENGLISH LAVENDER Yardley *Floral / Florale* 31 ●●●
ENGLISH ROSE *Floral / Florale* 31 ●●●
ENIGMA *Woody Oriental / Oriental Boisé* 61 ●●●
ENJOLI *Floral / Florale* 31 ●●●●
ENJOLI MIDNIGHT *Soft Oriental / Oriental Doux* 53 ●●●
ENRICO COVERI *Soft Oriental / Oriental Doux* 53 ●●●
ENVY *Floral / Florale* 36 ●
ERUPTION WOMAN *Floral Oriental / Fleuri Oriental* 46 ●●
ESCADA *Floral Oriental / Fleuri Oriental* 47 ●●●
ESCADA COLLECTION *Woody Oriental / Oriental Boisé* 60 ●
ESCADA EN FLEURS *Floral / Florale* 32 ●
ESENCIA DE DUENDE *Floral / Florale* 36 ●
ESCAPE *Water / Marine* 27 ●●●●
ESP STAFAST *Floral / Florale* 33 ●●●●
ESPRIT DE LAVANDE ♂ *Aromatic / Fougère* 76 ●
ESPRIT DU ROI ♂ *Citrus / Hespéridé* 16 ●●
ESSENTIALLY JAGUAR *Floral Oriental / Fleuri Oriental* 46 ●●
ESSENZA DI MEDITERRANEÒ DONNA *Floral / Florale* 32 ●
ESTÉE *Floral / Florale* 33 ●●●●
ESTIVALIA *Citrus / Hespéridé* 16 ●●
ETERNAL ROSE *Floral / Florale* 30 ●●
ETERNITY *Floral / Florale* 36 ●
ÉTHÉRÉ *Floral / Florale* 34 ●
ETIQUETTE BLEUE ♂ *Citrus / Hespéridé* 16 ●●
EUNECE *Woody Oriental / Oriental Boisé* 61 ●●●
ÉVÉ *Soft Oriental / Oriental Doux* 53 ●●●
EVELYN *Floral / Florale* 31 ●●●
EVENING IN PARIS → SOIR DE PARIS ORIGINAL
EXCEPTION *Oriental / Oriental* 56 ●
EXCITING ARROGANCE *Soft Floral / Fleuri Aldéhydé* 42 ●
EX'CLA.MA'TION *Floral Oriental / Fleuri Oriental* 46 ●●
EX'CLA.MA'TION BLUSH *Floral / Florale* 32 ●
EX'CLA.MA'TION DARE *Floral / Florale* 36 ●
EX'CLA.MA'TION EAU *Citrus / Hespéridé* 16 ●
EX'CLA.MA'TION NOIR *Mossy Woods / Chypre Boisé* 67 ●●●
EXPERIENCES *Floral / Florale* 33 ●●●●
EXPLOSIVE* *Mossy Woods / Chypre Boisé* 66 ●●
EXTASE BODY TALK ♂ *Citrus / Hespéridé* 16 ●
EXTASE DEVOTION WOMAN *Woody Oriental / Oriental Boisé* 60 ●
EXTASE EXOTIC NATURE *Floral / Florale* 36 ●●
EXTASE MUSK WOMAN *Oriental / Oriental* 57 ●●●
EXTRACT OF LIMES Penhaligon's ♂ *Citrus / Hespéridé* 17 ●●●●
EXTRAVAGANCE D'AMARIGE *Floral / Florale* 34 ●

FABERGÉ IMPERIAL *Floral / Florale* 33 ●●●●
FABLE *Woody Oriental / Oriental Boisé* 61 ●●●
FABULEUSE *Floral / Florale* 32 ●
FABULOUS *Floral Oriental / Fleuri Oriental* 47 ●●●
FACE À FACE FEMME *Floral / Florale* 34 ●
FANTASIA *Floral / Florale* 32 ●●
FANTASIA DE FLEURS *Floral / Florale* 33 ●●●●
FANTASME *Floral Oriental / Fleuri Oriental* 46 ●●
FARNESIANA *Floral / Florale* 30 ●●
FAROUCHE *Soft Floral / Fleuri Aldéhydé* 42 ●●
FASCINATION *Floral / Florale* 32 ●●
FASHION *Floral Oriental / Fleuri Oriental* 46 ●●
FASHION FAIR N° 1 *Floral / Florale* 34 ●●
FATH DE FATH *Oriental / Oriental* 56 ●●
FEELING FREE *Floral / Florale* 34 ●
FELCE AZZURRA *Soft Oriental / Oriental Doux* 53 ●●●
FEMINA *Floral / Florale* 36 ●
FEMINITÉ DU BOIS *Woody Oriental / Oriental Boisé* 61 ●●●
FEMME *Mossy Woods / Chypre Boisé* 67 ●●●
FENDI *Woody Oriental / Oriental Boisé* 61 ●●●●
FERENTINA *Floral Oriental / Fleuri Oriental* 47 ●●●
FERRARI DONNA *Floral / Florale* 36 ●●
FERRÉ BY FERRÉ *Soft Floral / Fleuri Aldéhydé* 43 ●●●
FÉTICHE *Floral Oriental / Fleuri Oriental* 47 ●●●
FETISH *Floral / Florale* 36 ●
FEU D'ISSEY → LE FEU D'ISSEY
FEUILLE D'HERBE FLORALE FRUITÉE *Mossy Woods / Chypre Boisé* 66 ●
FEUILLE D'HERBE FRAÎCHE EPICÉE
    Woody Oriental / Oriental Boisé 61 ●●●●
FEUILLE D'HERBE FRAÎCHE HERBACÉE *Green / Vert* 22 ●
FEUILLE DE VERVEINE ♂ *Citrus / Hespéridé* 16 ●
FIDJI *Floral / Florale* 34 ●
FILLE D'EVE *Mossy Woods / Chypre Boisé* 67 ●●●
FIORA *Dry Woods / Chypre Cuir* 72 ●●
FIORI DI KRIZIA *Floral / Florale* 32 ●
FIORILU EN FLEURS *Floral / Florale* 32 ●●
FIORUCCI *Floral / Florale* 32 ●●
FIRE & ICE *Oriental / Oriental* 56 ●●
FIRE & ICE COOL *Citrus / Hespéridé* 16 ●
FIRE & ICE SMOULDER FOR HER *Woody Oriental / Oriental Boisé* 60 ●
FIRENZE *Soft Floral / Fleuri Aldéhydé* 42 ●●
FIRST *Soft Floral / Fleuri Aldéhydé* 43 ●●●●
FLEUR Floris *Floral / Florale* 34 ●
FLEUR Morabito *Floral / Florale* 36 ●
FLEUR D'AMOUR *Floral / Florale* 32 ●●
FLEUR D'EAU *Floral / Florale* 36 ●
FLEUR D'INTERDIT *Floral / Florale* 36 ●
FLEUR D'IRIS *Soft Floral / Fleuri Aldéhydé* 43 ●●●
FLEUR DE DÉSIRADE *Soft Floral / Fleuri Aldéhydé* 42 ●●
FLEUR DE DIVA *Floral / Florale* 36 ●
FLEUR DE FIGUIER *Mossy Woods / Chypre Boisé* 66 ●
FLEUR DE FLEURS *Soft Floral / Fleuri Aldéhydé* 42 ●
FLEUR DE LOTUS *Water / Marine* 26 ●●
FLEUR DE ROCAILLE *Floral / Florale* 34 ●●
FLEUR DE WEIL* *Floral / Florale* 32 ●
FLEURAGE *Soft Floral / Fleuri Aldéhydé* 42 ●●
FLEURISSIMO *Floral / Florale* 36 ●
FLEURS D'ORLANE *Floral / Florale* 36 ●
FLEURS DE BULGARIE *Floral / Florale* 31 ●●●
FLEURS DE CHIARA BONI *Floral / Florale* 36 ●
FLEURS DE LA FORÊT *Mossy Woods / Chypre Boisé* 67 ●●●
FLEURS DE PÊCHER *Soft Floral / Fleuri Aldéhydé* 42 ●
FLEURS DE ROCAILLE *Floral / Florale* 33 ●●●
FLEURS DES COMORES *Mossy Woods / Chypre Boisé* 66 ●●
FLIRT *Floral / Florale* 34 ●●
FLORAMYE *Mossy Woods / Chypre Boisé* 66 ●●
FLORE Carolina Herrera *Floral / Florale* 30 ●
FLORE AUBUSSON *Floral / Florale* 34 ●
FLORET *Floral / Florale* 30 ●●
FLORISSA *Soft Floral / Fleuri Aldéhydé* 42 ●●
FLOWERS Gilles Cantuel *Floral / Florale* 32 ●
FOLAVRIL *Soft Floral / Fleuri Aldéhydé* 42 ●●
FOLIE DE CRÉATURE *Floral / Florale* 33 ●●●●
FOLIE DOUCE *Floral / Florale* 32 ●●

FOREVER Alfred Sung *Floral / Florale* 36 ●
FOREVER* Yardley *Floral Oriental / Fleuri Oriental* 48 ●●
FOREVER KRYSTLE *Floral Oriental / Fleuri Oriental* 47 ●●●
FORGET ME NOT *Soft Floral / Fleuri Aldéhydé* 43 ●●●
FORMIDABLE *Floral Oriental / Fleuri Oriental* 47 ●●●
FOU D'ELLE *Floral / Florale* 32 ●●
FRACAS *Floral / Florale* 31 ●●●●
FRAGILE *Floral / Florale* 31 ●●●●
FRAÎCHE PASSIFLORE *Citrus / Hespéridé* 16 ●●
FRAÎCHEUR MUSKISSIME ♂ *Citrus / Hespéridé* 17 ●●●●
FRANGIPANE *Floral / Florale* 31 ●●●●
FREE WORLD WOMAN *Floral / Florale* 34 ●
FREEDOM FOR HER *Floral / Florale* 36 ●
FREESIA Crabtree & Evelyn *Floral / Florale* 30 ●●
FREESIA Woods of Windsor *Floral / Florale* 30 ●●
FRENCH CANCAN *Floral Oriental / Fleuri Oriental* 48 ●●
FREEZIA D'OR *Floral / Florale* 33 ●●●●
FRENCH CONNECTION *Citrus / Hespéridé* 16 ●
FRENCH LIME BLOSSOM *Floral / Florale* 30 ●
FRENCH VANILLA *Woody Oriental / Oriental Boisé* 60 ●●
FRIDAY! *Floral Oriental / Fleuri Oriental* 48 ●
FRUITS SAUVAGES *Citrus / Hespéridé* 17 ●●●●
FUJIYAMA ♂ *Citrus / Hespéridé* 16 ●
FUN WATER WOMAN *Water / Marine* 26 ●●
FUSION *Citrus / Hespéridé* 16 ●

G *Soft Floral / Fleuri Aldéhydé* 42 ●
G GIGLI* *Soft Floral / Fleuri Aldéhydé* 42 ●
GABRIELA SABATINI *Floral Oriental / Fleuri Oriental* 48 ●●
GAI MATTIOLO *Floral Oriental / Fleuri Oriental* 46 ●
GALA DE DIA *Floral / Florale* 36 ●
GALA LOEWE *Floral Oriental / Fleuri Oriental* 46 ●●
GALANOS *Soft Floral / Fleuri Aldéhydé* 43 ●●●
GALANOS DE SERENE *Soft Oriental / Oriental Doux* 53 ●●●
GALICE *Floral Oriental / Fleuri Oriental* 46 ●
GALORÉ *Floral Oriental / Fleuri Oriental* 47 ●●●
GARDÉNIA Chanel *Floral / Florale* 30 ●●
GARDENIA Crabtree & Evelyn *Floral / Florale* 30 ●●
GARDENIA Floris *Floral / Florale* 30 ●●
GARDENIA Jo Malone *Floral / Florale* 30 ●●
GARDENIA Penhaligon's *Floral / Florale* 30 ●●
GARDÉNIA PASSION *Floral / Florale* 31 ●●●●
GATTINONI À PORTER *Floral / Florale* 32 ●●
GATTINONI COUTURE *Woody Oriental / Oriental Boisé* 60 ●
GAULOISE* *Mossy Woods / Chypre Boisé* 66 ●
GEM *Woody Oriental / Oriental Boisé* 61 ●●●●
GÉNÉRATION COURRÈGES *Floral / Florale* 32 ●
GENNY *Floral / Florale* 32 ●●
GENNY* (Original) *Dry Woods / Chypre Cuir* 72 ●
GENNY SHINE* *Floral Oriental / Fleuri Oriental* 46 ●●
GEOFFREY BEENE *Floral / Florale* 34 ●●
GERANI *Woody Oriental / Oriental Boisé* 60 ●
GFF DONNA *Floral / Florale* 34 ●●
GHOST MYST *Water / Marine* 26 ●
GIANFRANCO FERRÉ *Floral / Florale* 36 ●
GIANFRANCO FERRÉ 20 *Floral / Florale* 33 ●●●
GIANNI VERSACE *Mossy Woods / Chypre Boisé* 67 ●●●●
GIEFFEFFE ♂ *Citrus / Hespéridé* 16 ●
GILDA *Woody Oriental / Oriental Boisé* 60 ●
GINGHAM *Aromatic / Fougère* 77 ●●●
GIÒ *Floral / Florale* 33 ●●●●
GIORGIO *Floral / Florale* 36 ●●
GIORGIO AIRE* *Soft Floral / Fleuri Aldéhydé* 42 ●
GIORGIO HOLIDAY Ⓛ *Floral / Florale* 32 ●
GIVENCHY III *Mossy Woods / Chypre Boisé* 66 ●
GIVRINE (SICILE) ♂ *Citrus / Hespéridé* 17 ●●●
GLAMOUR *Floral Oriental / Fleuri Oriental* 47 ●●●
GMV DONNA *Floral Oriental / Fleuri Oriental* 46 ●●
GOLD *Woody Oriental / Oriental Boisé* 60 ●
GOLD JEANS FEMME *Citrus / Hespéridé* 16 ●
GOLDEN MOMENT *Floral Oriental / Fleuri Oriental* 46 ●
GOODLIFE WOMAN *Floral Oriental / Fleuri Oriental* 46 ●
GOSSIP *Woody Oriental / Oriental Boisé* 60 ●
GOURMANDISE DE RODIER *Citrus / Hespéridé* 16 ●

GRAFFITI VANILLA *Woody Oriental / Oriental Boisé* 60 ●●
GRAIN DE FOLIE *Green / Vert* 22 ●●
GRAIN DE PLAISIR ♂ *Mossy Woods / Chypre Boisé* 66 ●
GRAIN DE SOLEIL *Woody Oriental / Oriental Boisé* 61 ●●●
GRAND AMOUR *Soft Floral / Fleuri Aldéhydé* 43 ●●●●
GRAPEFRUIT ♂ *Citrus / Hespéridé* 16 ●●
GREEN GENERATION ♂ *Aromatic / Fougère* 76 ●●
GREEN GENERATION HER *Floral / Florale* 32 ●
GREEN TEA *Citrus / Hespéridé* 16 ●
GUCCI ACCENTI ➤ ACCENTI
GUCCI N° 1* *Soft Floral / Fleuri Aldéhydé* 42 ●●
GUCCI N° 3* *Mossy Woods / Chypre Boisé* 66 ●●
GUCCI RUSH *Woody Oriental / Oriental Boisé* 60 ●●
GUÉPARD *Mossy Woods / Chypre Boisé* 67 ●●●
GUESS* *Woody Oriental / Oriental Boisé* 60 ●●
GUET-APENS Ⓛ *Woody Oriental / Oriental Boisé* 60 ●
GUIRLANDES* *Soft Floral / Fleuri Aldéhydé* 42 ●

HABANITA *Woody Oriental / Oriental Boisé* 61 ●●●●
HALLOWEEN *Floral / Florale* 36 ●●
HALSTON *Mossy Woods / Chypre Boisé* 66 ●
HANAE MORI *Woody Oriental / Oriental Boisé* 60 ●●
HANAE MORI HAUTE COUTURE *Soft Floral / Aldéhydé* 42 ●
HAPPY *Floral / Florale* 32 ●
HAVANA POUR ELLE *Floral / Florale* 36 ●●
HEAD OVER HEELS *Floral / Florale* 32 ●
HEAVEN SENT *Aromatic / Fougère* 77 ●●●
HELIOTROPE *Floral Oriental / Fleuri Oriental* 47 ●●●
HERBA FRESCA ♂ *Green / Vert* 22 ●●
HEURE EXQUISE *Soft Floral / Fleuri Aldéhydé* 42 ●
HERVÉ LÉGER *Floral Oriental / Fleuri Oriental* 47 ●●●
HIGH TECH WOMEN *Floral / Florale* 32 ●
HIRIS *Floral / Florale* 30 ●
HISTOIRE D'AMOUR *Mossy Woods / Chypre Boisé* 67 ●●●
HOLLYWOOD FOR WOMEN *Woody Oriental / Oriental Boisé* 60 ●●
HONEYMOON *Woody Oriental / Oriental Boisé* 60 ●●
HONEYSUCKLE Woods of Windsor *Floral / Florale* 30 ●●
HONEYSUCKLE & JASMINE *Floral / Florale* 36 ●●
HOPE *Soft Floral / Fleuri Aldéhydé* 43 ●●●●
HOT *Floral Oriental / Fleuri Oriental* 46 ●
HUGO WOMAN *Floral / Florale* 36 ●●
HYPERSOUK *Soft Oriental / Oriental Doux* 53 ●●●
HYPNOTIC POISON *Woody Oriental / Oriental Boisé* 61 ●●●●

I AM ENERGY *Citrus / Hespéridé* 16 ●
I AM ETERNAL *Woody Oriental / Oriental Boisé* 61 ●●●
I AM PASSION *Floral / Florale* 34 ●
I AM SERENE *Green / Vert* 23 ●●●
I AM WILD *Oriental / Oriental* 56 ●
I EX'CLA.MA'TION *Floral / Florale* 32 ●●
I LOVE YOU *Floral / Florale* 32 ●
ICEBERG *Floral / Florale* 32 ●
ICEBERG TWICE *Floral / Florale* 36 ●
ICEBERG TWICE ICE *Citrus / Hespéridé* 16 ●
ICEBERG UNIVERSE FEMME *Floral Oriental / Fleuri Oriental* 47 ●●●
ICI *Floral Oriental / Fleuri Oriental* 46 ●●
IL BACIO *Floral / Florale* 32 ●
ÎLES D'OR *Floral / Florale* 32 ●
IMPERIAL VETYVER ♂ *Mossy Woods / Chypre Boisé* 67 ●●●
IMPLICITE *Soft Floral / Fleuri Aldéhydé* 42 ●
IMPRÉVU *Dry Woods / Chypre Cuir* 73 ●●●
IN LOVE AGAIN Ⓛ *Floral / Florale* 32 ●
INCLINATION *Floral / Florale* 32 ●
INCOGNITO *Floral Oriental / Fleuri Oriental* 46 ●●
INDÉCENCE ➤ ORGANZA INDÉCENCE
INDIANA *Floral / Florale* 36 ●●
INDIAN NIGHTS ➤ NUITS INDIENNES
INDIAN SUMMER *Floral Oriental / Fleuri Oriental* 46 ●
INDISCRET *Green / Vert* 22 ●●
INDIVIDUELLE *Floral / Florale* 36 ●
INDRA *Floral / Florale* 36 ●

INÈS DE LA FRESSANGE   *Floral / Fleuri*   30 ●
INFINI   *Soft Floral / Fleuri Aldéhydé*   43 ●●●●
INFINITIF   *Mossy Woods / Chypre Boisé*   67 ●●●
INIS ♂   *Water / Marine*   26 ●
INITIATION*   *Floral Oriental / Fleuri Oriental*   47 ●●●
INOUÏ   *Green / Vert*   23 ●●●
INSPIRATION   *Floral Oriental / Fleuri Oriental*   46 ●
INSTINCT D'ANIMALE   *Mossy Woods / Chypre Boisé*   67 ●●●
INTENSE DE SCAPA   *Citrus / Hespéridé*   17 ●●●●
INTERLUDE   *Oriental / Oriental*   57 ●●●
INTIMATE*   *Mossy Woods / Chypre Boisé*   66 ●
INTOXICATION D'AMOUR   *Woody Oriental / Oriental Boisé*   61 ●●●
INTRIGUE*   *Soft Floral / Fleuri Aldéhydé*   42 ●●
IO   *Mossy Woods / Chypre Boisé*   66 ●●
IQUITA*   *Mossy Woods / Chypre Boisé*   66 ●●
ISLAND GARDENIA   *Floral / Florale*   30 ●●
ISSEY   ➙ L'EAU D'ISSEY
IVANA   *Floral / Florale*   33 ●●●●
IVOIRE   *Soft Floral / Fleuri Aldéhydé*   42 ●

J

JACINTHE ROSE (ROMANTICA)   *Floral / Florale*   36 ●
JACQUELINE   *Oriental / Oriental*   56 ●●
JACQUI   *Soft Oriental / Oriental Doux*   53 ●●●
J'ADORE   *Floral / Florale*   36 ●
J'AI OSÉ   *Soft Oriental / Oriental Doux*   53 ●●●
JAÏPUR   *Floral / Florale*   32 ●●
JAÏPUR SAPHIR   *Oriental / Oriental*   56 ●●
JARDIN BLANC   *Floral / Florale*   36 ●●
JARDIN SECRET   *Mossy Woods / Chypre Boisé*   66 ●●
JARDINS DE BAGATELLE   *Floral / Florale*   33 ●●●●
JASMIN Le Jardin Retrouvé   *Floral / Florale*   31 ●●●
JASMIN Maître Parfumeur et Gantier   *Floral / Florale*   31 ●●●
JASMIN Molinard   *Floral / Florale*   31 ●●●
JASMIN DE PROVENCE   *Floral / Florale*   31 ●●●
JASMIN IMPÉRATRICE EUGÉNIE   *Floral / Florale*   33 ●●●
JASMIN MANDARINE   *Soft Floral / Fleuri Aldéhydé*   43 ●●●
JASMINE* Yardley   *Floral / Florale*   31 ●●●
JE T'AIME   *Floral Oriental / Fleuri Oriental*   47 ●●●
JEAN-LOUIS SCHERRER   *Green / Vert*   23 ●●●●
JEAN-MARIE FARINA ♂   *Citrus / Hespéridé*   17 ●●●
JEAN NATÉ   *Aromatic / Fougère*   77 ●●●
JEAN PAUL GAULTIER   *Floral Oriental / Fleuri Oriental*   46 ●●
JE REVIENS   *Soft Floral / Fleuri Aldéhydé*   43 ●●●●
JESS   *Floral / Florale*   33 ●●●●
JESSICA McCLINTOCK   *Floral / Florale*   30 ●
JICKY ♂   *Aromatic / Fougère*   77 ●●●
JIL   *Woody Oriental / Oriental Boisé*   60 ●
JIL SANDER BATH & BEAUTY   *Mossy Woods / Chypre Boisé*   67 ●●●
JIL SANDER N° 4   *Floral Oriental / Fleuri Oriental*   46 ●
JIL SANDER SUN   *Floral Oriental / Fleuri Oriental*   47 ●●●
JIL SANDER WOMAN PURE*   *Soft Floral / Fleuri Aldéhydé*   42 ●
JIL SANDER WOMAN II*   *Mossy Woods / Chypre Boisé*   66 ●●
JIL SANDER WOMAN III   *Dry Woods / Chypre Cuir*   72 ●●
JIN ABE   *Floral Oriental / Fleuri Oriental*   46 ●●
JITROIS   *Dry Woods / Chypre Cuir*   72 ●●
JIVAGO 7 NOTES   *Floral Oriental / Fleuri Oriental*   46 ●●
JIVAGO 24k WOMEN   *Floral / Florale*   33 ●●●●
JOLIE MADAME   *Woody Oriental / Oriental Boisé*   60 ●●
JONES NEW YORK   *Green / Vert*   22 ●●
JONTUE   *Floral / Florale*   31 ●●●●
JONTUE MOONLIGHT*   *Floral / Florale*   36 ●
JOOP!   *Woody Oriental / Oriental Boisé*   61 ●●●●
JOOP! BERLIN   *Soft Floral / Fleuri Aldéhydé*   42 ●
JOOP! LE BAIN   *Floral Oriental / Fleuri Oriental*   47 ●●●●
JOOP! NUIT D'ÉTÉ   *Woody Oriental / Oriental Boisé*   61 ●●●
JOSEPH DE JOUR   *Soft Floral / Fleuri Aldéhydé*   42 ●
JOVAN EVENING MUSK*   *Soft Floral / Fleuri Aldéhydé*   43 ●●●
JOVAN FRESH MUSK   *Floral / Florale*   32 ●
JOVAN MUSK   *Soft Floral / Fleuri Aldéhydé*   43 ●●●●
JOVAN WHITE MUSK   *Soft Oriental / Oriental Doux*   52 ●
JOY   *Floral / Florale*   33 ●●●
JUNGLE GARDENIA   *Floral / Florale*   30 ●●
JUNGLE: L'ÉLÉPHANT   *Soft Oriental / Oriental Doux*   53 ●●●
JUNGLE: LE TIGRE   *Floral Oriental / Fleuri Oriental*   46 ●

JUST ME   *Woody Oriental / Oriental Boisé*   60 ●●
JUSTE UN RÊVE   *Woody Oriental / Oriental Boisé*   60 ●●
JUSTINE   *Soft Floral / Fleuri Aldéhydé*   43 ●●●●

K

K de KRIZIA   *Soft Floral / Fleuri Aldéhydé*   42 ●●
KASHÂYA   *Floral Oriental / Fleuri Oriental*   46 ●
KENZO   *Floral / Florale*   32 ●●
KÉORA   *Oriental / Oriental*   57 ●●●●
KIRI   *Woody Oriental / Oriental Boisé*   61 ●●●
KISS & TELL   *Floral / Florale*   36 ●
KITON DONNA   *Floral / Florale*   32 ●●
KL   *Soft Oriental / Oriental Doux*   52 ●
KNOWING   *Mossy Woods / Chypre Boisé*   67 ●●●
KOOKAÏ OUI-NON   *Floral / Florale*   32 ●●
KRAZY KRIZIA*   *Oriental / Oriental*   56 ●●
KUMQUAT ♂   *Citrus / Hespéridé*   16 ●●

L

L de LOEWE   *Floral / Florale*   32 ●●
L'AIMANT   *Soft Floral / Fleuri Aldéhydé*   43 ●●●
L'AIR DU TEMPS   *Floral / Florale*   33 ●●●
L'ARTE DI GUCCI*   *Mossy Woods / Chypre Boisé*   67 ●●●
L'AUTRE ♂   *Dry Woods / Chypre Cuir*   73 ●●●●
L'EAU Diptyque ♂   *Soft Oriental / Oriental Doux*   52 ●●
L'EAU Laura Ashley   *Citrus / Hespéridé*   16 ●●
L'EAU D'AMBRE   *Oriental / Oriental*   57 ●●●
L'EAU D'ISSEY   *Water / Marine*   26 ●●
L'EAU DE KOOKAÏ   *Citrus / Hespéridé*   16 ●
L'EAU DE L'ARTISAN ♂   *Citrus / Hespéridé*   17 ●●●
L'EAU DE MONTEIL   *Floral / Florale*   33 ●●●●
L'EAU DE SONIA RYKIEL   *Floral / Florale*   32 ●
L'EAU DE SUCCÈS   *Floral / Florale*   32 ●●
L'EAU LILIAN   *Water / Marine*   26 ●●
L'EAU PAR KENZO   *Floral / Florale*   36 ●
L'EAU TROIS ♂   *Dry Woods / Chypre Cuir*   72 ●●
L'EFFLEUR   *Floral / Florale*   34 ●●
L'ELUE   *Floral Oriental / Fleuri Oriental*   46 ●●
L'ÉTÉ DE VENTILO   *Floral Oriental / Fleuri Oriental*   46 ●
L'HEURE ATTENDUE   *Woody Oriental / Oriental Boisé*   61 ●●●
L'HEURE BLEUE   *Floral Oriental / Fleuri Oriental*   47 ●●●
L'INSAISISSABLE   *Floral / Florale*   32 ●●
L'INSOLENT*   *Woody Oriental / Oriental Boisé*   60 ●●
L'INTERDIT   *Soft Floral / Fleuri Aldéhydé*   43 ●●●
L'OMBRE DANS L'EAU   *Floral / Florale*   34 ●●
L'ORIGAN*   *Floral Oriental / Fleuri Oriental*   47 ●●●
LA BASE FOR HER   *Floral / Florale*   30 ●●
LA CHASSE AUX PAPILLONS   *Floral / Florale*   36 ●●
LA COUPE D'OR   *Floral Oriental / Fleuri Oriental*   46 ●●
LA NUIT   *Dry Woods / Chypre Cuir*   73 ●●●●
LA PARISIENNE   *Soft Floral / Fleuri Aldéhydé*   42 ●●
LA PERLA   *Dry Woods / Chypre Cuir*   73 ●●●●
LA PLAGE   *Woody Oriental / Oriental Boisé*   60 ●
LA PRAIRIE   *Floral / Florale*   33 ●●●●
LA ROSE DE ROSINE   *Soft Floral / Fleuri Aldéhydé*   43 ●●●●
LE BAISER   *Floral / Florale*   32 ●●
LE CHIC*   *Soft Floral / Fleuri Aldéhydé*   42 ●●
LE CIRQUE DE POPY MORENI   *Soft Floral / Fleuri Aldéhydé*   42 ●
LE DE   *Floral / Florale*   33 ●●●
LE DIX   *Soft Floral / Fleuri Aldéhydé*   43 ●●●●
LE FEU D'ISSEY   *Woody Oriental / Oriental Boisé*   61 ●●●
LE JARDIN   *Floral / Florale*   38 ●
LE JARDIN D'AMOUR   *Floral Oriental / Fleuri Oriental*   47 ●●●●
LE MONDE EST BEAU   *Floral / Florale*   34 ●
LE MUGUET DE ROSINE   *Floral / Florale*   30 ●
LE PARFUM   *Woody Oriental / Oriental Boisé*   60 ●●
LE ROY SOLEIL   *Soft Oriental / Oriental Doux*   52 ●●
LE TEMPS D'AIMER*   *Mossy Woods / Chypre Boisé*   67 ●●●
LE TEMPS D'UNE FÊTE   *Floral / Florale*   34 ●
LES BELLES DE RICCI   ➙ LIBERTÉ ACIDULÉE
LES COPAINS   *Floral Oriental / Fleuri Oriental*   46 ●
LACE   *Mossy Woods / Chypre Boisé*   66 ●
LACOSTE FOR WOMEN   *Floral / Florale*   34 ●

LADY STETSON   *Soft Floral / Fleuri Aldéhydé   43* ●●●●
LAGUNA   *Floral Oriental / Fleuri Oriental   46* ●
LAILA   *Floral / Florale   38* ●
LAIT SUCRÉ   *Floral / Florale   32* ●●
LALIQUE   *Floral Oriental / Fleuri Oriental   46* ●●
LANCASTER BODY & BATH   *Oriental / Oriental   56* ●
LANCETTI   *Soft Floral / Fleuri Aldéhydé   43* ●●●
LANCETTI EAU DE JOIE   *Floral / Florale   34* ●●
LANCETTI MADAME   *Mossy Woods / Chypre Boisé   67* ●●●
LAPIS   *Woody Oriental / Oriental Boisé   60* ●●
LASTING   *Floral / Florale   32* ●●
LAURA   *Floral / Florale   36* ●
LAURA ASHLEY N° 1   *Soft Floral / Fleuri Aldéhydé   42* ●
LAUREN   *Floral / Florale   32* ●●
LAVANDA Myrurgia ♂   *Floral / Florale   31* ●●●
LAVANDE Molinard ♂   *Floral / Florale   31* ●●●●
LAVANDE ROYALE ♂   *Floral / Florale   31* ●●●
LAVANDE VELOURS ♂   *Floral / Florale   31* ●●●
LAVENDER Crabtree & Evelyn ♂   *Floral / Florale   31* ●●●
LAVENDER Floris ♂   *Floral / Florale   31* ●●●
LAVENDER Woods of Windsor   *Floral / Florale   31* ●●●
LELONG POUR FEMME   *Woody Oriental / Oriental Boisé   61* ●●●
LEMON SORBET ♂   *Aromatic / Fougère   76* ●
LÉONARD DE LÉONARD*   *Soft Floral / Fleuri Aldéhydé   42* ●
LIBERTÉ ACIDULÉE   *Floral / Florale   32* ●
LIGHT HER   *Floral / Florale   32* ●●
LILLIE RUBIN   *Floral / Florale   38* ●
LILY ⓛ   *Floral / Florale   30* ●
LILY OF THE VALLEY Crabtree & Evelyn   *Floral / Florale   30* ●
LILY OF THE VALLEY Floris   *Floral / Florale   30* ●
LILY OF THE VALLEY Penhaligon's   *Floral / Florale   30* ●
LILY OF THE VALLEY Woods of Windsor   *Floral / Florale   30* ●
LILY OF THE VALLEY Yardley   *Floral / Florale   30* ●
LIME, BASIL & MANDARIN ♂   *Citrus / Hespéridé   17* ●●●●
LIMES Floris ♂   *Citrus / Hespéridé   17* ●●●●
LIÙ   *Soft Floral / Fleuri Aldéhydé   43* ●●●
LIZ CLAIBORNE   *Floral / Florale   32* ●
LIZSPORT   *Floral / Florale   34* ●
LOLITA LEMPICKA   *Woody Oriental / Oriental Boisé   60* ●
LONG AGO / WISTFUL   *Floral / Florale   34* ●
LONGING   *Floral Oriental / Fleuri Oriental   46* ●
LORESTE FEMME   *Floral Oriental / Fleuri Oriental   46* ●●
LOULOU   *Soft Oriental / Oriental Doux   53* ●●●●
LOULOU BLUE*   *Floral Oriental / Fleuri Oriental   48* ●●
LOVE STORY   *Floral Oriental / Fleuri Oriental   47* ●●●●
LOVE'S BABY SOFT   *Soft Floral / Fleuri Aldéhydé   43* ●●●
LOVIN' GIRL   *Citrus / Hespéridé   16* ●●
LOVING BOUQUET ⓛ   *Floral / Florale   34* ●
LP N° 9   *Floral Oriental / Fleuri Oriental   46* ●
LUCKY BRAND WOMEN'S   *Floral / Florale   38* ●
LUMIÈRE   *Floral / Florale   38* ●
LUNE D'ÉTÉ   *Woody Oriental / Oriental Boisé   60* ●
LUTÈCE   *Floral Oriental / Fleuri Oriental   47* ●●●●
LYRA   *Oriental / Oriental   57* ●●●
LYRA 2   *Woody Oriental / Oriental Boisé   60* ●●
LYRA 3   *Floral / Florale   32* ●
LYS   *Floral / Florale   30* ●●

MA GRIFFE   *Mossy Woods / Chypre Boisé   66* ●●
MA LIBERTÉ*   *Aromatic / Fougère   77* ●●●
MACKIE   *Floral Oriental / Fleuri Oriental   46* ●●
MADAME CARVEN*   *Floral / Florale   33* ●●●●
MADAME ROCHAS   *Soft Floral / Fleuri Aldéhydé   43* ●●●●
MADELEINE   *Floral / Florale   31* ●●●●
MADELEINE VIONNET   *Floral Oriental / Fleuri Oriental   47* ●●●
MADLY   *Floral / Florale   32* ●●
MAGIC   *Mossy Woods / Chypre Boisé   66* ●
MAGIE NOIRE   *Woody Oriental / Oriental Boisé   60* ●●
MAGNETIC   *Floral Oriental / Fleuri Oriental   46* ●
MAGOT   *Oriental / Oriental   56* ●
MAJA   *Soft Oriental / Oriental Doux   53* ●●●
MALABAR   *Oriental / Oriental   57* ●●●
MALMAISON   *Floral / Florale   31* ●●●●
MANDARIN   *Floral / Florale   31* ●●●●

MANDARINE ♂   *Citrus / Hespéridé   16* ●●
MANIA   *Woody Oriental / Oriental Boisé   61* ●●●
MARBERT WOMAN   *Oriental / Oriental   57* ●●●
MARBERT WOMAN RED   *Floral / Florale   32* ●
MARE   *Water / Marine   26* ●●
MARECHALE 90   *Mossy Woods / Chypre Boisé   67* ●●●
MARECHALE ORIGINAL   *Floral / Florale   31* ●●●
MARIELLA   *Soft Oriental / Oriental Doux   52* ●
MARIELLA BURANI   *Soft Floral / Fleuri Aldéhydé   42* ●●
MARINA DE BOURBON   *Woody Oriental / Oriental Boisé   60* ●
MARJOLAINE   *Floral / Florale   34* ●●
MAROC*   *Mossy Woods / Chypre Boisé   67* ●●●●
MAROUSSIA   *Floral Oriental / Fleuri Oriental   47* ●●●
MARQUIS POUR FEMME   *Woody Oriental / Oriental Boisé   60* ●
MATSUKITA   *Floral Oriental / Fleuri Oriental   48* ●●
MAXIM'S DE PARIS   *Floral Oriental / Fleuri Oriental   46* ●
MCM   *Floral / Florale   32* ●●
MCM 1900*   *Floral Oriental / Fleuri Oriental   47* ●●●
MCM BLUE PARADISE*   *Floral / Florale   32* ●●
MCM OBELISK*   *Oriental / Oriental   56* ●
MEA CULPA   *Floral / Florale   36* ●●
MELODIE D'AMOUR   *Floral / Florale   32* ●
MENTHE FROISSÉE   *Green / Vert   22* ●
MERGE ♂   *Aromatic / Fougère   76* ●
MÉTAL   *Soft Floral / Fleuri Aldéhydé   42* ●
MICHEL JORDI   → THE SPIRIT OF SWITZERLAND
MICHELLE   *Floral / Florale   31* ●●●●
MIEL ORANGE   *Citrus / Hespéridé   17* ●●●●
MILA SCHÖN   *Mossy Woods / Chypre Boisé   67* ●●●
MILLENNIUM HOPE WOMAN   *Floral / Florale   32* ●●
MIMOSA Molinard   *Floral / Florale   30* ●●
MIMOSA Woods of Windsor   *Floral / Florale   30* ●●
MIMOSA POUR MOI   *Floral / Florale   30* ●●
MIMOSAÏQUE   *Floral / Florale   30* ●●
MING   *Woody Oriental / Oriental Boisé   61* ●●●
MIRA BAÏ   *Woody Oriental / Oriental Boisé   60* ●●
MISHA   *Mossy Woods / Chypre Boisé   67* ●●●●
MISS ARPELS   *Floral / Florale   32* ●
MISS BALAHÉ   *Floral / Florale   32* ●●
MISS BALMAIN   *Dry Woods / Chypre Cuir   73* ●●●
MISS BE BOP   *Floral / Florale   33* ●●●●
MISS DIOR   *Mossy Woods / Chypre Boisé   66* ●
MISS HABANITA   *Floral / Florale   32* ●
MISS JAGUAR   *Floral / Florale   36* ●
MISS MORABITO   *Floral / Florale   36* ●
MISS WORTH   *Floral / Florale   33* ●●●●
MISSONI   *Mossy Woods / Chypre Boisé   67* ●●●●
MISUKI   *Oriental / Oriental   57* ●●●
MITSOUKO   *Mossy Woods / Chypre Boisé   67* ●●●
MODERN QUARTZ   *Floral / Florale   32* ●
MOLINARD DE MOLINARD   *Floral / Florale   34* ●●
MOLTO MISSONI   *Oriental / Oriental   57* ●●●●
MOMENT SUPRÊME   *Floral / Florale   33* ●●●●
MOMENTS   *Woody Oriental / Oriental Boisé   61* ●●●
MON BOUQUET   *Floral / Florale   32* ●
MON CLASSIQUE   *Floral / Florale   36* ●
MON PARFUM   *Floral / Florale   32* ●●
MONDI PURSENSE   *Woody Oriental / Oriental Boisé   60* ●
MONSOON   *Floral / Florale   34* ●●
MONSOON EAU   *Water / Marine   26* ●●
MONTAIGNE   *Floral / Florale   32* ●●
MONTANA PARFUM D'ELLE*   *Mossy Woods / Chypre Boisé   66* ●
MONTANA PARFUM DE PEAU   *Dry Woods / Chypre Cuir   73* ●●●●
MONT ST MICHEL ♂   *Citrus / Hespéridé   17* ●●●
MOODS   *Floral / Florale   34* ●●
MOONDROPS   *Floral / Florale   33* ●●●●
MOOVING   *Aromatic / Fougère   77* ●●●
MORGANE LE FAY   *Floral / Florale   34* ●
MOSCHINO   *Oriental / Oriental   57* ●●●
MOTU   *Water / Marine   26* ●
MUGUET / LILY OF THE VALLEY Molinard   *Floral / Florale   30* ●
MUGUET DES BOIS   *Floral / Florale   30* ●
MUGUET DU BONHEUR   *Floral / Florale   30* ●
MULBERRY   *Soft Oriental / Oriental Doux   53* ●●●
MURASAKI   *Soft Floral / Fleuri Aldéhydé   42* ●
MÛRE   *Citrus / Hespéridé   17* ●●●●
MÛRE ET MUSC   *Citrus / Hespéridé   17* ●●●●

MÛRE ET MUSC EXTRÊME *Citrus / Hespéridé* 17 ●●●●
MUSC *Woody Oriental / Oriental Boisé* 61 ●●●
MUSK Bettina Barty *Soft Floral / Fleuri Aldéhydé* 43 ●●●
MUST DE CARTIER *Oriental / Oriental* 56 ●
MUST DE CARTIER (JOUR)* *Floral / Florale* 32 ●
MUST DE CARTIER II *Water / Marine* 26 ●
MV *Floral / Florale* 34 ●
MYSTÈRE *Woody Oriental / Oriental Boisé* 60 ●●
MYSTERY AUSTRALIA WOMAN *Woody Oriental / Oriental Boisé* 60 ●
MYSTIC *Floral / Florale* 32 ●●

N

N'AIMEZ QUE MOI *Floral / Florale* 33 ●●●
NAF NAF ➝ UNE TOUCHE DE NAF NAF
NAHÉMA *Floral Oriental / Fleuri Oriental* 47 ●●●●
NANTUCKET BRIAR *Floral Oriental / Fleuri Oriental* 46 ●●
NAOMI CAMPBELL *Woody Oriental / Oriental Boisé* 61 ●●●●
NARCISSE BLANC *Floral / Florale* 31 ●●●●
NARCISSE NOIR *Floral / Florale* 31 ●●●●
NATURE SYSTEM ♂ *Citrus / Hespéridé* 16 ●●
NATURE'S ONE FREESIA *Floral / Florale* 30 ●●
NATURE'S ONE GARDENIA *Floral / Florale* 30 ●●
NAUTICA WOMAN *Floral / Florale* 38 ●
NAVY *Floral Oriental / Fleuri Oriental* 47 ●●●●
NETWORK ♂ *Citrus / Hespéridé* 16 ●
NEW WEST FOR HER *Water / Marine* 27 ●●●
NICOLE *Floral / Florale* 38 ●
NICOLE MILLER *Floral Oriental / Fleuri Oriental* 46 ●●
NIGHT SCENTED STOCK *Floral / Florale* 31 ●●●●
NIKI DE SAINT PHALLE *Mossy Woods / Chypre Boisé* 66 ●
NILANG *Floral Oriental / Fleuri Oriental* 48 ●
NINA *Soft Floral / Fleuri Aldéhydé* 42 ●●
NINO CERRUTI* *Woody Oriental / Oriental Boisé* 60 ●
NIRMALA* *Woody Oriental / Oriental Boisé* 60 ●
N° 5 ➝ CHANEL N° 5
N° 19 ➝ CHANEL N° 19
N° 22 ➝ CHANEL N° 22
NO REGRETS *Floral / Florale* 36 ●●
NOA *Soft Floral / Fleuri Aldéhydé* 43 ●●●●
NOA NOA* *Floral Oriental / Fleuri Oriental* 46 ●●
NOCTURNES *Soft Floral / Fleuri Aldéhydé* 43 ●●●●
NOHIBA (TULIPE NOIRE) *Soft Oriental / Oriental Doux* 53 ●●●
NOI MISSONI *Citrus / Hespéridé* 16 ●●
NOKOMIS *Floral Oriental / Fleuri Oriental* 46 ●●
NONCHALANCE *Soft Floral / Fleuri Aldéhydé* 43 ●●●
NORELL *Floral / Florale* 34 ●●
NORMANDIE *Soft Oriental / Oriental Doux* 53 ●●●
NUAGE D'OR *Soft Floral / Fleuri Aldéhydé* 43 ●●●●
NUAGES D'EAU *Floral / Florale* 31 ●●●
NUBIADE *Woody Oriental / Oriental Boisé* 61 ●●●
NUDE *Soft Floral / Fleuri Aldéhydé* 42 ●
NUIT DE NOËL *Woody Oriental / Oriental Boisé* 61 ●●●
NUITS INDIENNES *Oriental / Oriental* 57 ●●●
NUMBER ONE *Floral / Florale* 36 ●●
NUTMEG & GINGER ♂ *Woody Oriental / Oriental Boisé* 60 ●●

O

Ô de LANCÔME *Citrus / Hespéridé* 17 ●●●
Ô OUI *Floral / Florale* 32 ●
O₂XYGEN WOMAN *Citrus / Hespéridé* 16 ●
OBSESSION *Oriental / Oriental* 56 ●
OCEAN DREAM *Floral / Florale* 36 ●
ODALISQUE *Floral / Florale* 38 ●
ODEUR 53 ♂ *Water / Marine* 26 ●●
OEILLET *Floral / Florale* 31 ●●●●
OFRÉSIA *Floral / Florale* 34 ●
OH! DE MOSCHINO *Soft Floral / Fleuri Aldéhydé* 42 ●
OH LA LA *Soft Oriental / Oriental Doux* 52 ●●
OLÈNE *Floral / Florale* 36 ●●
OMAR SHARIF *Floral / Florale* 33 ●●●
OMBRE BLEUE* *Floral / Florale* 33 ●●●●
OMBRE D'OR* *Soft Floral / Fleuri Aldéhydé* 42 ●
OMBRE ROSE *Floral Oriental / Fleuri Oriental* 47 ●●●●

OMBRE ROSE FRAÎCHE *Floral / Florale* 32 ●
ON AIR FEMME *Floral / Florale* 32 ●●
ONLY *Woody Oriental / Oriental Boisé* 61 ●●●
ONLY CRAZY *Floral Oriental / Fleuri Oriental* 47 ●●●●
OPHÉLIE *Soft Floral / Fleuri Aldéhydé* 43 ●●●
OPIUM *Soft Oriental / Oriental Doux* 53 ●●●
OPOPONAX *Aromatic/Fougère* 77 ●●●
OR DES INDES *Oriental / Oriental* 57 ●●●
OR ET NOIR *Floral Oriental / Fleuri Oriental* 47 ●●●
ORANGE BLOSSOM Penhaligon's *Floral / Florale* 31 ●●●●
ORANGE CAFÉ *Citrus / Hespéridé* 17 ●●●●
ORANGE-CANNELLE *Soft Oriental / Oriental Doux* 52 ●●
ORANGE SPICE ♂ *Aromatic / Fougère* 76 ●●
ORCHID* *Floral / Florale* 33 ●●●
ORGANZA *Woody Oriental / Oriental Boisé* 60 ●●
ORGANZA INDÉCENCE *Woody Oriental / Oriental Boisé* 61 ●●●●
ORGUEIL DE RODIER *Floral Oriental / Fleuri Oriental* 46 ●
ORIENT *Soft Oriental / Oriental Doux* 53 ●●●
ORMOLU *Woody Oriental / Oriental Boisé* 60 ●●
ORVAL *Floral / Florale* 33 ●●●
OSCAR DE LA RENTA *Floral Oriental / Fleuri Oriental* 47 ●●●
OTTOMANE *Woody Oriental / Oriental Boisé* 60 ●●
OUI-NON ➝ KOOKAÏ OUI-NON
OZBEK *Floral / Florale* 31 ●●●
OZBEK 1001 *Oriental / Oriental* 56 ●

P

PACO ♂ *Citrus / Hespéridé* 16 ●
PACO ENERGY ♂ *Citrus / Hespéridé* 16 ●●
PAIN D'ÉPICES *Woody Oriental / Oriental Boisé* 61 ●●●
PALACE *Soft Floral / Fleuri Aldéhydé* 42 ●●
PALAIS JAMAIS ♂ *Dry Woods / Chypre Cuir* 73 ●●●●
PALOMA PICASSO *Mossy Woods / Chypre Boisé* 67 ●●●
PAMPLELUNE ♂ *Citrus / Hespéridé* 17 ●●●●
PAMPLEMOUSSE ♂ *Citrus / Hespéridé* 16 ●●
PANACHE *Soft Floral / Fleuri Aldéhydé* 42 ●●
PANTHÈRE *Floral Oriental / Fleuri Oriental* 46 ●●
PARADOX *Floral Oriental / Fleuri Oriental* 48 ●
PARAH *Floral / Florale* 33 ●●●●
PARCE QUE!* *Soft Floral / Fleuri Aldéhydé* 43 ●●●
PARFUM D'ELLE ➝ MONTANA PARFUM D'ELLE
PARFUM D'ÉTÉ *Floral / Florale* 34 ●
PARFUM D'HERMÈS *Soft Oriental / Oriental Doux* 52 ●●
PARFUM D'OR *Mossy Woods / Chypre Boisé* 66 ●●
PARFUM PRIVÉ *Mossy Woods / Chypre Boisé* 67 ●●●
PARFUM SACRÉ *Floral Oriental / Fleuri Oriental* 47 ●●●
PARIS *Floral / Florale* 31 ●●●
PARESSE DE RODIER *Soft Floral / Fleuri Aldéhydé* 42 ●
PARURE *Mossy Woods / Chypre Boisé* 67 ●●●
PASSAGE D'ENFER *Dry Woods / Chypre Cuir* 72 ●●
PASSION Annick Goutal *Floral / Florale* 36 ●●
PASSION Elizabeth Taylor *Woody Oriental / Oriental Boisé* 61 ●●●
PASSION FLOWER *Floral / Florale* 32 ●
PASTEL DE CABOTINE *Floral / Florale* 32 ●
PATCHOULI Molinard ♂ *Mossy Woods / Chypre Boisé* 67 ●●●
PATCHOULY ♂ *Woody Oriental / Oriental Boisé* 61 ●●●
PATTI LaBELLE *Floral Oriental / Fleuri Oriental* 46 ●
PATOU FOR EVER *Floral / Florale* 32 ●●
PAVAROTTI DONNA *Mossy Woods / Chypre Boisé* 66 ●●
PAVLOVA *Floral / Florale* 31 ●●●●
PENHALIGON'S CASTILE ♂ *Citrus / Hespéridé* 17 ●●●
PEOPLE DONNA *Floral / Florale* 34 ●
PERHAPS *Floral Oriental / Fleuri Oriental* 46 ●
PERLE DE SILENCES *Soft Oriental / Oriental Doux* 52 ●
PERRY ELLIS FOR WOMEN *Soft Floral / Fleuri Aldéhydé* 42 ●●
PERSUASION *Floral / Florale* 34 ●●
PETITE CHÉRIE *Floral / Florale* 32 ●
PHANTOM OF THE OPERA* *Floral Oriental / Fleuri Oriental* 48 ●●
PHEROMONE *Green / Vert* 23 ●●●●
PHILOSYKOS ♂ *Mossy Woods / Chypre Boisé* 66 ●
PIAZZA DI SPAGNA *Floral / Florale* 34 ●
PLEASURES *Floral / Florale* 34 ●
PLEINE LUNE *Woody Oriental / Oriental Boisé* 60 ●
PLUMES *Floral / Florale* 32 ●
POÊME *Floral Oriental / Fleuri Oriental* 47 ●●●

POIS DE SENTEUR *Soft Oriental / Oriental Doux 53* ●●●
POISON *Floral Oriental / Fleuri Oriental 47* ●●●●
POIVRE *Soft Oriental / Oriental Doux 53* ●●●●
POLEMIC! *Floral Oriental / Fleuri Oriental 46* ●
POLO SPORT WOMAN *Water / Marine 26* ●●
POMME CANNELLE *Mossy Woods / Chypre Boisé 66* ●●
POMPEÏA *Dry Woods / Chypre Cuir 73* ●●●
POPY MORENI *Woody Oriental / Oriental Boisé 60* ●
POPY MORENI DE FÊTE *Floral / Florale 34* ●●
POUR UNE FEMME *Floral / Florale 38* ●
PRÉLUDE* *Soft Oriental / Oriental Doux 53* ●●●
PREMIER FIGUIER *Mossy Woods / Chypre Boisé 66* ●
PRIMROSE Penhaligon's *Floral / Florale 31* ●●●
PRINCESSE CHIPIE *Woody Oriental / Oriental Boisé 60* ●
PRIVATE COLLECTION *Green / Vert 23* ●●●●
PRIVATE NUMBER FOR WOMEN* *Floral / Florale 34* ●●
PROFUMO DI MONTECATINI ♂ *Water / Marine 27* ●●●
PURE *Floral / Florale 32* ●
PURE SILK* *Mossy Woods / Chypre Boisé 67* ●●●
PYTHON *Woody Oriental / Oriental Boisé 61* ●●●

Q

QUADRILLE *Mossy Woods / Chypre Boisé 67* ●●●
QUARTZ *Floral / Florale 32* ●
QUE SAIS-JE? *Mossy Woods / Chypre Boisé 67* ●●●
QUELQUES FLEURS *Floral / Florale 33* ●●●
QUELQUES ROSES *Floral / Florale 31* ●●●
QUELQUES VIOLETTES *Floral / Florale 31* ●●●●
QUERCUS ♂ *Citrus / Hespéridé 16* ●

R

RACINE ♂ *Mossy Woods / Chypre Boisé 66* ●●
RAFFINÉE *Floral Oriental / Fleuri Oriental 47* ●●●
RAVELLO *Floral Oriental / Fleuri Oriental 47* ●●●
REALITIES* *Floral / Florale 34* ●●
REALLY PARAH *Soft Floral / Fleuri Aldéhydé 42* ●●
REALM WOMEN *Soft Oriental / Oriental Doux 52* ●
RED *Mossy Woods / Chypre Boisé 66* ●●
RED 2* *Floral Oriental / Fleuri Oriental 46* ●
RED DOOR *Floral / Florale 33* ●●●●
RED JEANS *Floral / Florale 34* ●●
RED PEARL *Floral Oriental / Fleuri Oriental 46* ●●
RED ROSES *Floral / Florale 31* ●●●
RÉGINE'S *Woody Oriental / Oriental Boisé 61* ●●●
RELAXING FRAGRANCE *Floral / Florale 34* ●
RÉMY FOR WOMAN *Floral / Florale 34* ●●
RÉPLIQUE* *Mossy Woods / Chypre Boisé 67* ●●●
RÊVE D'OR *Soft Floral / Fleuri Aldéhydé 43* ●●●●
RÊVERIE *Floral Oriental / Fleuri Oriental 47* ●●●
REVOLUTION À VERSAILLES* *Floral Oriental / Fleuri Oriental 46* ●●
REYNALD KATZ ♂ *Citrus / Hespéridé 16* ●
RICHARDSON BAY ♂ *Green / Vert 22* ●
RIVE GAUCHE *Soft Floral / Fleuri Aldéhydé 42* ●●
ROCCOBAROCCO TRE *Floral / Florale 34* ●●
ROCOCO *Woody Oriental / Oriental Boisé 61* ●●●
RODIER *Woody Oriental / Oriental Boisé 60* ●
ROGER & GALLET EXTRA-VIEILLE ♂ *Citrus / Hespéridé 17* ●●●
ROMA *Oriental / Oriental 56* ●●
ROMANCE Ralph Lauren *Floral / Florale 33* ●●●
ROMANCE Royal Secret *Floral / Florale 33* ●●●●
ROMEO *Floral / Florale 34* ●●
ROOTS FOR HER *Floral / Florale 34* ●
ROOTS UNISCENT ♂ *Water / Marine 26* ●
ROSA MAGNIFICA *Floral / Florale 30* ●●
ROSE Caron *Floral / Florale 31* ●●●
ROSE Molinard *Floral / Florale 31* ●●●
ROSE* Yardley *Soft Floral / Fleuri Aldéhydé 42* ●●
ROSE ABSOLUE *Floral / Florale 31* ●●●
ROSE CARDIN *Mossy Woods / Chypre Boisé 67* ●●●
ROSE D'ÉTÉ *Floral / Florale 36* ●
ROSE MUSKISSIME *Floral / Florale 34* ●
ROSE NÉROLI *Floral / Florale 31* ●●●
ROSE OPULENTE *Floral / Florale 31* ●●●

ROSE-PIVOINE *Floral / Florale 31* ●●●
ROSE SANTAL *Floral / Florale 31* ●●●
ROSE THÉ *Floral / Florale 31* ●●●
ROSE VANILLE *Floral / Florale 33* ●●●
ROSEBERRY *Soft Floral / Fleuri Aldéhydé 42* ●●
ROSES AND MORE *Floral / Florale 31* ●●●
ROUGE *Woody Oriental / Oriental Boisé 60* ●
ROUGE FORMIDABLE *Soft Floral / Fleuri Aldéhydé 42* ●●
ROUTE DU THÉ *Citrus / Hespéridé 16* ●
ROY SOLEIL → LE ROY SOLEIL
ROYAL BAIN DE CHAMPAGNE ♂ *Soft Oriental / Oriental Doux 52* ●
ROYAL DELIGHT ♂ *Soft Oriental / Oriental Doux 53* ●●●●
ROYAL PAVILLON *Floral / Florale 34* ●●
ROYAL SECRET *Oriental / Oriental 57* ●●●
ROYAL SECRET II *Woody Oriental / Oriental Boisé 60* ●●
ROYALISSIME *Soft Floral / Fleuri Aldéhydé 42* ●●
RUBIS D'OR *Floral Oriental / Fleuri Oriental 46* ●
RUE PEROGLÈSE *Mossy Woods / Chypre Boisé 66* ●●
RUMBA *Dry Woods / Chypre Cuir 72* ●●
RUSH → GUCCI RUSH

S

SABI *Green / Vert 23* ●●●●
SACREBLEU! *Floral Oriental / Fleuri Oriental 47* ●●●
SAFARI *Soft Floral / Fleuri Aldéhydé 42* ●
SALVADOR DALI *Soft Oriental / Oriental Doux 53* ●●●
SALVATORE FERRAGAMO *Floral / Florale 34* ●●
SAMBA *Floral / Florale 34* ●●
SAMBA NATURAL *Water / Marine 26* ●●
SAMBA NOVA *Mossy Woods / Chypre Boisé 66* ●
SAMBA RED WOMAN *Soft Floral / Fleuri Aldéhydé 42* ●●
SAMSARA *Woody Oriental / Oriental Boisé 61* ●●●
UN AIR DE SAMSARA *Woody Oriental / Oriental Boisé 60* ●
SAND & SABLE *Floral / Florale 33* ●●●●
SANDALWOOD Yardley ♂ *Woody Oriental / Oriental Boisé 61* ●●●
SANGUINE MUSKISSIME ♂ *Citrus / Hespéridé 16* ●
SANS ADIEU *Water / Marine 26* ●●
SANTAL IMPÉRIAL ♂ *Woody Oriental / Oriental Boisé 61* ●●●
SARCANTHUS *Floral / Florale 34* ●●
SAVAGE VANILLA *Woody Oriental / Oriental Boisé 60* ●●
SAVANNA *Floral / Florale 34* ●●
SCAASI *Floral / Florale 34* ●●
SCAPA *Citrus / Hespéridé 16* ●●
SCARF *Woody Oriental / Oriental Boisé 60* ●●
SCARF TAORMINA *Floral / Florale 34* ●●
SCHERRER → JEAN-LOUIS SCHERRER
SCHERRER 2 *Floral Oriental / Fleuri Oriental 48* ●●
SCHÖN *Floral / Florale 34* ●●
SCULPTURE *Floral Oriental / Fleuri Oriental 48* ●
SEAWEST *Water / Marine 26* ●
SECRET DE VÉNUS *Woody Oriental / Oriental Boisé 61* ●●●
SECRETE DATURA *Oriental / Oriental 57* ●●●●
SENSES *Floral / Florale 33* ●●●●
SENSO *Floral / Florale 34* ●●
SERGIO TACCHINI DONNA *Water / Marine 26* ●●
SERINGA *Floral / Florale 36* ●
SÉXUAL *Floral Oriental / Fleuri Oriental 46* ●
SHAAL NUR ♂ *Soft Oriental / Oriental Doux 53* ●●●●
SHADES BY NAVY *Floral / Florale 34* ●●
SHAHI *Woody Oriental / Oriental Boisé 61* ●●●●
SHAHI AQUA *Floral / Florale 34* ●
SHAHI GOLDEN SUN *Floral Oriental / Fleuri Oriental 47* ●●●
SHALIMAR *Oriental / Oriental 57* ●●●
SHANGRI-LA *Floral / Florale 36* ●●
SHE* *Floral / Florale 34* ●●
SHEER HALSTON *Floral Oriental / Fleuri Oriental 48* ●
SHEER TIFFANY *Floral / Florale 38* ●
SHIMÓ *Floral Oriental / Fleuri Oriental 46* ●●
SHOCKING *Oriental / Oriental 57* ●●●
SI FLEURI *Floral / Florale 34* ●●
SI TENDRE *Soft Floral / Fleuri Aldéhydé 42* ●
SILENCES *Green / Vert 23* ●●●●
SILVER JEANS FEMME *Floral / Florale 34* ●
SINAÏ *Floral Oriental / Fleuri Oriental 46* ●
SIRÈNE *Floral Oriental / Fleuri Oriental 46* ●●

SISSI   Floral / Florale   33 ●●●
SKARLETT   Woody Oriental / Oriental Boisé   61 ●●●
SKARLETT SECRETS   Woody Oriental / Oriental Boisé   60 ●●
SMALTO DONNA*   Woody Oriental / Oriental Boisé   61 ●●●
SO…?   Woody Oriental / Oriental Boisé   61 ●●●
SO…? INSPIRED   Floral / Florale   34 ●
SO DE LA RENTA   Floral / Florale   34 ●
SO PRETTY   Soft Floral / Fleuri Aldéhydé   42 ●
SOCIETY*   Soft Floral / Fleuri Aldéhydé   42 ●●
SOIE ROUGE   Dry Woods / Chypre Cuir   72 ●●
SOIR DE PARIS ORIGINAL   Soft Floral / Fleuri Aldéhydé   43 ●●●●
SOIR DE PARIS   Floral / Florale   31 ●●●
SOIR D'ÉTÉ   Mossy Woods / Chypre Boisé   67 ●●●
SOLEIL   Floral / Florale   34 ●●
SOLEIL LEVANT   Woody Oriental / Oriental Boisé   61 ●●●
SOLILOQUY   Soft Floral / Fleuri Aldéhydé   43 ●●●●
SOLO FIORI FREESIA   Floral / Florale   30 ●●
SOLO FIORI JASMINE   Floral / Florale   31 ●●●
SOLO FIORI LILY OF THE VALLEY   Floral / Florale   30 ●
SOLO FIORI ROSE   Floral / Florale   31 ●●●
SOLO FIORI TUBEROSE   Floral / Florale   31 ●●●●
SOLO FIORI VIOLET   Floral / Florale   31 ●●●●
SOLO SOPRANI ♂   Citrus / Hespéridé   16 ●
SOLYTIS   Floral Oriental / Fleuri Oriental   46 ●●
SONG DE CHINE   Floral / Florale   36 ●
SONIA RYKIEL   Woody Oriental / Oriental Boisé   60 ●
SONOMA VALLEY   Green / Vert   22 ●
SOPRANI 2   Woody Oriental / Oriental Boisé   60 ●
SORENZA   Floral / Florale   33 ●●●
SORTILÈGE*   Soft Floral / Fleuri Aldéhydé   43 ●●●●
SOTTO VOCE   Woody Oriental / Oriental Boisé   61 ●●●
SOUTHERN EXPOSURE   Citrus / Hespéridé   16 ●●
SPAZIO KRIZIA DONNA   Floral Oriental / Fleuri Oriental   47 ●●●
SPECIAL N° 127 ♂   Citrus / Hespéridé   17 ●●●
SPELLBOUND   Floral Oriental / Fleuri Oriental   47 ●●●
SPIRIT OF ZEN   Floral / Florale   36 ●●
SPLENDOR   Floral / Florale   38 ●
SPORT SPIRIT ♂   Citrus / Hespéridé   16 ●
SPORTS EXTREME USA ♂   Citrus / Hespéridé   16 ●●
SPRING FEVER   Floral / Florale   34 ●●
SPRING FLOWER   Floral / Florale   34 ●
SPRING RAIN   Floral / Florale   36 ●
ST JOHN   Floral Oriental / Fleuri Oriental   47 ●●●●
S.T.DUPONT FEMME   Floral / Florale   34 ●
STARDUST   Floral Oriental / Fleuri Oriental   46 ●●
STÉPHANIE   Woody Oriental / Oriental Boisé   61 ●●●
STEPHANOTIS   Floral / Florale   31 ●●●●
STRADIVARIUS WHITE   Water / Marine   26 ●
STYLE   Floral Oriental / Fleuri Oriental   46 ●
SUBLIME   Soft Oriental / Oriental Doux   53 ●●●
SUGGESTION EAU CUIVRÉE   Floral Oriental / Fleuri Oriental   47 ●●●
SUGGESTION EAU D'ARGENT   Floral / Florale   36 ●●
SUGGESTION EAU D'OR   Floral / Florale   34 ●●
SULTRY / ANTICIPATE   Floral Oriental / Fleuri Oriental   48 ●●
SUMATRA RAIN WOMAN   Floral Oriental / Fleuri Oriental   46 ●
SUMMER HILL   Floral / Florale   38 ●
SUMMER SPLASH   Citrus / Hespéridé   16 ●
SUNFLOWERS   Water / Marine   27 ●●●
SUNG   Floral / Florale   38 ●
SUNG SPA   Green / Vert   22 ●
SUN MOON STARS   Floral Oriental / Fleuri Oriental   46 ●
SUNSET BOULEVARD   Floral Oriental / Fleuri Oriental   48 ●●
SUNSHINE   Floral / Florale   34 ●
SUN SPIRIT*   Floral / Florale   34 ●●
SUNWATER   Floral / Florale   36 ●
SWEET COURRÈGES   Soft Floral / Fleuri Aldéhydé   42 ●●
SYNTHETIC NIRVANA   Woody Oriental / Oriental Boisé   60 ●●

T

TABAC BLOND   Dry Woods / Chypre Cuir   73 ●●●
TABU   Oriental / Oriental   57 ●●●●
TALISMAN   Mossy Woods / Chypre Boisé   66 ●●
TALISMAN EAU TRANSPARENTE   Floral / Florale   34 ●
TAMANGO   Soft Floral / Fleuri Aldéhydé   42 ●●
TANGLEWOOD BOUQUET   Floral Oriental / Fleuri Oriental   47 ●●●

TATIANA   Floral / Florale   33 ●●●●
TÉ ♂   Citrus / Hespéridé   16 ●
TEA ROSE   Floral / Florale   31 ●●●
TEATRO ALLA SCALA*   Soft Oriental / Oriental Doux   53 ●●●
TEMPORE DONNA   Woody Oriental / Oriental Boisé   60 ●●
TENDRE POISON   Floral / Florale   34 ●●
TENTATIONS   Woody Oriental / Oriental Boisé   61 ●●●
THAÏS   Floral / Florale   36 ●
THÉ ♂   Woody Oriental / Oriental Boisé   61 ●●●
THÉ POUR UN ÉTÉ ♂   Citrus / Hespéridé   16 ●
THE SPIRIT OF SWITZERLAND   Floral / Florale   36 ●
THÉ VERT ♂   Citrus / Hespéridé   16 ●●
THEOREMA   Soft Oriental / Oriental Doux   53 ●●●
THEOREMA ESPRIT D'ÉTÉ   Soft Oriental / Oriental Doux   52 ●●
THIARA   Floral Oriental / Fleuri Oriental   47 ●●●
TIARÉ Comptoir Sud Pacifique   Floral / Florale   30 ●●
TIARÉ Sylvie Chantecaille   Floral / Florale   30 ●●
TIEMPE PASSATE   Mossy Woods / Chypre Boisé   67 ●●●
TIFFANY   Floral / Florale   33 ●●●●
TIGRESS*   Floral Oriental / Fleuri Oriental   47 ●●●
TILLEUL ♂   Floral / Florale   30 ●
TILLEUL CHÈVREFEUILLE   Soft Floral / Fleuri Aldéhydé   42 ●
TOCADE   Floral Oriental / Fleuri Oriental   47 ●●●
TOCADILLY   Floral / Florale   34 ●●
TODD OLDHAM*   Woody Oriental / Oriental Boisé   60 ●
TOMMY GIRL   Floral / Florale   36 ●
TOSCA   Soft Floral / Fleuri Aldéhydé   43 ●●●●
TOUCH FOR WOMEN   Floral / Florale   34 ●●
TOUJOURS MOI   Oriental / Oriental   57 ●●●●
TOVA   Soft Floral / Fleuri Aldéhydé   43 ●●●●
TRÈS CHIC   Soft Oriental / Oriental Doux   52 ●
TRÈS JOURDAN*   Floral / Florale   34 ●●
TRÉSOR   Floral Oriental / Fleuri Oriental   46 ●●●●
TRIANGLE*   Floral / Florale   34 ●●
TRIBÙ   Floral / Florale   34 ●●
TRIBÙ ACQUA FRESCA   Floral / Florale   36 ●
TRISH McEVOY 1   Citrus / Hespéridé   17 ●●●●
TRISH McEVOY 2   Floral / Florale   36 ●
TRISH McEVOY 3   Floral / Florale   36 ●
TRUE LOVE   Soft Floral / Fleuri Aldéhydé   42 ●
TRUESTE   Soft Floral / Fleuri Aldéhydé   42 ●
TRULY LACE   Floral Oriental / Fleuri Oriental   47 ●●●
TRUSSARDI   Dry Woods / Chypre Cuir   73 ●●●
TUBÉREUSE Annick Goutal   Floral / Florale   31 ●●●●
TUBÉREUSE Le Jardin Retrouvé   Floral / Florale   31 ●●●●
TUBÉREUSE Maître Parfumeur et Gantier   Floral / Florale   31 ●●●●
TUBEROSE Jo Malone   Floral / Florale   31 ●●●●
TURBULENCES   Mossy Woods / Chypre Boisé   67 ●●●●
TURQUOISE Comptoir Sud Pacifique   Soft Floral / Fleuri Aldéhydé   43 ●●●
TURQUOISE Morabito   Citrus / Hespéridé   17 ●●●●
TUSCANY PER DONNA   Woody Oriental / Oriental Boisé   60 ●
TWEED   Floral / Florale   33 ●●●●
TWICE ICEBERG   → ICEBERG TWICE

U

U   Floral / Florale   34 ●
U II SHEER SCENT   Mossy Woods / Chypre Boisé   66 ●
U de V POUR ELLE   Floral / Florale   34 ●●
UBAR   Mossy Woods / Chypre Boisé   67 ●●●
ULTRAVIOLET   Floral Oriental / Fleuri Oriental   46 ●
UN AIR DE SAMSARA   Woody Oriental / Oriental Boisé   60 ●
UN AMOUR DE PATOU   Floral / Florale   36 ●
UN MATIN D'ÉTÉ   Floral / Florale   30 ●●
UNE TOUCHE DE NAF NAF   Floral / Florale   34 ●
UNFORGETTABLE   Woody Oriental / Oriental Boisé   61 ●●●●
UNGARO   Woody Oriental / Oriental Boisé   61 ●●●●
UNINHIBITED*   Floral Oriental / Fleuri Oriental   47 ●●●●
UNRULY   Floral Oriental / Fleuri Oriental   47 ●●●●
UNTAMED MUSK   Oriental / Oriental   57 ●●●●
UNZIPPED   Woody Oriental / Oriental Boisé   60 ●
UNZIPPED SPORT   Floral / Florale   34 ●
UNZIPPED UNIVERSE   Floral Oriental / Fleuri Oriental   46 ●
URVASHI   Floral Oriental / Fleuri Oriental   46 ●●

V

V   *Soft Floral / Fleuri Aldéhydé   42* ●●
VACANCES   *Green / Vert   23* ●●●
VALENTINO   *Floral / Florale   34* ●●
VALERIA   *Floral / Florale   34* ●●
VALLÉE DES ROIS   *Floral Oriental / Fleuri Oriental   47* ●●●
VAN CLEEF   *Floral Oriental / Fleuri Oriental   46* ●●
VANDERBILT   *Floral Oriental / Fleuri Oriental   47* ●●●
VANILIA L'Artisan Parfumeur   *Oriental / Oriental   56* ●
VANILLA Crabtree & Evelyn   *Floral Oriental / Fleuri Oriental   48* ●
VANILLA FIELDS   *Woody Oriental / Oriental Boisé   60* ●●
VANILLA MUSK   *Woody Oriental / Oriental Boisé   61* ●●●
VANILLE Comptoir Sud Pacifique ♂   *Oriental / Oriental   56* ●●
VANILLE L'Occitane ♂   *Soft Oriental / Oriental Doux   53* ●●●
VANILLE Molinard   *Oriental / Oriental   57* ●●●
VANILLE ABRICOT   *Oriental / Oriental   56* ●
VANILLE AMANDE   *Oriental / Oriental   56* ●
VANILLE CAFÉ ♂   *Oriental / Oriental   57* ●●●
VANILLE CANNELLE   *Oriental / Oriental   57* ●●●
VANILLE CERISE   *Oriental / Oriental   56* ●
VANILLE COCO   *Woody Oriental / Oriental Boisé   60* ●
VANILLE FLEURIE   *Floral / Florale   31* ●●●●
VANILLE FRAÎCHEUR   *Oriental / Oriental   56* ●●
VANILLE FRUITÉE   *Oriental / Oriental   56* ●●
VANILLE MARINE   *Water / Marine   27* ●●●●
VANILLE PATCHOULI   *Woody Oriental / Oriental Boisé   61* ●●●
VANILLE TIARÉ   *Oriental / Oriental   56* ●
VANILLE-TONKA   *Oriental / Oriental   57* ●●●
VANISIA   *Oriental / Oriental   57* ●●●
VARENSIA   *Mossy Woods / Chypre Boisé   66* ●●
V'E VERSACE   *Mossy Woods / Chypre Boisé   66* ●●
VENDETTA*   *Woody Oriental / Oriental Boisé   60* ●
VENET   *Floral Oriental / Fleuri Oriental   47* ●●●
VENEZIA   *Woody Oriental / Oriental Boisé   61* ●●●
VENEZIA PASTELLO*   *Soft Floral / Fleuri Aldéhydé   42* ●
VENT VERT   *Green / Vert   23* ●●●
VENTILO   *Floral Oriental / Fleuri Oriental   46* ●●
VÉNUS DE L'AMOUR   *Floral Oriental / Fleuri Oriental   47* ●●●
VERANDA   *Floral Oriental / Fleuri Oriental   46* ●
VERBENAS OF PROVENCE ♂   *Citrus / Hespéridé   17* ●●●
VERINO   *Floral Oriental / Fleuri Oriental   46* ●●
VERSACE   → GIANNI VERSACE
VERSACE'S BLONDE   *Floral / Florale   31* ●●●●
VERSUS DONNA   *Floral Oriental / Fleuri Oriental   46* ●●
VERTIGO FOR WOMEN   *Aromatic / Fougère   76* ●●
VERVEINE Le Jardin Retrouvé ♂   *Citrus / Hespéridé   17* ●●●
VERY M.C. ♂   *Citrus / Hespéridé   16* ●
VERY VALENTINO   *Oriental / Oriental   56* ●
VETYVER Jo Malone ♂   *Mossy Woods / Chypre Boisé   66* ●●
VETYVER HAITI ♂   *Mossy Woods / Chypre Boisé   66* ●●
VICE VERSA Ⓛ   *Floral / Florale   34* ●●
VICKY TIEL ORIGINALÉ   *Floral / Florale   33* ●●●●
VICOLO FIORI   *Floral Oriental / Fleuri Oriental   48* ●
VICTORIAN POSY   *Floral / Florale   33* ●●●●
VIOLET Woods of Windsor   *Floral / Florale   31* ●●●●
VIOLETTA Penhaligon's   *Floral / Florale   31* ●●●●
VIOLETTA DI PARMA   *Floral / Florale   31* ●●●●
VIOLETTE Molinard   *Floral / Florale   31* ●●●●
VIOLETTE PRÉCIEUSE   *Floral / Florale   31* ●●●●
VIRGILIO ♂   *Green / Vert   22* ●●
VIVA DI TOSCA   *Floral Oriental / Fleuri Oriental   47* ●●●
VIVID   *Floral / Florale   33* ●●●●
VIVRE   *Soft Floral / Fleuri Aldéhydé   42* ●●
VOCALISE Maître Parfumeur et Gantier   *Citrus / Hespéridé   16* ●●
VOCALISE Shiseido   *Floral Oriental / Fleuri Oriental   46* ●
VOICE BY BETTY BARCLAY   *Floral Oriental / Fleuri Oriental   47* ●●●
VOL DE NUIT   *Woody Oriental / Oriental Boisé   60* ●●
VOLEUR DE ROSES ♂   *Dry Woods / Chypre Cuir   72* ●
VOLUPTÉ   *Floral Oriental / Fleuri Oriental   46* ●●
V/S   *Floral / Florale   34* ●

W

WATT   *Floral / Florale   36* ●
WEEKEND FOR WOMEN   *Floral / Florale   36* ●●
WEIL DE WEIL   *Green / Vert   23* ●●●
WEIL EAU DE FRAÎCHEUR ♂   *Citrus / Hespéridé   16* ●
WHITE CAMELLIA   *Floral / Florale   38* ●
WHITE CHANTILLY   *Floral / Florale   34* ●
WHITE DIAMONDS   *Soft Floral / Fleuri Aldéhydé   42* ●●
WHITE JEANS   *Mossy Woods / Chypre Boisé   67* ●●●
WHITE LAVENDER   *Floral / Florale   34* ●●
WHITE LINEN   *Soft Floral / Fleuri Aldéhydé   42* ●●
WHITE LINEN BREEZE   *Soft Floral / Fleuri Aldéhydé   42* ●
WHITE SATIN   *Soft Floral / Fleuri Aldéhydé   42* ●●
WHITE SHOULDERS   *Floral / Florale   33* ●●●
WHITE SPELL   *Floral / Florale   38* ●
WILD MUGUET   *Floral / Florale   30* ●
WILD MUSK Coty   *Oriental / Oriental   57* ●●●●
WILD ROSE Woods of Windsor   *Floral / Florale   31* ●●●
WILD WIND   *Water / Marine   26* ●●
WIND SONG   *Floral / Florale   33* ●●●
WINGS   *Floral / Florale   33* ●●●●
WISH   *Woody Oriental / Oriental Boisé   60* ●
WISTFUL / LONG AGO   *Floral / Florale   34* ●
WISTERIA   *Floral / Florale   30* ●●
WITH LOVE*   *Woody Oriental / Oriental Boisé   60* ●
WITH PLEASURE   *Green / Vert   23* ●●●●
WOMAN*   *Woody Oriental / Oriental Boisé   61* ●●●
WOMENSWEAR   *Soft Floral / Fleuri Aldéhydé   42* ●●
WOODHUE*   *Woody Oriental / Oriental Boisé   61* ●●●
WRAPPINGS   *Water / Marine   26* ●

X

X LIMITED ♂   *Citrus / Hespéridé   16* ●
XI'A XI'ANG*   *Floral Oriental / Fleuri Oriental   46* ●●
XS POUR ELLE   *Floral / Florale   38* ●
XTC ♂   *Citrus / Hespéridé   16* ●

Y

Y   *Mossy Woods / Chypre Boisé   66* ●
YELLOW JEANS   *Floral / Florale   34* ●
YENDI*   *Soft Floral / Fleuri Aldéhydé   43* ●●●●
YIN   *Floral / Florale   34* ●●
YLANG & VANILLE   *Floral / Florale   31* ●●●
YOHJI   *Oriental / Oriental   56* ●
YOHJI ESSENTIAL   *Mossy Woods / Chypre Boisé   66* ●●
YPNO*   *Woody Oriental / Oriental Boisé   60* ●●
YOU'RE THE FIRE FOR WOMEN   *Soft Oriental / Oriental Doux   53* ●●●
YOUTH-DEW   *Soft Oriental / Oriental Doux   53* ●●●
YSATIS   *Woody Oriental / Oriental Boisé   60* ●
YVRESSE (CHAMPAGNE)   *Mossy Woods / Chypre Boisé   66* ●

Z

ZAHAROFF   *Floral Oriental / Fleuri Oriental   46* ●
ZAHRA   *Floral Oriental / Fleuri Oriental   46* ●●
ZEN   *Floral / Florale   33* ●●●
ZESTE MANDARINE PAMPLEMOUSSE ♂   *Citrus / Hespéridé   17* ●●●●
ZIBELINE   *Mossy Woods / Chypre Boisé   67* ●●●
ZINNIA   *Floral / Florale   38* ●
ZOA   *Floral / Florale   34* ●●
ZOE   *Floral Oriental / Fleuri Oriental   46* ●
ZUT   *Woody Oriental / Oriental Boisé   60* ●

Perfume Legends

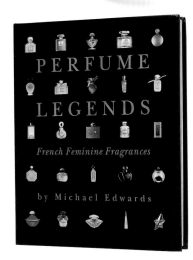

'A fascinating book for anyone with even a passing interest in perfume. Charting all the great scents since the launch of Guerlain's Jicky in 1889 to Mugler's Angel in 1992, this tells the story of some of the world's most famous fragrances. Edwards's passion for the subject makes this more a great read than just a reference book. Information value: Outstanding.'
Harpers & Queen

Critical acclaim for Michael Edwards's book, *Perfume Legends: French Feminine Fragrances*

'This book is unique, nothing else is comparable'
Edmond Roudnitska, celebrated French perfumer

'Magnificent ... the world's leading writer on the subject'
The Observer

'Michael Edwards's book is marvellously documented. It is an invaluable contribution to the history of modern perfumery. I am particularly proud to appear among the legends, and can't wait to read the next two Perfume Legends: *The Rise of American Fragrances* and *Men and Men's Fragrances*.'
Pierre Dinand, designer of the Opium, Ysatis, Obsession and Pleasures bottles

π *Woody Oriental / Oriental Boisé* 63 ●●●
3ᵉ HOMME / THIRD MAN *Aromatic / Fougère* 79 ●●●●
57 FOR HIM *Woody Oriental / Oriental Boisé* 62 ●
212 MEN *Mossy Woods / Chypre Boisé* 68 ●
273 FOR MEN *Dry Woods / Chypre Cuir* 72 ●●
360° FOR MEN *Aromatic / Fougère* 80 ●
4711 ORIGINAL ♂ *Citrus / Hespéridé* 19 ●●●

A

ACIER *Aromatic / Fougère* 82 ●●
ACIER ALUMINIUM *Mossy Woods / Chypre Boisé* 69 ●●●●
ACQUA CLASSICA DI BORSARI ♂ *Citrus / Hespéridé* 19 ●●●
ACQUA DI GIÒ HOMME *Water / Marine* 26 ●●
ACQUA DI PARMA ♂ *Citrus / Hespéridé* 19 ●●●
ACQUA DI SELVA *Mossy Woods / Chypre Boisé* 69 ●●●
ACTEUR *Dry Woods / Chypre Cuir* 72 ●●
ACTION SPORT *Citrus / Hespéridé* 19 ●●●●
ACTION UOMO* *Aromatic / Fougère* 80 ●
ADIDAS ACTION *Aromatic / Fougère* 82 ●
ADIDAS ACTIVE BODIES *Aromatic / Fougère* 78 ●●
ADIDAS ADVENTURE *Aromatic / Fougère* 78 ●●
ADIDAS CLASSIC *Dry Woods / Chypre Cuir* 72 ●●
ADIDAS DYNAMIC *Aromatic / Fougère* 82 ●
ADIDAS MOVES *Aromatic / Fougère* 80 ●
ADIDAS SPORT *Citrus / Hespéridé* 18 ●●
ADOLFO DOMINGUEZ *Aromatic / Fougère* 80 ●
ADVENTURE QUASAR *Aromatic / Fougère* 78 ●
AGUA BRAVA *Mossy Woods / Chypre Boisé* 69 ●●●
AGUA FRESCA *Mossy Woods / Chypre Boisé* 69 ●●●
AGUA LAVANDA ♂ *Floral / Florale* 39 ●●●
AGUIRRE *Woody Oriental / Oriental Boisé* 62 ●●
AIGNER Nº 1 → ETIENNE AIGNER Nº 1
AIGNER Nº 2 → ETIENNE AIGNER Nº 2
ALLURE HOMME *Woody Oriental / Oriental Boisé* 62 ●
ALVIERO MARTINI UOMO *Aromatic / Fougère* 82 ●
AMBER & LAVENDER ♂ *Woody Oriental / Oriental Boisé* 63 ●●●
AMBRE PRECIEUX ♂ *Oriental / Oriental* 57 ●●●●
AMBRO DE JACOMO *Woody Oriental / Oriental Boisé* 63 ●●●
A*MEN / ANGEL MEN *Woody Oriental / Oriental Boisé* 62 ●●
AMERICA FOR MEN *Aromatic / Fougère* 80 ●
AMOUAGE HOMME *Soft Floral / Fleuri Aldéhydé* 43 ●●●●
ANDY WARHOL FOR MEN *Aromatic / Fougère* 78 ●
ANGEL MEN / A*MEN *Woody Oriental / Oriental Boisé* 62 ●●
ANIMALE FOR MEN *Aromatic / Fougère* 80 ●
ANIMALE ANIMALE FOR MEN *Woody Oriental / Oriental Boisé* 62 ●
ANTAEUS *Dry Woods / Chypre Cuir* 73 ●●●●
ANTHRACITE POUR L'HOMME *Aromatic / Fougère* 82 ●●
AQUA QUORUM *Aromatic / Fougère* 82 ●
AQUA VELVA ICE BLUE *Mossy Woods / Chypre Boisé* 68 ●●
ARAMIS *Dry Woods / Chypre Cuir* 73 ●●●
ARAMIS 900 *Dry Woods / Chypre Cuir* 72 ●
ARAMIS GOLD *Dry Woods / Chypre Cuir* 73 ●●●
ARIOS *Aromatic / Fougère* 79 ●●●●
ARMANI POUR HOMME *Citrus / Hespéridé* 19 ●●●●
ARÔME 3 ♂ *Floral / Florale* 39 ●●●
ARÔME 3 TRADITION ♂ *Floral / Florale* 39 ●●●●
ARROGANCE UOMO *Aromatic / Fougère* 78 ●●
ARROGANCE YOU *Aromatic / Fougère* 82 ●●
ARSENAL *Woody Oriental / Oriental Boisé* 62 ●
ASPEN FOR MEN *Aromatic / Fougère* 80 ●
ATKINSON GOLD MEDAL ♂ *Citrus / Hespéridé* 19 ●●●
ATMAN *Dry Woods / Chypre Cuir* 73 ●●●
AUBUSSON HOMME *Mossy Woods / Chypre Boisé* 68 ●●
AVATAR *Aromatic / Fougère* 78 ●
AZZARO POUR HOMME *Aromatic / Fougère* 78 ●

B

BACKGROUND *Woody Oriental / Oriental Boisé* 62 ●●
BAD BOYS *Aromatic / Fougère* 80 ●●
BAIE DE GENIÈVRE *Woody Oriental / Oriental Boisé* 63 ●●●
BALADIN *Dry Woods / Chypre Cuir* 73 ●●●
BALENCIAGA POUR HOMME *Woody Oriental / Oriental Boisé* 63 ●●●●
BARBIER DES ISLES *Dry Woods / Chypre Cuir* 73 ●●●

BARON → THE BARON
BARYSHNIKOV *Aromatic / Fougère* 78 ●●
BARYSHNIKOV SPORT *Aromatic / Fougère* 80 ●
BASALA *Aromatic / Fougère* 79 ●●●●
BASILE UOMO *Dry Woods / Chypre Cuir* 72 ●●
BAYWATCH MAN *Aromatic / Fougère* 78 ●●
BE BOP MAN *Dry Woods / Chypre Cuir* 72 ●
BE BOP POUR HOMME *Aromatic / Fougère* 78 ●●
BEL AMI *Dry Woods / Chypre Cuir* 73 ●●●●
BENETTON SPORT MAN *Aromatic / Fougère* 80 ●●
BEST MAN *Woody Oriental / Oriental Boisé* 62 ●
BEST OF CHEVIGNON ♂ *Water / Marine* 27 ●●●
BIJAN FOR MEN *Aromatic / Fougère* 78 ●●
BLACK JEANS Gianni Versace *Aromatic / Fougère* 78 ●●
BLACK JEANS HOMME *Woody Oriental / Oriental Boisé* 62 ●●
BLACK SILVER ♂ *Aromatic / Fougère* 78 ●●
BLENHEIM BOUQUET *Citrus / Hespéridé* 19 ●●●
BLEU FORMIDABLE *Aromatic / Fougère* 82 ●
BLEU MARINE *Woody Oriental / Oriental Boisé* 62 ●
BLUE *Aromatic / Fougère* 82 ●
BLUE JEANS *Woody Oriental / Oriental Boisé* 62 ●●
BLUE STRATOS *Aromatic / Fougère* 82 ●
BODY KOUROS *Woody Oriental / Oriental Boisé* 62 ●
BOGART *Aromatic / Fougère* 80 ●●
BOGNER MAN *Citrus / Hespéridé* 18 ●●
BOGNER MAN II *Aromatic / Fougère* 78 ●●
BOIS DE CÉDRAT ♂ *Citrus / Hespéridé* 19 ●●●
BOIS DU PORTUGAL *Woody Oriental / Oriental Boisé* 63 ●●●●
BOIS PRÉCIEUX *Mossy Woods / Chypre Boisé* 69 ●●●●
BOOSTER *Citrus / Hespéridé* 18 ●●
BORSALINO *Aromatic / Fougère* 82 ●●
BOSS *Woody Oriental / Oriental Boisé* 62 ●●
BOSS NUMBER ONE *Aromatic / Fougère* 78 ●●
BOSS SPIRIT* *Dry Woods / Chypre Cuir* 72 ●●
BOSS SPORT* *Aromatic / Fougère* 78 ●●
BOSTON MAN *Aromatic / Fougère* 78 ●●
BOUCHERON POUR HOMME *Citrus / Hespéridé* 19 ●●●●
BOUQUET IMPÉRIAL ♂ *Citrus / Hespéridé* 19 ●●●●
BOURBON HOMME *Mossy Woods / Chypre Boisé* 69 ●●●●
BOWLING GREEN *Aromatic / Fougère* 78 ●●
BRISTOL BLUE *Aromatic / Fougère* 78 ●●
BRITISH STERLING *Aromatic / Fougère* 79 ●●●
BROOKS BROS *Aromatic / Fougère* 80 ●
BRUT *Aromatic / Fougère* 79 ●●●
BRUT ACTIF BLUE *Aromatic / Fougère* 82 ●
BRUT INSTINCT *Aromatic / Fougère* 78 ●●
BUCKINGHAM *Aromatic / Fougère* 78 ●●
BUGATTI *Aromatic / Fougère* 80 ●
BULGARI BLACK ♂ *Dry Woods / Chypre Cuir* 72 ●●
BULGARI EAU PARFUMÉE ♂ *Citrus / Hespéridé* 18 ●
BULGARI POUR HOMME *Aromatic / Fougère* 80 ●
BURBERRY FOR MEN *Aromatic / Fougère* 78 ●●
BY MAN *Woody Oriental / Oriental Boisé* 62 ●●
BYBLOS UOMO *Aromatic / Fougère* 80 ●●

C

CACHAREL POUR L'HOMME *Aromatic / Fougère* 82 ●●
CAESARS MAN *Aromatic / Fougère* 78 ●●
CAFÉ-CAFÉ POUR HOMME *Aromatic / Fougère* 82 ●
CALIFORNIA FOR MEN *Aromatic / Fougère* 78 ●●
CALVIN *Aromatic / Fougère* 78 ●●
CAMP BEVERLY HILLS FOR MEN* *Citrus / Hespéridé* 19 ●●●●
CANDIE'S MEN *Aromatic / Fougère* 80 ●
CANOÉ *Aromatic / Fougère* 79 ●●●
CANNELLE ORANGE ♂ *Citrus / Hespéridé* 18 ●
CAPTAIN* *Aromatic / Fougère* 78 ●●
CAPUCCI POUR HOMME *Citrus / Hespéridé* 18 ●●
CARACTÈRE *Dry Woods / Chypre Cuir* 72 ●●
CARLO CORINTO *Dry Woods / Chypre Cuir* 72 ●●
CARRÉ D'AS *Aromatic / Fougère* 80 ●
CARVEN HOMME *Dry Woods / Chypre Cuir* 72 ●●
CASRAN *Woody Oriental / Oriental Boisé* 62 ●
CASSINI FOR MEN *Aromatic / Fougère* 78 ●
CASUAL FRIDAY *Woody Oriental / Oriental Boisé* 62 ●
CATALYST FOR MEN *Woody Oriental / Oriental Boisé* 62 ●●
CÉDRAT POMELO ♂ *Citrus / Hespéridé* 18 ●●

CELSIUS *Aromatic / Fougère* 80 ●
CENTAURE *Aromatic / Fougère* 79 ●●●
CENTAURE CUIR AMBRE *Woody Oriental / Oriental Boisé* 62 ●●
CENTAURE CUIR BLANC *Mossy Woods / Chypre Boisé* 68 ●●
CENTAURE CUIR CASAQUE *Aromatic / Fougère* 82 ●●
CENTAURE CUIR ÉTALON *Dry Woods / Chypre Cuir* 73 ●●●
CENTAURE CUIR FOUGÈRE *Aromatic / Fougère* 78 ●
CENTAURE DIAMANT NOIR *Aromatic / Fougère* 78 ●●
CENTAURE TÊTE D'OR *Aromatic / Fougère* 78 ●●
CERRUTI 1881 *Citrus / Hespéridé* 18 ●●
C'EST MAGIQUE HOMME *Aromatic / Fougère* 78 ●●
CHAMADE POUR HOMME ℒ *Mossy Woods / Chypre Boisé* 68 ●
CHALLENGE → PUMA CHALLENGE
CHANEL POUR MONSIEUR *Mossy Woods / Chypre Boisé* 69 ●●●
CHAPEAU *Aromatic / Fougère* 78 ●
CHAPS *Woody Oriental / Oriental Boisé* 63 ●●●
CHAPS MUSK *Woody Oriental / Oriental Boisé* 63 ●●●
CHEMISTRY *Aromatic / Fougère* 80 ●
CHEVALIER D'ORSAY *Citrus / Hespéridé* 19 ●●●●
CHEVIGNON *Mossy Woods / Chypre Boisé* 68 ●●
CHÈVREFEUILLE ORIGINAL ♂ *Green / Vert* 22 ●
CHIARA BONI UOMO *Aromatic / Fougère* 82 ●
CHRISTOS MAN *Woody Oriental / Oriental Boisé* 62 ●●
CHROME *Citrus / Hespéridé* 18 ●●
CIGAR *Woody Oriental / Oriental Boisé* 62 ●●
CIGAR AFICIONADO *Aromatic / Fougère* 79 ●●●●
CIGARILLO *Dry Woods / Chypre Cuir* 73 ●●●●
CITRON VERT ♂ *Citrus / Hespéridé* 18 ●
CITRUS BIGARRADE ♂ *Citrus / Hespéridé* 19 ●●●
cK BE ♂ *Aromatic / Fougère* 80 ●
cK ONE ♂ *Citrus / Hespéridé* 18 ●
CLAIBORNE FOR MEN* *Citrus / Hespéridé* 18 ●
CLAIBORNE SPORT *Aromatic / Fougère* 82 ●
CLASSIC *Mossy Woods / Chypre Boisé* 69 ●●●
CLEAR DAY FOR MEN *Aromatic / Fougère* 80 ●
ᶜN *Dry Woods / Chypre Cuir* 73 ●●●
COLD ♂ *Citrus / Hespéridé* 19 ●●●●
COLOGNE SOLOGNE ♂ *Citrus / Hespéridé* 19 ●●●
COLORS FOR MEN *Woody Oriental / Oriental Boisé* 62 ●
COMME DES GARÇONS ♂ *Mossy Woods / Chypre Boisé* 69 ●●●●
COMME DES GARÇONS 2 ♂ *Mossy Woods / Chypre Boisé* 68 ●
CONSENT MAN *Aromatic / Fougère* 78 ●
CONTRADICTION FOR MEN *Woody Oriental / Oriental Boisé* 62 ●
CONVICTION MEN *Woody Oriental / Oriental Boisé* 62 ●●
COOL WATER *Aromatic / Fougère* 80 ●
CORIOLAN *Mossy Woods / Chypre Boisé* 68 ●●
COTONNADE ♂ *Soft Oriental / Oriental Doux* 52 ●●
COUNTRY ROAD MAN *Aromatic / Fougère* 82 ●
COUNTRY WEEKEND ♂ *Aromatic / Fougère* 82 ●●
CRABTREE & EVELYN FOR MEN *Dry Woods / Chypre Cuir* 73 ●●●
CROSSROADS *Aromatic / Fougère* 82 ●
CROWN FOUGÈRE *Aromatic / Fougère* 79 ●●●
CROWN IMPERIAL *Citrus / Hespéridé* 19 ●●●●
CROWN PARK ROYAL *Dry Woods / Chypre Cuir* 72 ●●
CROWN SPICED LIMES *Citrus / Hespéridé* 19 ●●●●
CRUISE FOR MEN *Mossy Woods / Chypre Boisé* 68 ●●
CRUISER FOR MEN *Aromatic / Fougère* 78 ●●
CUIR DE RUSSIE Le Jardin Retrouvé → EAU DE CUIR DE RUSSIE
CUIR DE RUSSIE L.T. Piver ♂ *Dry Woods / Chypre Cuir* 73 ●●●
CULTURE by TABAC *Aromatic / Fougère* 82 ●●
CULTURE by TABAC BLUE *Aromatic / Fougère* 82 ●
CURVE FOR MEN *Aromatic / Fougère* 78 ●
CYBERSP@CE ♂ *Water / Marine* 26 ●
CYCLE* *Aromatic / Fougère* 80 ●

D

D Dunhill *Aromatic / Fougère* 80 ●
D & G MASCULINE *Citrus / Hespéridé* 19 ●●●●
DALI *Aromatic / Fougère* 78 ●
DALIMIX ♂ *Citrus / Hespéridé* 18 ●
DALIMIX GOLD ♂ *Green / Vert* 22 ●
DANIEL HECHTER SPORT *Aromatic / Fougère* 78 ●
DAVIDOFF *Dry Woods / Chypre Cuir* 73 ●●●●
DAVINCI CLASSICO *Dry Woods / Chypre Cuir* 73 ●●●●
DEAUVILLE POUR HOMME *Aromatic / Fougère* 78 ●

DÉCLARATION *Dry Woods / Chypre Cuir* 72 ●
DEEP BLUE *Aromatic / Fougère* 80 ●
DEEP FOREST *Dry Woods / Chypre Cuir* 73 ●●●●
DERBY *Dry Woods / Chypre Cuir* 73 ●●●●
DERRICK *Woody Oriental / Oriental Boisé* 63 ●●●
DESIGN FOR MEN *Aromatic / Fougère* 80 ●
DESTINY *Mossy Woods / Chypre Boisé* 69 ●●●
DEVIN *Green / Vert* 23 ●●●●
DIESEL *Woody Oriental / Oriental Boisé* 63 ●●●
DIESEL PLUS PLUS MASCULINE *Woody Oriental / Oriental Boisé* 61 ●
DIESEL ZERO PLUS MASCULINE *Woody Oriental / Oriental Boisé* 63 ●●●
DISCOVER *Aromatic / Fougère* 78 ●●
DISCOVERY *Aromatic / Fougère* 78 ●
DK MEN* *Dry Woods / Chypre Cuir* 72 ●●
DK MEN UNLEADED* *Dry Woods / Chypre Cuir* 72 ●
DKNY MEN *Aromatic / Fougère* 80 ●
DNA FOR MEN *Woody Oriental / Oriental Boisé* 62 ●●
DOLCE & GABBANA HOMME *Aromatic / Fougère* 79 ●●●
DRAKKAR DYNAMIK *Aromatic / Fougère* 82 ●
DRAKKAR NOIR *Aromatic / Fougère* 78 ●●
DREAMER → THE DREAMER
DUC DE VERVINS *Aromatic / Fougère* 78 ●●
DUNE POUR HOMME *Woody Oriental / Oriental Boisé* 62 ●
DUNHILL *Dry Woods / Chypre Cuir* 73 ●●●
DUNHILL D → D
DUNHILL EDITION *Aromatic / Fougère* 82 ●●
DV8 FOR MEN *Aromatic / Fougère* 80 ●

E

EAU D'ÉLIDE ♂ *Aromatic / Fougère* 79 ●●●
EAU D'HADRIEN ♂ *Citrus / Hespéridé* 19 ●●●
EAU D'HERMÈS ♂ *Dry Woods / Chypre Cuir* 73 ●●●
EAU D'ORANGE VERTE ♂ *Citrus / Hespéridé* 19 ●●●●
EAU DE CAMPAGNE ♂ *Green / Vert* 23 ●●●
EAU DE CARON FORTE ♂ *Citrus / Hespéridé* 19 ●●●●
EAU DE CÈDRE ♂ *Dry Woods / Chypre Cuir* 72 ●
EAU DE CHEVERNY ♂ *Mossy Woods / Chypre Boisé* 69 ●●●
EAU DE COLOGNE Penhaligon's ♂ *Citrus / Hespéridé* 19 ●●●
EAU DE COLOGNE EXTRA FINE L'Occitane *Citrus / Hespéridé* 19 ●●●●
EAU DE CUIR DE RUSSIE *Dry Woods / Chypre Cuir* 72 ●●
EAU DE FLEURS DE CÉDRAT ♂ *Citrus / Hespéridé* 19 ●●●
EAU DE GREY FLANNEL *Mossy Woods / Chypre Boisé* 68 ●
EAU DE GUERLAIN ♂ *Citrus / Hespéridé* 19 ●●●
EAU DE LAVANDE Annick Goutal ♂ *Floral / Florale* 39 ●●●
EAU DE LAVANDE Mont St Michel ♂ *Floral / Florale* 39 ●●●
EAU DE MONSIEUR *Mossy Woods / Chypre Boisé* 69 ●●●
EAU DE PROVENCE ♂ *Floral / Florale* 39 ●●●
EAU DE QUININE *Citrus / Hespéridé* 19 ●●●
EAU DE ROCHAS HOMME *Citrus / Hespéridé* 19 ●●●●
EAU DE RUSSE Crown *Oriental / Oriental* 56 ●●
EAU DE SANDALWOOD *Woody Oriental / Oriental Boisé* 63 ●●●
EAU DE SPORT Alain Delon* *Aromatic / Fougère* 80 ●●
EAU DE VARENS N° 2 ♂ *Citrus / Hespéridé* 18 ●
EAU DE VARENS N° 3 ♂ *Citrus / Hespéridé* 18 ●●
EAU DE VARENS N° 4 ♂ *Citrus / Hespéridé* 19 ●●●●
EAU DE VERVEINE Penhaligon's ♂ *Citrus / Hespéridé* 19 ●●●●
EAU DE VÉTYVER *Mossy Woods / Chypre Boisé* 68 ●●
EAU DES 4 VOLEURS *Aromatic / Fougère* 80 ●
EAU DES ÎLES *Dry Woods / Chypre Cuir* 73 ●●●●
EAU DES PRINCES *Citrus / Hespéridé* 19 ●●●
EAU DES TROPIQUES *Citrus / Hespéridé* 19 ●●●
EAU DU BADIAN *Citrus / Hespéridé* 18 ●●
EAU DU CONTADOUR *Aromatic / Fougère* 79 ●●●
EAU DU COQ ♂ *Citrus / Hespéridé* 19 ●●●
EAU DU GANTIER ♂ *Citrus / Hespéridé* 19 ●●●
EAU DU NAVIGATEUR *Dry Woods / Chypre Cuir* 73 ●●●●
EAU DU SUD ♂ *Citrus / Hespéridé* 18 ●●
EAU DU TSAR *Aromatic / Fougère* 80 ●
EAU DYNAMISANTE ♂ *Citrus / Hespéridé* 19 ●●●
EAU FRAÎCHE Caron ♂ *Citrus / Hespéridé* 19 ●●●
EAU FRAÎCHE Molinard ♂ *Citrus / Hespéridé* 18 ●●
EAU FRANCE ♂ *Citrus / Hespéridé* 19 ●●●
EAU FRESH Jacques Bogart *Aromatic / Fougère* 80 ●
EAU GRISE *Mossy Woods / Chypre Boisé* 68 ●
EAU IMPÉRIALE ♂ *Citrus / Hespéridé* 19 ●●●

EAU LENTE ♂ *Oriental / Oriental* 57 ●●●
EAU POUR HOMME Le Jardin Retrouvé *Aromatic / Fougère* 80 ●●
EAU POUR HOMME L.T. Piver *Citrus / Hespéridé* 19 ●●●●
EAU PURE ♂ *Water / Marine* 26 ●
EAU SANS PAREIL ♂ *Aromatic / Fougère* 78 ●●
EAU SAUVAGE *Citrus / Hespéridé* 19 ●●●
EAU SAUVAGE EXTRÊME *Citrus / Hespéridé* 19 ●●●●
ÉBÈNE *Aromatic / Fougère* 80 ●●
ÉGOÏSTE / L'ÉGOÏSTE *Woody Oriental / Oriental Boisé* 63 ●●●
ÉGOÏSTE PLATINUM *Aromatic / Fougère* 78 ●
EL PASO *Aromatic / Fougère* 78 ●●
ELEMENTS *Aromatic / Fougère* 78 ●
ELEMENTS AQUA *Aromatic / Fougère* 82 ●●
ELITE *Citrus / Hespéridé* 19 ●●●●
ELYSEOS HOMME *Dry Woods / Chypre Cuir* 73 ●●●●
EMOZIONI FOR MAN *Aromatic / Fougère* 82 ●
EMPORIO ARMANI HE / LUI *Mossy Woods / Chypre Boisé* 68 ●●
ENGLISH BLAZER *Aromatic / Fougère* 78 ●●
ENGLISH FERN ♂ *Aromatic / Fougère* 79 ●●●
ENGLISH FINE COLOGNE ♂ *Citrus / Hespéridé* 19 ●●●
ENGLISH LAVENDER Atkinson ♂ *Floral / Florale* 39 ●●●
ENGLISH LEATHER *Dry Woods / Chypre Cuir* 72 ●●
ENIGME *Aromatic / Fougère* 82 ●●
ENVY FOR MEN *Woody Oriental / Oriental Boisé* 62 ●
EPICÉA *Aromatic / Fougère* 82 ●●
EQUATEUR *Aromatic / Fougère* 79 ●●●
ÉQUIPAGE *Aromatic / Fougère* 79 ●●●●
EROLFA *Water / Marine* 26 ●
ERUPTION MAN *Woody Oriental / Oriental Boisé* 62 ●●
ESCADA POUR HOMME *Woody Oriental / Oriental Boisé* 62 ●●
ESCAPE FOR MEN *Aromatic / Fougère* 82 ●
ESENCIA LOEWE *Dry Woods / Chypre Cuir* 72 ●●
ESPRIT DE LAVANDE ♂ *Aromatic / Fougère* 78 ●
ESPRIT DU ROI ♂ *Citrus / Hespéridé* 18 ●●
ESSENZA DI MEDITERRANEÒ UOMO *Dry Woods / Chypre Cuir* 72 ●
ETERNITY FOR MEN *Aromatic / Fougère* 80 ●
ETIENNE AIGNER N° 1* *Dry Woods / Chypre Cuir* 73 ●●●
ETIENNE AIGNER N° 2 *Aromatic / Fougère* 79 ●●●●
ETIQUETTE BLEUE ♂ *Citrus / Hespéridé* 18 ●●
EVASION *Citrus / Hespéridé* 18 ●●
EXTASE BODY TALK ♂ *Citrus / Hespéridé* 18 ●
EXTASE EXOTIC NATURE MAN *Aromatic / Fougère* 78 ●●
EXTASE MAGMA MAN *Woody Oriental / Oriental Boisé* 63 ●●●
EXTASE MUSK MAN *Oriental / Oriental* 57 ●●●●
EXTRACT OF LIMES Penhaligon's ♂ *Citrus / Hespéridé* 19 ●●●●

F

FACE À FACE HOMME *Aromatic / Fougère* 82 ●
FAÇONNABLE *Aromatic / Fougère* 82 ●
FAHRENHEIT *Mossy Woods / Chypre Boisé* 68 ●
FEELING MAN → JIL SANDER FEELING MAN
FENDI UOMO *Dry Woods / Chypre Cuir* 73 ●●●●
FERRARI *Woody Oriental / Oriental Boisé* 62 ●
FERRARI BLACK *Mossy Woods / Chypre Boisé* 68 ●●
FERRARI COLOGNE WATER *Citrus / Hespéridé* 19 ●●●
FERRÉ FOR MAN *Woody Oriental / Oriental Boisé* 63 ●●●
FEUILLE DE VERVEINE ♂ *Citrus / Hespéridé* 18 ●
FIRE & ICE FOR MEN *Aromatic / Fougère* 80 ●
FIRE & ICE SMOULDER FOR HIM *Mossy Woods / Chypre Boisé* 68 ●●
FOR GENTLEMEN Woods of Windsor
    Mossy Woods / Chypre Boisé 69 ●●●
FORCE MAJEURE *Woody Oriental / Oriental Boisé* 62 ●●
FORMIDABLE HOMME *Aromatic / Fougère* 80 ●●
FOUGÈRE ROYALE* *Aromatic / Fougère* 79 ●●●
FRAÎCHE BADIANE *Mossy Woods / Chypre Boisé* 68 ●●
FRAÎCHEUR MUSKISSIME ♂ *Citrus / Hespéridé* 19 ●●●●
FREE WORLD MAN *Aromatic / Fougère* 80 ●
FREEDOM FOR HIM *Aromatic / Fougère* 80 ●●
FUJIYAMA ♂ *Citrus / Hespéridé* 18 ●
FUN WATER FOR MEN *Aromatic / Fougère* 80 ●
FURYO* *Woody Oriental / Oriental Boisé* 63 ●●●●

G

GAI MATTIOLO UOMO *Citrus / Hespéridé* 18 ●
GALE HAYMAN MAN *Aromatic / Fougère* 82 ●●
GALILEO 21st CENTURY *Aromatic / Fougère* 82 ●
GALILEO DE VIENTO *Aromatic / Fougère* 80 ●●
GARRIGUE *Aromatic / Fougère* 78 ●●
GENDARME *Citrus / Hespéridé* 19 ●●●●
GENGIS KHAN *Woody Oriental / Oriental Boisé* 62 ●
GERANI UOMO *Woody Oriental / Oriental Boisé* 62 ●
GFF UOMO *Aromatic / Fougère* 78 ●
GIEFFEFFE ♂ *Citrus / Hespéridé* 18 ●
GIGLI PER UOMO *Woody Oriental / Oriental Boisé* 62 ●●
GINSENG N.R.G *Woody Oriental / Oriental Boisé* 62 ●●
GIORGIO MEN* *Mossy Woods / Chypre Boisé* 69 ●●●●
GIVENCHY GENTLEMAN *Mossy Woods / Chypre Boisé* 69 ●●●●
GIVRINE (SICILE) ♂ *Citrus / Hespéridé* 19 ●●●
GLOBE* *Aromatic / Fougère* 80 ●●
GMV ENERGY *Aromatic / Fougère* 82 ●
GMV UOMO *Aromatic / Fougère* 80 ●
GOLD *Aromatic / Fougère* 78 ●
GOLD JEANS HOMME *Aromatic / Fougère* 82 ●●
GOODLIFE *Aromatic / Fougère* 80 ●●
GRABAZZI *Soft Oriental / Oriental Doux* 53 ●●●
GRAIN DE PLAISIR ♂ *Mossy Woods / Chypre Boisé* 68 ●
GRANITE BLUE *Aromatic / Fougère* 80 ●
GRANITE ORIGINAL *Aromatic / Fougère* 82 ●
GRAPEFRUIT ♂ *Citrus / Hespéridé* 18 ●●
GRAVITY *Woody Oriental / Oriental Boisé* 62 ●●
GREEN GENERATION ♂ *Aromatic / Fougère* 80 ●●
GREEN GENERATION HIM *Aromatic / Fougère* 78 ●
GREEN IRISH TWEED *Green / Vert* 23 ●●●
GREEN JEANS *Aromatic / Fougère* 80 ●
GREEN VALLEY *Mossy Woods / Chypre Boisé* 68 ●
GREEN WATER *Citrus / Hespéridé* 18 ●●
GREY FLANNEL *Mossy Woods / Chypre Boisé* 68 ●
EAU DE GREY FLANNEL *Mossy Woods / Chypre Boisé* 68 ●
GRIGIO PERLA *Aromatic / Fougère* 78 ●
GUCCI NOBILE* *Aromatic / Fougère* 82 ●●
GUÉPARD HOMME *Mossy Woods / Chypre Boisé* 68 ●●
GUESS FOR MEN* *Aromatic / Fougère* 79 ●●●●

H

HABIT ROUGE *Oriental / Oriental* 57 ●●●
HALSTON 1-12 *Green / Vert* 23 ●●●
HALSTON Z *Mossy Woods / Chypre Boisé* 68 ●●
HALSTON Z-14 *Mossy Woods / Chypre Boisé* 68 ●●
HAMMAM BOUQUET *Woody Oriental / Oriental Boisé* 63 ●●●
HAPPY FOR MEN *Citrus / Hespéridé* 18 ●
HAVANA *Aromatic / Fougère* 79 ●●●●
HEAVEN *Aromatic / Fougère* 80 ●●
HERBA FRESCA ♂ *Green / Vert* 22 ●●
HÉRITAGE *Woody Oriental / Oriental Boisé* 62 ●●
HÉROS *Woody Oriental / Oriental Boisé* 62 ●●
HÉROS SPORT *Aromatic / Fougère* 80 ●
HERRERA FOR MEN *Woody Oriental / Oriental Boisé* 62 ●●
HIGH TECH MEN *Mossy Woods / Chypre Boisé* 68 ●●
HILFIGER ATHLETICS *Citrus / Hespéridé* 18 ●
H.M. *Woody Oriental / Oriental Boisé* 62 ●
HO HANG *Aromatic / Fougère* 82 ●●
HO HANG CLUB* *Dry Woods / Chypre Cuir* 73 ●●●●
HOLLYWOOD FOR MEN *Aromatic / Fougère* 78 ●●
HOMME I → MOLINARD HOMME I
HOMME II → MOLINARD HOMME II
HOMME III → MOLINARD HOMME III
HOMME DE GRÈS *Dry Woods / Chypre Cuir* 73 ●●●●
HORIZON *Aromatic / Fougère* 80 ●
HUGO *Aromatic / Fougère* 82 ●
HUGO DARK BLUE *Mossy Woods / Chypre Boisé* 68 ●
HUNGARY WATER *Citrus / Hespéridé* 19 ●●●

I

ICE WATER* *Aromatic / Fougère* 82 ●
ICEBERG HOMME *Citrus / Hespéridé* 19 ●●●●
ICEBERG TWICE HOMME *Aromatic / Fougère* 78 ●
ICEBERG UNIVERSE HOMME *Woody Oriental / Oriental Boisé* 62 ●
IGNIS *Dry Woods / Chypre Cuir* 73 ●●●
IMAGE *Aromatic / Fougère* 80 ●
IMPERIAL LEATHER *Dry Woods / Chypre Cuir* 73 ●●●
IMPERIAL VETYVER ♂ *Mossy Woods / Chypre Boisé* 69 ●●●
IMPLICITE HOMME *Mossy Woods / Chypre Boisé* 68 ●●
INDEPENDENCE → PUMA INDEPENDENCE
INIS ♂ *Water / Marine* 26 ●
INSATIABLE *Aromatic / Fougère* 78 ●
INSENSÉ *Floral / Florale* 38 ●●
INSENSÉ ULTRAMARINE *Aromatic / Fougère* 82 ●
INSTINCT *Aromatic / Fougère* 78 ●●
IQUITOS* *Mossy Woods / Chypre Boisé* 69 ●●●●
IRIS BLEU GRIS *Mossy Woods / Chypre Boisé* 68 ●

J

J.F. *Aromatic / Fougère* 80 ●
J.H.L. *Soft Oriental / Oriental Doux* 53 ●●●
JACOMO DE JACOMO *Woody Oriental / Oriental Boisé* 62 ●●
JACQUES FATH → POUR L'HOMME
JADE EAST *Aromatic / Fougère* 79 ●●●
JAGUAR *Aromatic / Fougère* 79 ●●●●
JAGUAR MARK II *Woody Oriental / Oriental Boisé* 62 ●●
JAGUAR SPECIAL EDITION *Aromatic / Fougère* 82 ●
JAÏPUR HOMME *Woody Oriental / Oriental Boisé* 62 ●●
JAKO *Woody Oriental / Oriental Boisé* 62 ●●
JARDIN DU NIL *Floral / Florale* 38 ●●
JAZZ *Aromatic / Fougère* 78 ●
JEAN-MARIE FARINA ♂ *Citrus / Hespéridé* 19 ●●●
JICKY ♂ *Aromatic / Fougère* 79 ●●●
JIL SANDER FEELING MAN *Soft Oriental / Oriental Doux* 52 ●
JIL SANDER MAN III* *Aromatic / Fougère* 78 ●●
JIL SANDER MAN PURE *Dry Woods / Chypre Cuir* 73 ●●●●
JIMMY'Z *Woody Oriental / Oriental Boisé* 62 ●●
JIVAGO 7 ELEMENTS *Woody Oriental / Oriental Boisé* 62 ●●
JIVAGO 24k MEN *Aromatic / Fougère* 78 ●
JOHNNY LAMBS *Woody Oriental / Oriental Boisé* 62 ●●
JOOP! HOMME *Woody Oriental / Oriental Boisé* 63 ●●●
JORDAN BY MICHAEL *Woody Oriental / Oriental Boisé* 62 ●
JOSEPH ABBOUD *Aromatic / Fougère* 80 ●●
JOVAN EVENING MUSK* *Soft Oriental / Oriental Doux* 52 ●●
JOVAN MUSK FOR MEN *Soft Floral / Fleuri Aldéhydé* 43 ●●●●
JOVAN WHITE MUSK *Woody Oriental / Oriental Boisé* 62 ●
JULES *Aromatic / Fougère* 79 ●●●●
JUNGLE POUR HOMME *Woody Oriental / Oriental Boisé* 62 ●●

K

KANØN *Woody Oriental / Oriental Boisé* 63 ●●●
KENZO POUR HOMME *Water / Marine* 26 ●
KIPLING *Woody Oriental / Oriental Boisé* 62 ●●
KITON MEN *Mossy Woods / Chypre Boisé* 68 ●
KITON NAPOLI *Woody Oriental / Oriental Boisé* 62 ●
KL HOMME* *Oriental / Oriental* 57 ●●●
KNIZE TEN *Dry Woods / Chypre Cuir* 73 ●●●
KOUROS *Aromatic / Fougère* 79 ●●●●
KOUROS FRAÎCHEUR *Aromatic / Fougère* 80 ●●
KRIZIA UOMO *Dry Woods / Chypre Cuir* 73 ●●●●
KUMQUAT ♂ *Citrus / Hespéridé* 18 ●●
KYRIAZ *Aromatic / Fougère* 80 ●

L

L'AUTRE ♂ *Dry Woods / Chypre Cuir* 73 ●●●●
L'EAU Diptyque ♂ *Soft Oriental / Oriental Doux* 52 ●●
L'EAU D'ISSEY POUR HOMME *Water / Marine* 27 ●●●
L'EAU DE L'ARTISAN ♂ *Citrus / Hespéridé* 19 ●●●

L'EAU PAR KENZO POUR HOMME *Citrus / Hespéridé* 18 ●●
L'EAU TROIS ♂ *Dry Woods / Chypre Cuir* 72 ●●
L'ÉGOÏSTE → ÉGOÏSTE
L'ÉGOÏSTE PLATINUM → ÉGOÏSTE PLATINUM
L'HOMME Comptoir Sud Pacifique *Dry Woods / Chypre Cuir* 72 ●●
L'HOMME Roger & Gallet *Aromatic / Fougère* 78 ●●
L'HOMME DE VENTILO *Dry Woods / Chypre Cuir* 73 ●●●●
L'UOMO TRUSSARDI *Aromatic / Fougère* 78 ●●
LA BASE FOR HIM *Dry Woods / Chypre Cuir* 73 ●●●●
LE DANDY *Dry Woods / Chypre Cuir* 72 ●
LE MÂLE *Woody Oriental / Oriental Boisé* 62 ●●
LE ROY SOLEIL HOMME *Mossy Woods / Chypre Boisé* 68 ●●
LES COPAINS L'HOMME *Mossy Woods / Chypre Boisé* 68 ●●
LACOSTE *Aromatic / Fougère* 80 ●●
LACOSTE 2000 *Aromatic / Fougère* 80 ●
LAGERFELD *Woody Oriental / Oriental Boisé* 63 ●●●
LALIQUE POUR HOMME *Woody Oriental / Oriental Boisé* 62 ●●
LANCETTI MONSIEUR *Dry Woods / Chypre Cuir* 73 ●●●
LANCETTI POUR HOMME *Aromatic / Fougère* 80 ●
LAND *Woody Oriental / Oriental Boisé* 62 ●
LANVIN L'HOMME *Aromatic / Fougère* 78 ●
LAPIDUS POUR HOMME *Aromatic / Fougère* 79 ●●●●
LATITUDE *Aromatic / Fougère* 78 ●●
LATITUDE SPORT *Water / Marine* 27 ●●●
LAUDER FOR MEN *Aromatic / Fougère* 80 ●●
LAVANDA Myrurgia ♂ *Floral / Florale* 39 ●●
LAVANDE L'Occitane *Aromatic / Fougère* 79 ●●●●
LAVANDE Molinard ♂ *Floral / Florale* 39 ●●●●
LAVANDE Mont St Michel ♂ *Floral / Florale* 39 ●●●
LAVANDE DES PRINCES L.T. Piver *Floral / Florale* 39 ●●●●
LAVANDE VELOURS Guerlain ♂ *Floral / Florale* 39 ●●●
LAVENDER Crabtree & Evelyn ♂ *Floral / Florale* 39 ●●●
LAVENDER Floris ♂ *Floral / Florale* 39 ●●●
LEGENDARY *Dry Woods / Chypre Cuir* 72 ●●
LEMON SORBET ♂ *Aromatic / Fougère* 80 ●
LÉONARD POUR HOMME* *Dry Woods / Chypre Cuir* 73 ●●●●
LIFE ESSENCE *Mossy Woods / Chypre Boisé* 68 ●●
LIGHT HIM *Woody Oriental / Oriental Boisé* 62 ●
LIME, BASIL & MANDARIN ♂ *Citrus / Hespéridé* 19 ●●●●
LIMES Floris ♂ *Citrus / Hespéridé* 19 ●●●●
LIVE JAZZ *Aromatic / Fougère* 82 ●
LOEWE POUR HOMME *Aromatic / Fougère* 82 ●●
LOMANI *Aromatic / Fougère* 78 ●●
LORD Molyneux* *Dry Woods / Chypre Cuir* 72 ●●
LORDS Penhaligon's *Citrus / Hespéridé* 19 ●●●●
LORESTE *Aromatic / Fougère* 78 ●●
LP N° 9 FOR MEN *Woody Oriental / Oriental Boisé* 63 ●●●
LUCIANO *Aromatic / Fougère* 82 ●
LUCIANO PAVAROTTI *Dry Woods / Chypre Cuir* 73 ●●●
LUCKY BRAND MEN'S *Aromatic / Fougère* 80 ●

M

M de BOURBON *Aromatic / Fougère* 82 ●●
M de M *Soft Oriental / Oriental Doux* 52 ●●
M de MORABITO *Woody Oriental / Oriental Boisé* 63 ●●●●
M pour MONSIEUR *Aromatic / Fougère* 80 ●
MACASSAR *Dry Woods / Chypre Cuir* 73 ●●●●
MACKIE FOR MEN *Aromatic / Fougère* 80 ●
MADRIGAL *Mossy Woods / Chypre Boisé* 68 ●●
MAN DE RAUCH *Woody Oriental / Oriental Boisé* 63 ●●●●
MANDARINE ♂ *Citrus / Hespéridé* 18 ●●
MANDATE *Aromatic / Fougère* 78 ●●
MANÈS *Woody Oriental / Oriental Boisé* 62 ●●
MANÈS ICE *Aromatic / Fougère* 80 ●
MARBERT GENTLEMAN* *Mossy Woods / Chypre Boisé* 68 ●●
MARBERT HOMME* *Dry Woods / Chypre Cuir* 72 ●●
MARBERT MAN *Aromatic / Fougère* 82 ●●
MARBERT MAN PURE *Mossy Woods / Chypre Boisé* 68 ●
MARBERT MAN TOO *Aromatic / Fougère* 80 ●
MARE ♂ *Water / Marine* 26 ●●
MARK II → JAGUAR MARK II
MARK BIRLEY FOR MEN *Dry Woods / Chypre Cuir* 72 ●●
MARQUIS Crown *Aromatic / Fougère* 80 ●
MARQUIS Rémy Marquis *Aromatic / Fougère* 80 ●
MASERATI *Aromatic / Fougère* 78 ●●

MATCH PLAY *Aromatic / Fougère* 78 ●
MAXIM'S POUR HOMME *Woody Oriental / Oriental Boisé* 63 ●●●●
MCM SUCCESS* *Mossy Woods / Chypre Boisé* 69 ●●●●
MCM 24 MORNING* *Aromatic / Fougère* 80 ●
MCM 24 EVENING* *Woody Oriental / Oriental Boisé* 63 ●●●
MÉCHANT LOUP *Dry Woods / Chypre Cuir* 73 ●●●●
MENNEN SKIN BRACER *Aromatic / Fougère* 79 ●●●
MERGE ♂ *Aromatic / Fougère* 80 ●
MESSIRE *Citrus / Hespéridé* 19 ●●●
METROPOLIS *Mossy Woods / Chypre Boisé* 68 ●●
MICHAEL JORDAN *Aromatic / Fougère* 78 ●
MILA SCHÖN UOMO *Green / Vert* 23 ●●●●
MILLENNIUM HOPE MAN *Aromatic / Fougère* 82 ●
MILLÉSIME IMPÉRIAL *Water / Marine* 27 ●●●●
MINOTAURE *Woody Oriental / Oriental Boisé* 62 ●●
MISSONI SPORT *Citrus / Hespéridé* 19 ●●●●
MISSONI UOMO *Dry Woods / Chypre Cuir* 73 ●●●
MOLINARD HOMME I *Aromatic / Fougère* 82 ●●
MOLINARD HOMME II *Woody Oriental / Oriental Boisé* 62 ●
MOLINARD HOMME III *Water / Marine* 27 ●●●
MOLTO SMALTO* *Aromatic / Fougère* 78 ●
MONSIEUR BALMAIN *Citrus / Hespéridé* 19 ●●●●
MONSIEUR CARVEN* *Soft Oriental / Oriental Doux* 52 ●●
MONSIEUR DE GIVENCHY *Citrus / Hespéridé* 19 ●●●
MONSIEUR JOVAN* *Dry Woods / Chypre Cuir* 73 ●●●●
MONSIEUR LÉONARD *Aromatic / Fougère* 79 ●●●●
MONSIEUR MORABITO *Aromatic / Fougère* 82 ●
MONSIEUR MUSK *Oriental / Oriental* 57 ●●●●
MONSIEUR ROCHAS *Aromatic / Fougère* 79 ●●●
MONTANA HOMME *Woody Oriental / Oriental Boisé* 62 ●●
MONT ST MICHEL ♂ *Citrus / Hespéridé* 19 ●●●
MOODS UOMO *Woody Oriental / Oriental Boisé* 63 ●●●
MOSCHINO POUR HOMME *Dry Woods / Chypre Cuir* 72 ●●
MOUCHOIR DE MONSIEUR *Aromatic / Fougère* 79 ●●●
MOUSTACHE *Mossy Woods / Chypre Boisé* 68 ●●
MOVES → ADIDAS MOVES
MR J *Aromatic / Fougère* 78 ●●
MULBERRY FOR MEN *Dry Woods / Chypre Cuir* 72 ●●
MUSK FOR MEN Coty *Woody Oriental / Oriental Boisé* 63 ●●●
MUSK FOR MEN Jovan → JOVAN MUSK FOR MEN
MYSTERY AUSTRALIA MAN *Aromatic / Fougère* 80 ●

NATURE SYSTEM ♂ *Citrus / Hespéridé* 18 ●●
NAUTICA *Water / Marine* 26 ●
NAUTICA COMPETITION *Woody Oriental / Oriental Boisé* 62 ●●
NAUTILUS AQUA *Water / Marine* 27 ●●●●
NAVIGATOR *Aromatic / Fougère* 80 ●
NAVY FOR MEN *Aromatic / Fougère* 80 ●
NEMO *Woody Oriental / Oriental Boisé* 62 ●●
NÉROLI SAUVAGE *Citrus / Hespéridé* 19 ●●●●
NETWORK ♂ *Citrus / Hespéridé* 18 ●
NEW WEST FOR HIM *Water / Marine* 27 ●●●●
NEW YORK *Woody Oriental / Oriental Boisé* 62 ●●
NIAGARA *Dry Woods / Chypre Cuir* 72 ●●
NICKI LAUDA *Aromatic / Fougère* 78 ●●
NICOLE MILLER MEN *Woody Oriental / Oriental Boisé* 62 ●●
NIGHTFLIGHT *Aromatic / Fougère* 80 ●
NIKE *Aromatic / Fougère* 80 ●
NINO CERRUTI *Green / Vert* 23 ●●●●
NK *Aromatic / Fougère* 82 ●
N° 89 *Aromatic / Fougère* 79 ●●●
NOI UOMINI *Citrus / Hespéridé* 18 ●
NOMAD *Aromatic / Fougère* 80 ●
NUTMEG & GINGER ♂ *Woody Oriental / Oriental Boisé* 62 ●●

Ô POUR HOMME *Green / Vert* 22 ●●
O₂XYGEN *Citrus / Hespéridé* 18 ●
OBSESSION FOR MEN *Woody Oriental / Oriental Boisé* 62 ●
ODEUR 53 ♂ *Water / Marine* 26 ●●
OLD SPICE *Soft Oriental / Oriental Doux* 53 ●●●
OLD SPICE WHITEWATER *Aromatic / Fougère* 78 ●●

OLYMPIOS *Aromatic / Fougère* 80 ●
OMAR SHARIF POUR HOMME *Aromatic / Fougère* 80 ●●
ON AIR HOMME *Aromatic / Fougère* 78 ●
ONE MAN SHOW *Dry Woods / Chypre Cuir* 73 ●●●●
ONLY FOR MEN *Aromatic / Fougère* 79 ●●●
OPEN *Aromatic / Fougère* 82 ●●
OPIUM POUR HOMME *Woody Oriental / Oriental Boisé* 62 ●●
OPPORTUNE / PERIPHERY *Woody Oriental / Oriental Boisé* 62 ●
ORANGE SPICE ♂ *Aromatic / Fougère* 82 ●●
ORPHÉE *Aromatic / Fougère* 80 ●●
OSCAR DE LA RENTA POUR LUI *Dry Woods / Chypre Cuir* 72 ●●
OSCAR FOR MEN *Dry Woods / Chypre Cuir* 72 ●●
OURAGAN *Woody Oriental / Oriental Boisé* 62 ●

PACO ♂ *Citrus / Hespéridé* 18 ●
PACO ENERGY ♂ *Citrus / Hespéridé* 18 ●●
PACO RABANNE POUR HOMME *Aromatic / Fougère* 78 ●●
PALAIS JAMAIS ♂ *Dry Woods / Chypre Cuir* 73 ●●●●
PAMPLELUNE ♂ *Citrus / Hespéridé* 19 ●●●●
PAMPLEMOUSSE ♂ *Citrus / Hespéridé* 18 ●●
PARADOX FOR MEN *Woody Oriental / Oriental Boisé* 62 ●
PARFUM D'HABIT *Dry Woods / Chypre Cuir* 73 ●●●●
PARFUM D'HOMME *Aromatic / Fougère* 78 ●●
PASHA *Aromatic / Fougère* 78 ●●
PASSION D'HOMME *Woody Oriental / Oriental Boisé* 62 ●●
PASSION FOR MEN *Woody Oriental / Oriental Boisé* 63 ●●●
PATCHOULI Crabtree *Woody Oriental / Oriental Boisé* 62 ●●
PATCHOULI Molinard ♂ *Mossy Woods / Chypre Boisé* 69 ●●●
PATCHOULY Etro ♂ *Woody Oriental / Oriental Boisé* 63 ●●●
PATOU POUR HOMME *Woody Oriental / Oriental Boisé* 63 ●●●
PATOU POUR HOMME PRIVÉ *Aromatic / Fougère* 79 ●●●
PEN DUICK *Aromatic / Fougère* 82 ●
PENHALIGON'S CASTILE ♂ *Citrus / Hespéridé* 19 ●●●
PEOPLE UOMO *Woody Oriental / Oriental Boisé* 62 ●
PERIPHERY / OPPORTUNE *Woody Oriental / Oriental Boisé* 62 ●
PERRY ELLIS FOR MEN *Dry Woods / Chypre Cuir* 73 ●●●
PERRY ELLIS PORTFOLIO *Aromatic / Fougère* 78 ●
PERRY ELLIS RESERVE *Aromatic / Fougère* 80 ●
PHAROS *Aromatic / Fougère* 82 ●
PHEROMONE FOR MEN *Dry Woods / Chypre Cuir* 72 ●●
PHILOSYKOS ♂ *Mossy Woods / Chypre Boisé* 68 ●
PHOTO *Aromatic / Fougère* 80 ●●
PIAZZA DI SPAGNA UOMO *Aromatic / Fougère* 82 ●
PIERRE CARDIN POUR MONSIEUR *Soft Oriental / Oriental Doux* 52 ●
PIERRE CARDIN MUSK *Aromatic / Fougère* 79 ●●●●
PINO SILVESTRE EXTREME *Citrus / Hespéridé* 19 ●●●●
PINO SILVESTRE ORIGINAL *Mossy Woods / Chypre Boisé* 69 ●●●
PIROGUIER *Dry Woods / Chypre Cuir* 73 ●●●
PLEASURES FOR MEN *Aromatic / Fougère* 82 ●
POLICE *Aromatic / Fougère* 79 ●●●
POLO *Dry Woods / Chypre Cuir* 72 ●●
POLO CREST *Dry Woods / Chypre Cuir* 72 ●●
POLO SPORT *Aromatic / Fougère* 82 ●
POLO SPORT EXTREME *Dry Woods / Chypre Cuir* 72 ●●
PONTACCIO 21 *Dry Woods / Chypre Cuir* 72 ●●
PORTOS* *Dry Woods / Chypre Cuir* 73 ●●●
POUR L'HOMME Jacques Fath *Woody Oriental / Oriental Boisé* 62 ●●
POUR L'HOMME Roger & Gallet *Citrus / Hespéridé* 18 ●●
POUR LE JEUNE HOMME *Citrus / Hespéridé* 18 ●
POUR MONSIEUR → CHANEL POUR MONSIEUR
POUR UN HOMME Caron *Floral / Florale* 39 ●●●●
PREFERRED STOCK *Aromatic / Fougère* 78 ●
PRESSURE *Aromatic / Fougère* 82 ●●
PRIVATE NUMBER FOR MEN* *Mossy Woods / Chypre Boisé* 68 ●●●
PROFUMO DI MONTECATINI ♂ *Water / Marine* 27 ●●●
PS *Soft Oriental / Oriental Doux* 53 ●●●
PUB *Aromatic / Fougère* 79 ●●●
PUMA CHALLENGE *Aromatic / Fougère* 80 ●●
PUMA INDEPENDENCE *Aromatic / Fougère* 82 ●

Q

QUARTZ POUR HOMME *Citrus / Hespéridé 18* ●●
QUASAR *Aromatic / Fougère 82* ●
QUERCUS ♂ *Citrus / Hespéridé 18* ●
QUORUM *Dry Woods / Chypre Cuir 72* ●●

R

R Révillon *Mossy Woods / Chypre Boisé 68* ●
R de CAPUCCI *Aromatic / Fougère 78* ●
RACINE ♂ *Mossy Woods / Chypre Boisé 68* ●●
RACQUETS FORMULA *Aromatic / Fougère 79* ●●●
RAFALE *Aromatic / Fougère 78* ●●
RÄKS *Aromatic / Fougère 80* ●●
RAPPORT *Aromatic / Fougère 78* ●●
RAW VANILLA *Woody Oriental / Oriental Boisé 62* ●
REALM MEN *Woody Oriental / Oriental Boisé 62* ●●
REBEL Salle *Citrus / Hespéridé 18* ●
REBEL ... JAMES DEAN *Aromatic / Fougère 82* ●
RED FOR MEN *Aromatic / Fougère 78* ●●
RÉGINE'S FOR MEN *Woody Oriental / Oriental Boisé 62* ●
RELAX *Woody Oriental / Oriental Boisé 62* ●●
RÉMY *Woody Oriental / Oriental Boisé 62* ●●
REPLAY *Woody Oriental / Oriental Boisé 62* ●
REYNALD KATZ ♂ *Citrus / Hespéridé 18* ●
RICCI-CLUB *Woody Oriental / Oriental Boisé 62* ●●
RICHARDSON BAY ♂ *Green / Vert 22* ●
ROCABAR *Dry Woods / Chypre Cuir 73* ●●●●
ROCCOBAROCCO* *Aromatic / Fougère 79* ●●●●
ROGER & GALLET → POUR L'HOMME
ROGER & GALLET EXTRA-VIEILLE ♂ *Citrus / Hespéridé 19* ●●●
ROI SANTAL *Woody Oriental / Oriental Boisé 63* ●●●
ROLAND GARROS *Aromatic / Fougère 80* ●
ROMA UOMO *Woody Oriental / Oriental Boisé 62* ●●
ROMANCE MEN *Aromatic / Fougère 82* ●
ROMEO GIGLI PER UOMO → GIGLI PER UOMO
ROOTS UNISCENT ♂ *Water / Marine 26* ●
ROUTE 66 *Aromatic / Fougère 78* ●●
ROUTE 66 COLORADO RAIN *Aromatic / Fougère 78* ●
ROUTE DU VÉTIVER *Mossy Woods / Chypre Boisé 69* ●●●
ROY SOLEIL → LE ROY SOLEIL HOMME
ROYAL BAIN DE CHAMPAGNE ♂ *Soft Oriental / Oriental Doux 52* ●
ROYAL COPENHAGEN *Woody Oriental / Oriental Boisé 63* ●●●
ROYAL COPENHAGEN MUSK *Soft Oriental / Oriental Doux 53* ●●●●
ROYAL COPENHAGEN SPORT* *Aromatic / Fougère 82* ●
ROYAL DELIGHT ♂ *Soft Oriental / Oriental Doux 53* ●●●●
ROYAL ENGLISH LEATHER *Dry Woods / Chypre Cuir 73* ●●●
ROYAL GREEN *Aromatic / Fougère 82* ●
ROYAL SCOTTISH LAVENDER *Floral / Florale 39* ●●●
ROYAL WATER *Aromatic / Fougère 79* ●●●●
RYKIEL HOMME *Aromatic / Fougère 82* ●

S

SABLES *Woody Oriental / Oriental Boisé 62* ●●
SAFARI FOR MEN *Aromatic / Fougère 78* ●
SAFRANIER *Woody Oriental / Oriental Boisé 62* ●●
SALVADOR *Aromatic / Fougère 78* ●●
SALVADOR DALI POUR HOMME *Woody Oriental / Oriental Boisé 62* ●●
SALVATORE FERRAGAMO POUR HOMME
  Mossy Woods / Chypre Boisé 68 ●
SAMBA FOR MEN *Citrus / Hespéridé 19* ●●●●
SAMBA NATURAL MAN *Aromatic / Fougère 82* ●
SAMBA NOVA HOMME *Woody Oriental / Oriental Boisé 62* ●●
SAMBA RED MAN *Mossy Woods / Chypre Boisé 68* ●●
SAMOURAÏ *Soft Oriental / Oriental Doux 52* ●
SANDALO *Woody Oriental / Oriental Boisé 63* ●●●●
SANDALWOOD Crabtree & Evelyn
  Woody Oriental / Oriental Boisé 63 ●●●
SANDALWOOD Yardley ♂ *Woody Oriental / Oriental Boisé 63* ●●●
SANDER FOR MEN *Aromatic / Fougère 78* ●●
SANDRINGHAM *Woody Oriental / Oriental Boisé 63* ●●●

SANGUINE MUSKISSIME ♂ *Citrus / Hespéridé 18* ●
SANTA FE FOR MEN *Woody Oriental / Oriental Boisé 62* ●
SANTAL L'Artisan Parfumeur *Dry Woods / Chypre Cuir 73* ●●●
SANTAL IMPÉRIAL ♂ *Woody Oriental / Oriental Boisé 63* ●●●
SANTAL NOBLE *Mossy Woods / Chypre Boisé 69* ●●●●
SANTOS *Aromatic / Fougère 78* ●●
SANTOS EAU DE SPORT *Citrus / Hespéridé 19* ●●●●
SCAPA POUR HOMME *Aromatic / Fougère 78* ●
SCOTT McCLINTOCK *Soft Oriental / Oriental Doux 52* ●
SCULPTURE HOMME *Woody Oriental / Oriental Boisé 62* ●●
SECRET MÉLANGE *Aromatic / Fougère 78* ●
SÉLECTION VERTE *Citrus / Hespéridé 18* ●●
SERGIO TACCHINI *Aromatic / Fougère 78* ●
SERGIO TACCHINI SPORT EXTREME *Aromatic / Fougère 82* ●
SERGIO TACCHINI UOMO *Aromatic / Fougère 78* ●●
SEX APPEAL FOR MEN* *Woody Oriental / Oriental Boisé 63* ●●●
SÉXUAL POUR HOMME *Woody Oriental / Oriental Boisé 62* ●
SHAAL NUR ♂ *Soft Oriental / Oriental Doux 53* ●●●●
SIENNA *Mossy Woods / Chypre Boisé 68* ●
SIESTE *Dry Woods / Chypre Cuir 73* ●●●
SIGNORICCI *Citrus / Hespéridé 19* ●●●
SILVER *Aromatic / Fougère 79* ●●●
SILVER JEANS HOMME *Aromatic / Fougère 78* ●
SILVER LIGHT *Citrus / Hespéridé 18* ●●
SILVER MOUNTAIN WATER *Water / Marine 26* ●●
SILVESTRE *Mossy Woods / Chypre Boisé 69* ●●●
SIR IRISH MOSS *Mossy Woods / Chypre Boisé 68* ●●
SMALTO *Mossy Woods / Chypre Boisé 68* ●●
SO ... FOR HIM *Aromatic / Fougère 82* ●
SOLO SOPRANI ♂ *Citrus / Hespéridé 18* ●
SOPRANI ACTIVE MAN *Aromatic / Fougère 80* ●●
SPAZIO KRIZIA UOMO *Dry Woods / Chypre Cuir 72* ●
SPECIAL N° 127 ♂ *Citrus / Hespéridé 19* ●●●
SPORT 2000 *Aromatic / Fougère 78* ●
SPORT DE PACO RABANNE *Citrus / Hespéridé 18* ●●
SPORT MAXIMUM *Aromatic / Fougère 82* ●
SPORTIF *Aromatic / Fougère 82* ●
SPORT SPIRIT ♂ *Citrus / Hespéridé 18* ●
SPORTS EXTREME USA ♂ *Citrus / Hespéridé 18* ●●
SPRINGFIELD *Dry Woods / Chypre Cuir 72* ●
STATEMENT FOR MEN *Aromatic / Fougère 78* ●
S.T.DUPONT HOMME *Dry Woods / Chypre Cuir 73* ●●●●
STETSON *Woody Oriental / Oriental Boisé 63* ●●●
STETSON COUNTRY *Mossy Woods / Chypre Boisé 68* ●●
STETSON SIERRA *Aromatic / Fougère 78* ●
STREET GAMES *Aromatic / Fougère 82* ●
SUD EST *Aromatic / Fougère 82* ●
SUMARE *Citrus / Hespéridé 19* ●●●●
SUMATRA RAIN *Aromatic / Fougère 82* ●●
SUMATRA RAIN FRESH *Aromatic / Fougère 80* ●
SUMATRA RAIN WOOD *Woody Oriental / Oriental Boisé 62* ●●
SUNG HOMME *Aromatic / Fougère 78* ●●
SWISS ARMY *Aromatic / Fougère 82* ●
SYBARIS *Woody Oriental / Oriental Boisé 62* ●●

T

TABAC ORIGINAL (Aftershave) *Aromatic / Fougère 80* ●●
TABAC ORIGINAL (EdC) *Soft Floral / Fleuri Aldéhydé 42* ●●
TABAC EXTREME *Aromatic / Fougère 78* ●
TABAROME *Dry Woods / Chypre Cuir 73* ●●●●
TACTICS *Green / Vert 23* ●●●●
TÉ ♂ *Citrus / Hespéridé 18* ●
TECK *Dry Woods / Chypre Cuir 73* ●●●
TED *Woody Oriental / Oriental Boisé 62* ●●
TED BAKER *Citrus / Hespéridé 19* ●●●●
TEMPORE UOMO *Woody Oriental / Oriental Boisé 62* ●
TENAZ *Aromatic / Fougère 79* ●●●●
TÉNÉRÉ *Floral / Florale 39* ●●●●
THAT MAN *Citrus / Hespéridé 19* ●●●●
THÉ ♂ *Woody Oriental / Oriental Boisé 63* ●●●
THE BARON *Aromatic / Fougère 79* ●●●
THE DREAMER *Woody Oriental / Oriental Boisé 62* ●●
THÉ POUR UN ÉTÉ ♂ *Citrus / Hespéridé 18* ●
THÉ VERT ♂ *Citrus / Hespéridé 18* ●●
THIRD MAN / 3e HOMME *Aromatic / Fougère 79* ●●●●

TIFFANY FOR MEN *Woody Oriental / Oriental Boisé* 63 ●●●
TIFFANY FOR MEN SPORT *Green / Vert* 22 ●
TILLEUL ♂ *Floral / Florale* 38 ●
TOM TAILOR *Citrus / Hespéridé* 18 ●
TOMMY *Aromatic / Fougère* 80 ●
TOUCH FOR MEN* *Aromatic / Fougère* 79 ●●●
TOWN & COUNTRY *Mossy Woods / Chypre Boisé* 68 ●●
TRIESTE *Aromatic / Fougère* 78 ●●
TROPHÉE LANCÔME *Citrus / Hespéridé* 19 ●●●●
TRUSSARDI UOMO FRESH *Dry Woods / Chypre Cuir* 72 ●●
TSAR *Aromatic / Fougère* 78 ●
TUSCANY PER UOMO *Aromatic / Fougère* 78 ●
TYCOON *Woody Oriental / Oriental Boisé* 62 ●●

U de V Ulric de Varens *Aromatic / Fougère* 82 ●
U de V N° 2 *Woody Oriental / Oriental Boisé* 62 ●●
ULYSSE *Woody Oriental / Oriental Boisé* 62 ●
UNGARO L'HOMME I* *Woody Oriental / Oriental Boisé* 62 ●●
UNGARO L'HOMME II* *Citrus / Hespéridé* 19 ●●●●
UNGARO L'HOMME III *Aromatic / Fougère* 78 ●
UNIVERSO *Aromatic / Fougère* 78 ●
UOMO? MOSCHINO *Woody Oriental / Oriental Boisé* 62 ●

VAN CLEEF & ARPELS *Dry Woods / Chypre Cuir* 73 ●●●●
VAN GILS *Aromatic / Fougère* 79 ●●●●
VANILLE L'Occitane ♂ *Soft Oriental / Oriental Doux* 53 ●●●
VANILLE CAFÉ ♂ *Oriental / Oriental* 57 ●●●
VANITECK *Dry Woods / Chypre Cuir* 73 ●●●●
VENDETTA POUR HOMME* *Dry Woods / Chypre Cuir* 72 ●●
VENEZIA UOMO *Woody Oriental / Oriental Boisé* 62 ●●
VERBENAS OF PROVENCE ♂ *Citrus / Hespéridé* 19 ●●●
VERDI 800 *Woody Oriental / Oriental Boisé* 63 ●●●
VERINO POUR HOMME *Aromatic / Fougère* 78 ●●
VERSACE L'HOMME *Woody Oriental / Oriental Boisé* 63 ●●●
VERSAILLES *Oriental / Oriental* 56 ●●
VERSION HOMME* *Mossy Woods / Chypre Boisé* 68 ●●
VERSUS UOMO *Woody Oriental / Oriental Boisé* 62 ●
VERTIGO FOR MEN *Aromatic / Fougère* 82 ●
VERVEINE Le Jardin Retrouvé ♂ *Citrus / Hespéridé* 19 ●●●
VERVEINE Molinard *Citrus / Hespéridé* 19 ●●●
VERY M.C. ♂ *Citrus / Hespéridé* 18 ●
VERY VALENTINO POUR HOMME *Woody Oriental / Oriental Boisé* 62 ●●
VÉTIVER Annick Goutal *Dry Woods / Chypre Cuir* 73 ●●●
VÉTIVER Carven *Mossy Woods / Chypre Boisé* 69 ●●●
VETIVER Creed *Mossy Woods / Chypre Boisé* 69 ●●●
VETIVER Etro *Dry Woods / Chypre Cuir* 73 ●●●
VETIVER Guerlain *Mossy Woods / Chypre Boisé* 69 ●●●
VETIVER L'Artisan Parfumeur *Dry Woods / Chypre Cuir* 72 ●
VÉTIVER DRY Carven *Aromatic / Fougère* 80 ●●
VETIVER HOMBRE ♂ *Mossy Woods / Chypre Boisé* 68 ●●
VETYVER Jo Malone ♂ *Mossy Woods / Chypre Boisé* 68 ●●
VÉTYVER Le Jardin Retrouvé ➔ EAU DE VÉTYVER
VÉTYVER L.T. Piver *Mossy Woods / Chypre Boisé* 69 ●●●
VETYVER Molinard *Mossy Woods / Chypre Boisé* 69 ●●●
VÉTYVER Roger & Gallet *Mossy Woods / Chypre Boisé* 69 ●●●
VETYVER HAITI ♂ *Mossy Woods / Chypre Boisé* 68 ●●
VIKING *Aromatic / Fougère* 82 ●
VIRGILIO ♂ *Green / Vert* 22 ●●
VOLCANO HOMME *Aromatic / Fougère* 82 ●
VOLEUR DE ROSES ♂ *Dry Woods / Chypre Cuir* 72 ●
VORAGO *Aromatic / Fougère* 78 ●●
VORAGO ACTION *Citrus / Hespéridé* 19 ●●●
VOYAGEUR *Mossy Woods / Chypre Boisé* 68 ●
VUARNET *Aromatic / Fougère* 80 ●

WATT FOR MEN *Aromatic / Fougère* 78 ●●
WEEKEND FOR MEN *Mossy Woods / Chypre Boisé* 68 ●●
WEIL EAU DE FRAÎCHEUR ♂ *Citrus / Hespéridé* 18 ●

WEIL POUR HOMME *Aromatic / Fougère* 82 ●●
WHAT ABOUT ADAM *Aromatic / Fougère* 82 ●
WILD WIND FOR MEN *Aromatic / Fougère* 80 ●
WILKES SAN FRANCISCO *Aromatic / Fougère* 80 ●
WINGS FOR MEN *Aromatic / Fougère* 82 ●
WITNESS* *Woody Oriental / Oriental Boisé* 62 ●●
WORTH POUR HOMME *Aromatic / Fougère* 78 ●●

X *Woody Oriental / Oriental Boisé* 62 ●
X LIMITED ♂ *Citrus / Hespéridé* 18 ●
XERYUS *Aromatic / Fougère* 78 ●●
XERYUS ROUGE *Woody Oriental / Oriental Boisé* 62 ●●
XS POUR HOMME *Aromatic / Fougère* 78 ●
XTC ♂ *Citrus / Hespéridé* 18 ●
XXL Hechter *Woody Oriental / Oriental Boisé* 62 ●

YANG *Woody Oriental / Oriental Boisé* 62 ●
YARDLEY CLASSIC *Mossy Woods / Chypre Boisé* 69 ●●●
YARDLEY GOLD *Aromatic / Fougère* 78 ●
YARDLEY ORIGINAL *Aromatic / Fougère* 82 ●
YATAGAN *Dry Woods / Chypre Cuir* 73 ●●●●
YOHJI HOMME *Aromatic / Fougère* 79 ●●●●
YOU'RE THE FIRE FOR MEN *Dry Woods / Chypre Cuir* 73 ●●●
YSL POUR HOMME *Citrus / Hespéridé* 19 ●●●●

ZAHAROFF POUR HOMME *Woody Oriental / Oriental Boisé* 63 ●●●●
ZEGNA *Aromatic / Fougère* 78 ●●
ZESTE MANDARINE PAMPLEMOUSSE ♂ *Citrus / Hespéridé* 19 ●●●●
ZINO DAVIDOFF *Woody Oriental / Oriental Boisé* 63 ●●●●
ZIPPED *Citrus / Hespéridé* 18 ●●
ZIPPED SPORTS *Aromatic / Fougère* 82 ●
ZIPPED UNIVERSE *Woody Oriental / Oriental Boisé* 62 ●●
ZIZANIE *Woody Oriental / Oriental Boisé* 63 ●●●

Parfums de Légende

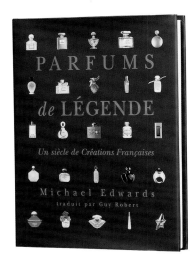

Accueil enthousiaste fait au livre de Michael Edwards traduit par Guy Robert: *Parfums de Légende: un Siècle de Créations Françaises*

« Ce livre est tout à fait unique, il n'en existe aucun qui lui soit comparable »
Edmond Roudnitska, le parfumeur le plus célèbre

« La 'bible' des parfums »
Le Figaro

« Ex-cep-tion-nel! Signé Michael Edwards, cet album Parfums de Légende est une petite oeuvre d'art que tous les amoureux du parfum se doivent de posséder.

Voilà en effet, un livre extraordinaire. Pour la première fois, les parfumeurs, les couturiers, les créateurs de flacons et les dirigeants des grandes maisons de parfums parlent de leur art comme ils ne l'ont jamais fait.

Un voyage fascinant dans l'univers des parfums au travers de leur histoire, du savoir-faire français, illustré par une iconographie superbe et rare, des photographies, des croquis, des dessins et des documents d'archives.

Pour le prix d'une eau de toilette, Parfums de Légende est un livre-révélation à consulter - presque - comme un incunable. »
Paris Match

ADIDAS
1988/97 ADIDAS WOMAN *Floral / Florale* ●
1997 ADIDAS WOMAN SPORT *Floral / Florale* ●
1986 ADIDAS CLASSIC *Dry Woods / Chypre Cuir* ●●
1990 ADIDAS ACTIVE BODIES *Aromatic / Fougère* ●●
1992 ADIDAS ADVENTURE *Aromatic / Fougère* ●●
1994 ADIDAS SPORT *Citrus / Hespéridé* ●●
1997 ADIDAS DYNAMIC *Aromatic / Fougère* ●
1998 ADIDAS ACTION *Aromatic / Fougère* ●
1999 ADIDAS MOVES *Aromatic / Fougère* ●

ADOLFO DOMINGUEZ
1995 AGUA FRESCA DE ROSAS *Floral / Florale* ●●
1999 ALEGRIA *Floral / Florale* ●●
1991 ADOLFO DOMINGUEZ *Aromatic / Fougère* ●
1996 AGUA FRESCA *Mossy Woods / Chypre Boisé* ●●●
1998 VETIVER HOMBRE *Mossy Woods / Chypre Boisé* ●●

ADRIENNE VITTADINI
1994 AV *Floral / Florale* ●●
1999 ADRIENNE VITTADINI *Oriental / Oriental* ●

AIGNER → ETIENNE AIGNER

ALAIN DELON
1981 LE TEMPS D'AIMER* *Mossy Woods / Chypre Boisé* ●●●
1993 LYRA *Oriental / Oriental* ●●●
1995 LYRA 2 *Woody Oriental / Oriental Boisé* ●●
1996 IQUITA* *Mossy Woods / Chypre Boisé* ●●
1998 LYRA 3 *Floral / Florale* ●
1987 IQUITOS* *Mossy Woods / Chypre Boisé* ●●●●
1995 SAMOURAÏ *Soft Oriental / Oriental Doux* ●
1997 EAU DE SPORT* *Aromatic / Fougère* ●●
1997 PHAROS *Aromatic / Fougère* ●

ALBERTA FERRETTI
1993 FEMINA *Floral / Florale* ●

ALEXANDER JULIAN
1992 WOMENSWEAR *Soft Floral / Fleuri Aldéhydé* ●●
1993 COLORS *Soft Floral / Fleuri Aldéhydé* ●

ALEXANDRA DE MARKOFF
1972 ENIGMA *Woody Oriental / Oriental Boisé* ●●●
1979 ALEXANDRA *Soft Oriental / Oriental Doux* ●●●
1994 NO REGRETS *Floral / Florale* ●●

ALFRED SUNG
1986 SUNG *Floral / Florale* ●
1990 E.N.C.O.R.E *Woody Oriental / Oriental Boisé* ●
1992 SUNG SPA *Green / Vert* ●
1995 FOREVER *Floral / Florale* ●
1997 PURE *Floral / Florale* ●
1988 SUNG HOMME *Aromatic / Fougère* ●●

ALYSSA ASHLEY
1992 ALYSSA ASHLEY MUSK *Soft Floral / Fleuri Aldéhydé* ●●●●
1996 ALYSSA ASHLEY VANILLA *Woody Oriental / Oriental Boisé* ●

AMOUAGE
1983 AMOUAGE *Soft Floral / Fleuri Aldéhydé* ●●●●
1995 UBAR *Mossy Woods / Chypre Boisé* ●●●
1983 AMOUAGE HOMME *Soft Floral / Fleuri Aldéhydé* ●●●●

AMWAY
1997 LONG AGO / WISTFUL *Floral / Florale* ●
1997 SOLILOQUY *Soft Floral / Fleuri Aldéhydé* ●●●●
1998 ANTICIPATE / SULTRY *Floral Oriental / Fleuri Oriental* ●●
1998 CONSIDERATIONS / CONFIDENT *Mossy Woods / Chypre Boisé* ●
1997 CROSSROADS *Aromatic / Fougère* ●
1998 PERIPHERY / OPPORTUNE *Woody Oriental / Oriental Boisé* ●

ANDRÉ BARNWELL
1998 RÄKS *Aromatic / Fougère* ●●

ANNA SUI
1999 ANNA SUI *Soft Floral / Fleuri Aldéhydé* ●●

ANNABELLA
1997 ANNABELLA *Green / Vert* ●
1999 ROUGE *Woody Oriental / Oriental Boisé* ●

ANNE PLISKA
1987 ANNE PLISKA *Soft Oriental / Oriental Doux* ●●●

ANNICK GOUTAL
1981 EAU D'HADRIEN ♂ *Citrus / Hespéridé* ●●●
1981 EAU DE LAVANDE ♂ *Floral / Florale* ●●●
1981 FOLAVRIL *Soft Floral / Fleuri Aldéhydé* ●●
1982 EAU DE CHARLOTTE *Floral / Florale* ●
1983 EAU DE CAMILLE *Floral / Florale* ●
1983 PASSION *Floral / Florale* ●●
1984 HEURE EXQUISE *Soft Floral / Fleuri Aldéhydé* ●
1984 ROSE ABSOLUE *Floral / Florale* ●●●
1984 TUBÉREUSE *Floral / Florale* ●●●●
1985 EAU DU CIEL *Floral / Florale* ●●
1989 GARDÉNIA PASSION *Floral / Florale* ●●●●
1995 EAU DU SUD ♂ *Citrus / Hespéridé* ●●
1996 GRAND AMOUR *Soft Floral / Fleuri Aldéhydé* ●●●●
1998 PETITE CHÉRIE *Floral / Florale* ●
1999 CE SOIR OU JAMAIS *Floral / Florale* ●●
1981 EAU DE MONSIEUR *Mossy Woods / Chypre Boisé* ●●●
1985 SABLES *Woody Oriental / Oriental Boisé* ●●
1985 VÉTIVER *Dry Woods / Chypre Cuir* ●●●

ANTONIA'S FLOWERS
1984 ANTONIA'S FLOWERS *Floral / Florale* ●●
1995 FLORET *Floral / Florale* ●●
1999 TIEMPE PASSATE *Mossy Woods / Chypre Boisé* ●●●

APPLEWOODS
1996 BRISTOL BLUE *Aromatic / Fougère* ●●

ARAMIS
1990 NEW WEST FOR HER *Water / Marine* ●●●
1992 TUSCANY PER DONNA *Woody Oriental / Oriental Boisé* ●
1995 HAVANA POUR ELLE *Floral / Florale* ●●
1965 ARAMIS *Dry Woods / Chypre Cuir* ●●●
1973 ARAMIS 900 *Dry Woods / Chypre Cuir* ●
1978 DEVIN *Green / Vert* ●●●●
1982 J.H.L. *Soft Oriental / Oriental Doux* ●●●
1984 TUSCANY PER UOMO *Aromatic / Fougère* ●
1988 NEW WEST FOR HIM *Water / Marine* ●●●●
1994 HAVANA *Aromatic / Fougère* ●●●●
1998 ARAMIS GOLD *Dry Woods / Chypre Cuir* ●●●

ARDEN → ELIZABETH ARDEN

ARMAN
1997 STRADIVARIUS WHITE *Water / Marine* ●

ARMANI → GIORGIO ARMANI

ARROGANCE
1982 ARROGANCE POUR FEMME *Floral / Florale* ●●
1997 ARROGANCE ME *Floral / Florale* ●
1999 EXCITING ARROGANCE *Soft Floral / Fleuri Aldéhydé* ●
1987 ARROGANCE UOMO *Aromatic / Fougère* ●●
1997 ARROGANCE YOU *Aromatic / Fougère* ●●

ASHLEY → LAURA ASHLEY

ATKINSON
1799 ATKINSON GOLD MEDAL ♂ *Citrus / Hespéridé* ●●●
1910 ENGLISH LAVENDER ♂ *Floral / Florale* ●●●
1997 ALVIERO MARTINI DONNA *Floral Oriental / Fleuri Oriental* ●
1997 ALVIERO MARTINI UOMO *Aromatic / Fougère* ●

ATMAN
1998 ATMAN *Dry Woods / Chypre Cuir* ●●●

AUBUSSON
1984 HISTOIRE D'AMOUR *Mossy Woods / Chypre Boisé* ●●●
1990 DÉSIRADE *Floral Oriental / Fleuri Oriental* ●●
1994 25 *Woody Oriental / Oriental Boisé* ●

1995 FLEUR DE DÉSIRADE *Soft Floral / Fleuri Aldéhydé* ●●
1997 AUBUSSON COULEURS *Floral / Florale* ●
1998 FLORE AUBUSSON *Floral / Florale* ●
1992 AUBUSSON HOMME *Mossy Woods / Chypre Boisé* ●●

AZUREL
1997 SPORTS EXTREME USA ♂ *Citrus / Hespéridé* ●●

AZZARO → LORIS AZZARO

BALENCIAGA
1947 LE DIX *Soft Floral / Fleuri Aldéhydé* ●●●●
1955 QUADRILLE *Mossy Woods / Chypre Boisé* ●●●
1973 CIALENGA *Soft Floral / Fleuri Aldéhydé* ●
1979 MICHELLE *Floral / Florale* ●●●●
1982 PRÉLUDE* *Soft Oriental / Oriental Doux* ●●●
1988 RUMBA *Dry Woods / Chypre Cuir* ●●
1994 TALISMAN *Mossy Woods / Chypre Boisé* ●●
1996 TALISMAN EAU TRANSPARENTE *Floral / Florale* ●
1998 CRISTOBAL *Woody Oriental / Oriental Boisé* ●
1971 HO HANG *Aromatic / Fougère* ●●
1980 PORTOS* *Dry Woods / Chypre Cuir* ●●●
1986 HO HANG CLUB* *Dry Woods / Chypre Cuir* ●●●●
1990 BALENCIAGA POUR HOMME *Woody Oriental / Oriental Boisé* ●●●●

BALMAIN → PIERRE BALMAIN

BARNEYS NEW YORK
1986 ROUTE DU THÉ *Citrus / Hespéridé* ●

BARONY → LILIAN BARONY
BARYSHNIKOV → MIKHAIL BARYSHNIKOV

BASILE
1987 BASILE UOMO *Dry Woods / Chypre Cuir* ●●

BAYWATCH
1996 BAYWATCH WOMAN *Floral / Florale* ●●
1996 BAYWATCH MAN *Aromatic / Fougère* ●●

BEENE → GEOFFREY BEENE

BENETTON
1987/93 COLORS OF BENETTON *Floral Oriental / Fleuri Oriental* ●
1993 TRIBÙ *Floral / Florale* ●●
1995 TRIBÙ ACQUA FRESCA *Floral / Florale* ●
1997 COLD ♂ *Citrus / Hespéridé* ●●●●
1997 HOT *Floral Oriental / Fleuri Oriental* ●
1999 BENETTON SPORT WOMAN *Floral / Florale* ●
1988 COLORS FOR MEN *Woody Oriental / Oriental Boisé* ●
1999 BENETTON SPORT MAN *Aromatic / Fougère* ●

BERNINI
1996 BERNINI WOMEN *Floral Oriental / Fleuri Oriental* ●

BETTINA BARTY
1990 MUSK *Soft Floral / Fleuri Aldéhydé* ●●●

BIAGIOTTI → LAURA BIAGIOTTI

BIJAN
1987 BIJAN *Woody Oriental / Oriental Boisé* ●●●
1993 DNA *Soft Floral / Fleuri Aldéhydé* ●●●●
1981 BIJAN FOR MEN *Aromatic / Fougère* ●●
1993 DNA FOR MEN *Woody Oriental / Oriental Boisé* ●●
1996 MICHAEL JORDAN *Aromatic / Fougère* ●
1999 JORDAN BY MICHAEL *Woody Oriental / Oriental Boisé* ●

BILL BLASS
1978 BILL BLASS *Floral / Florale* ●●●●
1990 NUDE *Soft Floral / Fleuri Aldéhydé* ●
1999 AMAZING *Soft Floral / Fleuri Aldéhydé* ●●

BIOTHERM
1997 EAU VITAMINÉE *Citrus / Hespéridé* ●●
1999 AQUA RELAX *Aromatic / Fougère* ●

BLUMARINE
1988 BLUMARINE *Soft Floral / Fleuri Aldéhydé* ●●
1995 BLU BLUMARINE *Floral / Florale* ●●

BOB MACKIE
1985/91 MACKIE *Floral Oriental / Fleuri Oriental* ●●
1997 PERHAPS *Floral Oriental / Fleuri Oriental* ●
1992 MACKIE FOR MEN *Aromatic / Fougère* ●

BOBBI BROWN
1998 BOBBI *Floral / Florale* ●

BOGART → JACQUES BOGART

BOGNER
1985/90 BOGNER MAN *Citrus / Hespéridé* ●●
1988 BOGNER MAN II *Aromatic / Fougère* ●●
1995 DEEP FOREST *Dry Woods / Chypre Cuir* ●●●●

BOND → JAMES BOND
BOND STREET → YARDLEY / BOND STREET

BONJOUR
1994 BONJOUR *Floral Oriental / Fleuri Oriental* ●●

BONNE BELL
1989 FRIDAY! *Floral Oriental / Fleuri Oriental* ●

BORGHESE → MARCELLA BORGHESE

BORSALINO
1995 DONNA BORSALINO *Floral Oriental / Fleuri Oriental* ●●
1984 BORSALINO *Aromatic / Fougère* ●●
1997 CHAPEAU *Aromatic / Fougère* ●

BORSARI
1870 VIOLETTA DI PARMA *Floral / Florale* ●●●●
1880 ACQUA CLASSICA DI BORSARI ♂ *Citrus / Hespéridé* ●●●

BOSS → HUGO BOSS

BOUCHERON
1988 BOUCHERON *Floral Oriental / Fleuri Oriental* ●●●
1994 JAÏPUR *Floral / Florale* ●●
1999 JAÏPUR SAPHIR *Oriental / Oriental* ●●
1991 BOUCHERON POUR HOMME *Citrus / Hespéridé* ●●●●
1997 JAÏPUR HOMME *Woody Oriental / Oriental Boisé* ●●

BOURJOIS
1925/95 MON PARFUM *Floral / Florale* ●●
1928 SOIR DE PARIS ORIGINAL *Soft Floral / Aldéhydé* ●●●●
1928/91 SOIR DE PARIS *Floral / Florale* ●●●
1988 ACIER *Aromatic / Fougère* ●●
1991 AGUIRRE *Woody Oriental / Oriental Boisé* ●●
1993 EQUATEUR *Aromatic / Fougère* ●●●
1996 EVASION *Citrus / Hespéridé* ●●
1997 OURAGAN *Woody Oriental / Oriental Boisé* ●

BROOKS BROS
1998 BROOKS BROS *Aromatic / Fougère* ●

BROSSEAU → JEAN-CHARLES BROSSEAU

BULGARI
1993 BULGARI EAU PARFUMÉE ♂ *Citrus / Hespéridé* ●
1994 BULGARI POUR FEMME *Floral / Florale* ●●●
1998 BULGARI BLACK ♂ *Dry Woods / Chypre Cuir* ●●
1995 BULGARI POUR HOMME *Aromatic / Fougère* ●

BURANI → MARIELLA BURANI

BURBERRY
1991 SOCIETY* *Soft Floral / Fleuri Aldéhydé* ●●
1995 BURBERRY FOR WOMEN *Floral Oriental / Fleuri Oriental* ●
1997 WEEKEND FOR WOMEN *Floral / Florale* ●●
1992/95 BURBERRY FOR MEN *Aromatic / Fougère* ●●
1997 WEEKEND FOR MEN *Mossy Woods / Chypre Boisé* ●●

BYBLOS
1990 BYBLOS   *Floral / Florale* ●●
1993 BYBLOS UOMO   *Aromatic / Fougère* ●●

CACHAREL
1978 ANAÏS ANAÏS   *Floral / Florale* ●
1987 LOULOU   *Soft Oriental / Oriental Doux* ●●●●
1994 EDEN   *Floral Oriental / Fleuri Oriental* ●
1995 LOULOU BLUE*   *Floral Oriental / Fleuri Oriental* ●●
1996 EAU D'EDEN   *Floral / Florale* ●
1998 NOA   *Soft Floral / Fleuri Aldéhydé* ●●●●
1981 CACHAREL POUR L'HOMME   *Aromatic / Fougère* ●●
1999 NEMO   *Woody Oriental / Oriental Boisé* ●●

CAESARS WORLD
1988 CAESARS WOMAN   *Floral / Florale* ●●●●
1994 FERENTINA   *Floral Oriental / Fleuri Oriental* ●●●
1988 CAESARS MAN   *Aromatic / Fougère* ●●

CALIFORNIA FRAGRANCES
1987 VORAGO   *Aromatic / Fougère* ●●
1992 VORAGO ACTION   *Citrus / Hespéridé* ●●●

CALIFORNIA NORTH
1991 RICHARDSON BAY ♂   *Green / Vert* ●
1996 O₂XYGEN WOMAN   *Citrus / Hespéridé* ●
1994 O₂XYGEN   *Citrus / Hespéridé* ●
1995 ⁽N   *Dry Woods / Chypre Cuir* ●●●

CALVIN KLEIN
1985 OBSESSION   *Oriental / Oriental* ●
1988 ETERNITY   *Floral / Florale* ●
1991 ESCAPE   *Water / Marine* ●●●●
1994 cK ONE ♂   *Citrus / Hespéridé* ●
1996 cK BE ♂   *Aromatic / Fougère* ●
1997 CONTRADICTION   *Floral Oriental / Fleuri Oriental* ●
1981 CALVIN   *Aromatic / Fougère* ●
1986 OBSESSION FOR MEN   *Woody Oriental / Oriental Boisé* ●
1989 ETERNITY FOR MEN   *Aromatic / Fougère* ●
1993 ESCAPE FOR MEN   *Aromatic / Fougère* ●
1998 CONTRADICTION FOR MEN   *Woody Oriental / Oriental Boisé* ●

CALYPSO
1998 CALYPSO MIMOSA   *Floral / Florale* ●●
1999 CALYPSO JASMINE   *Floral / Florale* ●●●
1999 CALYPSO VIOLET   *Floral / Florale* ●●●●

CANTUEL → GILLES CANTUEL
CAPUCCI → ROBERTO CAPUCCI
CARDIN → PIERRE CARDIN

CARITA
1996 CARITA   *Water / Marine* ●●

CARLO CORINTO
1984 CARLO CORINTO   *Dry Woods / Chypre Cuir* ●●

CARNIVAL
1996 CRUISE FOR WOMEN   *Oriental / Oriental* ●●●
1996 CRUISE FOR MEN   *Mossy Woods / Chypre Boisé* ●●

CAROLINA HERRERA
1988 CAROLINA HERRERA   *Floral / Florale* ●●●●
1994 FLORE   *Floral / Florale* ●
1996 AQUAFLORE   *Water / Marine* ●
1997 212   *Soft Floral / Fleuri Aldéhydé* ●
1991 HERRERA FOR MEN   *Woody Oriental / Oriental Boisé* ●●
1999 212 MEN   *Mossy Woods / Chypre Boisé* ●

CARON
1911 NARCISSE NOIR   *Floral / Florale* ●●●●
1912/70 INFINI   *Soft Floral / Fleuri Aldéhydé* ●●●●
1916 N'AIMEZ QUE MOI   *Floral / Florale* ●●●
1918 VIOLETTE PRÉCIEUSE   *Floral / Florale* ●●●●
1919 TABAC BLOND   *Dry Woods / Chypre Cuir* ●●●
1922 NUIT DE NOËL   *Woody Oriental / Oriental Boisé* ●●●
1923 NARCISSE BLANC   *Floral / Florale* ●●●●

1924 ACACIOSA   *Floral / Florale* ●
1927 BELLODGIA   *Floral / Florale* ●●●●
1927 POIS DE SENTEUR   *Soft Oriental / Oriental Doux* ●●●
1930 EN AVION   *Floral Oriental / Fleuri Oriental* ●●●●
1933 FLEURS DE ROCAILLE   *Floral / Florale* ●●●
1936 FRENCH CANCAN   *Floral Oriental / Fleuri Oriental* ●●
1939 ALPONA   *Citrus / Hespéridé* ●●●●
1941 ROYAL BAIN DE CHAMPAGNE ♂   *Soft Oriental / Oriental Doux* ●
1947 FARNESIANA   *Floral / Florale* ●●
1949 OR ET NOIR   *Floral Oriental / Fleuri Oriental* ●●●
1949 ROSE   *Floral / Florale* ●●●
1949 WITH PLEASURE   *Green / Vert* ●●●●
1952 MUGUET DU BONHEUR   *Floral / Florale* ●
1954 POIVRE   *Soft Oriental / Oriental Doux* ●●●●
1980 EAU DE CARON   *Oriental / Oriental* ●●
1981 NOCTURNES   *Soft Floral / Fleuri Aldéhydé* ●●●●
1986 MONTAIGNE   *Floral / Florale* ●●
1990 PARFUM SACRÉ   *Floral Oriental / Fleuri Oriental* ●●●
1993 FLEUR DE ROCAILLE   *Floral / Florale* ●●
1996 AIMEZ-MOI   *Soft Floral / Fleuri Aldéhydé* ●●●●
1996 EAU PURE ♂   *Water / Marine* ●
1997 EAU FRAÎCHE ♂   *Citrus / Hespéridé* ●●●
1999 EAU DE CARON FORTE ♂   *Citrus / Hespéridé* ●●●●
1934 POUR UN HOMME   *Floral / Florale* ●●●●
1976 YATAGAN   *Dry Woods / Chypre Cuir* ●●●●
1985 THIRD MAN / 3ᵉ HOMME   *Aromatic / Fougère* ●●●●

CARTIER
1981 MUST DE CARTIER   *Oriental / Oriental* ●
1981 MUST DE CARTIER (JOUR)*   *Floral / Florale* ●
1987 PANTHÈRE   *Floral Oriental / Fleuri Oriental* ●●
1993 MUST DE CARTIER II   *Water / Marine* ●
1995 SO PRETTY   *Soft Floral / Fleuri Aldéhydé* ●
1981 SANTOS   *Aromatic / Fougère* ●●
1989 SANTOS EAU DE SPORT   *Citrus / Hespéridé* ●●●●
1992 PASHA   *Aromatic / Fougère* ●●
1998 DÉCLARATION   *Dry Woods / Chypre Cuir* ●

CARVEN
1946 MA GRIFFE   *Mossy Woods / Chypre Boisé* ●●
1966/95 EAU VIVE   *Citrus / Hespéridé* ●●
1979 MADAME CARVEN*   *Floral / Florale* ●●●●
1982 GUIRLANDES*   *Soft Floral / Fleuri Aldéhydé* ●
1986 INTRIGUE*   *Soft Floral / Fleuri Aldéhydé* ●●
1957 VÉTIVER   *Mossy Woods / Chypre Boisé* ●●●
1978 MONSIEUR CARVEN*   *Soft Oriental / Oriental Doux* ●●
1988 VÉTIVER DRY   *Aromatic / Fougère* ●●
1999 CARVEN HOMME   *Dry Woods / Chypre Cuir* ●●

CASSINI → OLEG CASSINI

CATHERINE DENEUVE
1986 DENEUVE*   *Mossy Woods / Chypre Boisé* ●

CBH
1986 CAMP BEVERLY HILLS*   *Soft Floral / Fleuri Aldéhydé* ●●
1988 CAMP BEVERLY HILLS FOR MEN*   *Citrus / Hespéridé* ●●●●

CÉLINE
1996 MAGIC   *Mossy Woods / Chypre Boisé* ●

CELSIUS
1989 CELSIUS   *Aromatic / Fougère* ●

CERRUTI
1987 NINO CERRUTI*   *Woody Oriental / Oriental Boisé* ●
1995 CERRUTI 1881 POUR FEMME   *Floral / Florale* ●●
1979 NINO CERRUTI   *Green / Vert* ●●●●
1990 CERRUTI 1881   *Citrus / Hespéridé* ●●
1998 IMAGE   *Aromatic / Fougère* ●

CHANEL
1921 CHANEL N° 5   *Soft Floral / Fleuri Aldéhydé* ●●●
1922 CHANEL N° 22   *Floral / Florale* ●●●
1924 CUIR DE RUSSIE   *Dry Woods / Chypre Cuir* ●●●
1925 GARDÉNIA   *Floral / Florale* ●●
1926 BOIS DES ÎLES   *Woody Oriental / Oriental Boisé* ●●●

1971 CHANEL Nº 19 *Soft Floral / Fleuri Aldéhydé* ●
1974 CRISTALLE *Citrus / Hespéridé* ●●
1984 COCO *Soft Oriental / Oriental Doux* ●●●
1996 ALLURE *Floral Oriental / Fleuri Oriental* ●
1955 CHANEL POUR MONSIEUR *Mossy Woods / Chypre Boisé* ●●●
1981 ANTAEUS *Dry Woods / Chypre Cuir* ●●●●
1990 ÉGOÏSTE / L'ÉGOÏSTE *Woody Oriental / Oriental Boisé* ●●●
1993 ÉGOÏSTE PLATINUM *Aromatic / Fougère* ●
1998 ALLURE HOMME *Woody Oriental / Oriental Boisé* ●

CHARLES JOURDAN
1992 TRES JOURDAN* *Floral / Florale* ●●
1995 L'INSOLENT* *Woody Oriental / Oriental Boisé* ●●
1996 INDIVIDUELLE *Floral / Florale* ●
1998 INSPIRATION *Floral Oriental / Fleuri Oriental* ●

CHAUMET
1999 CHAUMET *Floral / Florale* ●

CHER
1989 UNINHIBITED* *Floral Oriental / Fleuri Oriental* ●●●●

CHEVIGNON
1996 BEST OF CHEVIGNON ♂ *Water / Marine* ●●●
1999 57 FOR HER *Floral / Florale* ●●
1992 CHEVIGNON *Mossy Woods / Chypre Boisé* ●●
1999 57 FOR HIM *Woody Oriental / Oriental Boisé* ●

CHIARA BONI
1990 CHIARA BONI *Floral / Florale* ●●●●
1997 CHIARA BONI LIGHT *Soft Floral / Fleuri Aldéhydé* ●●
1998 SUNSHINE *Floral / Florale* ●
1999 FLEURS DE CHIARA BONI *Floral / Florale* ●
1997 CHIARA BONI UOMO *Aromatic / Fougère* ●

CHIEMSEE
1999 CHIEMSEE *Floral / Florale* ●

CHLOÉ
1975 CHLOÉ *Floral / Florale* ●●●●
1992 CHLOÉ NARCISSE *Floral Oriental / Fleuri Oriental* ●●
1996 CHLOÉ INNOCENCE* *Floral / Florale* ●

CHOPARD
1991 CASMIR *Woody Oriental / Oriental Boisé* ●●
1997 WISH *Woody Oriental / Oriental Boisé* ●
1998 MIRA BAÏ *Woody Oriental / Oriental Boisé* ●●
1994 HEAVEN *Aromatic / Fougère* ●●
1999 CASRAN *Woody Oriental / Oriental Boisé* ●

CHRISTIAN DIOR
1947 MISS DIOR *Mossy Woods / Chypre Boisé* ●
1949 DIORAMA *Mossy Woods / Chypre Boisé* ●●●
1953 EAU FRAÎCHE *Mossy Woods / Chypre Boisé* ●●●
1956 DIORISSIMO *Floral / Florale* ●
1963 DIORLING *Dry Woods / Chypre Cuir* ●●●
1969/79 DIORESSENCE *Soft Oriental / Oriental Doux* ●●●
1972 DIORELLA *Citrus / Hespéridé* ●●
1985 POISON *Floral Oriental / Fleuri Oriental* ●●●●
1991 DUNE *Woody Oriental / Oriental Boisé* ●
1994 TENDRE POISON *Floral / Florale* ●●
1995 DOLCE VITA *Woody Oriental / Oriental Boisé* ●●
1995 EAU SVELTE *Floral / Florale* ●
1998 EAU DE DOLCE VITA *Floral / Florale* ●
1998 HYPNOTIC POISON *Woody Oriental / Oriental Boisé* ●●●●
1999 J'ADORE *Floral / Florale* ●
1999 LILY ⓛ *Floral / Florale* ●
1966 EAU SAUVAGE *Citrus / Hespéridé* ●●●
1980 JULES *Aromatic / Fougère* ●●●●
1984 EAU SAUVAGE EXTRÊME *Citrus / Hespéridé* ●●●●
1988 FAHRENHEIT *Mossy Woods / Chypre Boisé* ●
1997 DUNE POUR HOMME *Woody Oriental / Oriental Boisé* ●

CHRISTIAN LACROIX
1990 C'EST LA VIE* *Floral Oriental / Fleuri Oriental* ●
1999 CHRISTIAN LACROIX *Floral / Florale* ●●

CHRISTIAN TORTU
1998 EAU FRAÎCHE *Citrus / Hespéridé* ●●●

CHRISTOPHER CHRONIS
1998 CHRISTOS WOMAN *Woody Oriental / Oriental Boisé* ●
1998 CHRISTOS MAN *Woody Oriental / Oriental Boisé* ●●

CHYPRON
1995 SHAHI *Woody Oriental / Oriental Boisé* ●●●●
1997 SHAHI GOLDEN SUN *Floral Oriental / Fleuri Oriental* ●●●
1998 SHAHI AQUA *Floral / Florale* ●

CIGAR AFICIONADO
1997 CIGAR AFICIONADO *Aromatic / Fougère* ●●●●

CINDY ADAMS
1997 GOSSIP *Woody Oriental / Oriental Boisé* ●

CLAIBORNE → LIZ CLAIBORNE
CLAIRE → HOUBIGANT / CLAIRE

CLARINS
1987 EAU DYNAMISANTE ♂ *Citrus / Hespéridé* ●●●
1993 ELYSIUM *Floral / Florale* ●

CLINIQUE
1971 AROMATICS ELIXIR *Dry Woods / Chypre Cuir* ●
1990 WRAPPINGS *Water / Marine* ●
1997 HAPPY *Floral / Florale* ●
1995 CHEMISTRY *Aromatic / Fougère* ●
1999 HAPPY FOR MEN *Citrus / Hespéridé* ●

COFINLUXE
1978 CAFÉ *Soft Oriental / Oriental Doux* ●●●
1993 WATT *Floral / Florale* ●
1996 CAFÉ-CAFÉ *Soft Floral / Fleuri Aldéhydé* ●●
1999 ANDY WARHOL FOR WOMEN *Floral / Florale* ●
1991 WATT FOR MEN *Aromatic / Fougère* ●●
1996 CAFÉ-CAFÉ POUR HOMME *Aromatic / Fougère* ●
1999 ANDY WARHOL FOR MEN *Aromatic / Fougère* ●

COLONIA
1916 ACQUA DI PARMA ♂ *Citrus / Hespéridé* ●●●

COMME DES GARÇONS
1994 COMME DES GARÇONS ♂ *Mossy Woods / Chypre Boisé* ●●●●
1998 ODEUR 53 ♂ *Water / Marine* ●●
1999 COMME DES GARÇONS 2 ♂ *Mossy Woods / Chypre Boisé* ●

COMPTOIR SUD PACIFIQUE
1975 EAU DE CÈDRE ♂ *Dry Woods / Chypre Cuir* ●
1975 SOLEIL LEVANT *Woody Oriental / Oriental Boisé* ●●●
1976 FLEURS DE PÊCHER *Soft Floral / Fleuri Aldéhydé* ●
1976 MANDARINE ♂ *Citrus / Hespéridé* ●●
1977 VETYVER HAITI ♂ *Mossy Woods / Chypre Boisé* ●●
1978 VANILLE ♂ *Oriental / Oriental* ●●
1984 TIARÉ *Floral / Florale* ●●
1985 PAMPLEMOUSSE ♂ *Citrus / Hespéridé* ●●
1986 CRISTAL DE MUSC *Soft Oriental / Oriental Doux* ●
1986 PAIN D'ÉPICES *Woody Oriental / Oriental Boisé* ●●●
1987 FRUITS SAUVAGES *Citrus / Hespéridé* ●●●●
1987 VANILLE CAFÉ ♂ *Oriental / Oriental* ●●●
1988 COTONNADE ♂ *Soft Oriental / Oriental Doux* ●●
1989 ROSE VANILLE *Floral / Florale* ●●●
1989 VANILLE TIARÉ *Oriental / Oriental* ●
1991 TURQUOISE *Soft Floral / Fleuri Aldéhydé* ●●●
1992 MOTU *Water / Marine* ●
1992 OPOPONAX *Aromatic / Fougère* ●●●
1993 AMOUR DE CACAO *Oriental / Oriental* ●●
1994 VANILLE ABRICOT *Oriental / Oriental* ●
1994 VANILLE AMANDE *Oriental / Oriental* ●
1995 EAU DE BIARRITZ *Soft Floral / Fleuri Aldéhydé* ●●
1997 THÉ ♂ *Woody Oriental / Oriental Boisé* ●●●
1997 VANILLE CERISE *Oriental / Oriental* ●
1998 KUMQUAT ♂ *Citrus / Hespéridé* ●●
1999 ENFANTS DU SOLEIL *Floral Oriental / Fleuri Oriental* ●●
1999 LAIT SUCRÉ *Floral / Florale* ●●

1976 EAU GRISE *Mossy Woods / Chypre Boisé* ●
1978 BARBIER DES ISLES *Dry Woods / Chypre Cuir* ●●●
1988 EAU DES TROPIQUES *Citrus / Hespéridé* ●●●
1988 ROI SANTAL *Woody Oriental / Oriental Boisé* ●●●
1990 PIROGUIER *Dry Woods / Chypre Cuir* ●●●
1993 L'HOMME *Dry Woods / Chypre Cuir* ●●
1996 SAFRANIER *Woody Oriental / Oriental Boisé* ●●

CONROY
1992 DISCOVERY *Aromatic / Fougère* ●
1993 TRIESTE *Aromatic / Fougère* ●●

CONSENT
2000 CONSENT WOMAN *Floral / Florale* ●
2000 CONSENT MAN *Aromatic / Fougère* ●

COTY
1905 L'ORIGAN* *Floral Oriental / Fleuri Oriental* ●●●
1917 CHYPRE DE COTY* *Mossy Woods / Chypre Boisé* ●●●
1921 ÉMERAUDE *Oriental / Oriental* ●●●
1927 L'AIMANT *Soft Floral / Fleuri Aldéhydé* ●●●
1942 MUGUET DES BOIS *Floral / Florale* ●
1950/95 JUNGLE GARDENIA *Floral / Florale* ●●
1966 IMPRÉVU *Dry Woods / Chypre Cuir* ●●●
1973 WILD MUSK *Oriental / Oriental* ●●●●
1983 SAND & SABLE *Floral / Florale* ●●●●
1986 LADY STETSON *Soft Floral / Fleuri Aldéhydé* ●●●●
1988 EX'CLA.MA'TION *Floral Oriental / Fleuri Oriental* ●●
1990 ASPEN FOR WOMEN *Water / Marine* ●●●
1990 L'EFFLEUR *Floral / Florale* ●●
1992 TRULY LACE *Floral Oriental / Fleuri Oriental* ●●●
1993 VANILLA FIELDS *Woody Oriental / Oriental Boisé* ●●
1994 LONGING *Floral Oriental / Fleuri Oriental* ●
1994 VANILLA MUSK *Woody Oriental / Oriental Boisé* ●●●
1995 CHANSON D'EAU *Citrus / Hespéridé* ●●●
1995 CHIPIE *Floral Oriental / Fleuri Oriental* ●
1995 GHOST MYST *Water / Marine* ●
1995 ICI *Floral Oriental / Fleuri Oriental* ●●
1996 CELEBRATE *Floral / Florale* ●●
1996 EX'CLA.MA'TION BLUSH *Floral / Florale* ●
1996 EX'CLA.MA'TION DARE *Floral / Florale* ●
1996 EX'CLA.MA'TION EAU *Citrus / Hespéridé* ●
1996 ROOTS UNISCENT ♂ *Water / Marine* ●
1997 CHANSON D'AIR *Floral / Florale* ●
1997 NOKOMIS *Floral Oriental / Fleuri Oriental* ●●
1997 PRINCESSE CHIPIE *Woody Oriental / Oriental Boisé* ●
1998 100% PURE CHIPIE GREEN *Floral / Florale* ●
1998 100% PURE CHIPIE PURPLE *Woody Oriental / Oriental Boisé* ●
1998 ASPEN SENSATION *Floral / Florale* ●
1998 DARK VANILLA *Floral Oriental / Fleuri Oriental* ●●●●
1998 EXC'LA.MA'TION NOIR *Mossy Woods / Chypre Boisé* ●●●
1998 I EX'CLA.MA'TION *Floral / Florale* ●●
1998 ROOTS FOR HER *Floral / Florale* ●
1999 APRIL FIELDS *Floral / Florale* ●
1999 CHANSON DE VIE *Citrus / Hespéridé* ●
1999 DULCE VANILLA *Woody Oriental / Oriental Boisé* ●
1974 MUSK FOR MEN *Woody Oriental / Oriental Boisé* ●●●
1981 STETSON *Woody Oriental / Oriental Boisé* ●●●
1989 ASPEN FOR MEN *Aromatic / Fougère* ●
1990 PREFERRED STOCK *Aromatic / Fougère* ●
1992 GRAVITY *Woody Oriental / Oriental Boisé* ●●
1992 ROLAND GARROS *Aromatic / Fougère* ●
1993 STETSON SIERRA *Aromatic / Fougère* ●
1994 UNIVERSO *Aromatic / Fougère* ●
1995 ROUTE 66 *Aromatic / Fougère* ●●
1996 RAW VANILLA *Woody Oriental / Oriental Boisé* ●
1997 AVATAR *Aromatic / Fougère* ●
1997 ROUTE 66 COLORADO RAIN *Aromatic / Fougère* ●
1998 STETSON COUNTRY *Mossy Woods / Chypre Boisé* ●●

COUDRAY → E.COUDRAY

COUNTRY ROAD WOMAN
1999 COUNTRY ROAD WOMAN *Soft Floral / Fleuri Aldéhydé* ●●
1999 COUNTRY ROAD MAN *Aromatic / Fougère* ●

COURRÈGES
1971/92 EMPREINTE *Dry Woods / Chypre Cuir* ●●●
1983 COURRÈGES IN BLUE *Floral / Florale* ●●●●
1993 SWEET COURRÈGES *Soft Floral / Fleuri Aldéhydé* ●●
1996 GÉNÉRATION COURRÈGES *Floral / Florale* ●
1997 COURRÈGES 2020 *Floral / Florale* ●●
1995 NIAGARA *Dry Woods / Chypre Cuir* ●●

COUTURIER → JEAN COUTURIER
COVER GIRL / DANA → DANA
COVERI → ENRICO COVERI

CRABTREE & EVELYN
1970 JASMIN DE PROVENCE *Floral / Florale* ●●●
1970 LAVENDER ♂ *Floral / Florale* ●●●
1970 LILY OF THE VALLEY *Floral / Florale* ●
1974 GARDENIA *Floral / Florale* ●
1976/91 DAMASK ROSE *Soft Floral / Fleuri Aldéhydé* ●●
1979 SPRING RAIN *Floral / Florale* ●
1985 NANTUCKET BRIAR *Floral Oriental / Fleuri Oriental* ●●
1988 SUMMER HILL *Floral / Florale* ●
1990 VERANDA *Floral Oriental / Fleuri Oriental* ●
1993 EVELYN *Floral / Florale* ●●●
1993 FREESIA *Floral / Florale* ●●
1994 VANILLA *Floral Oriental / Fleuri Oriental* ●
1996 PASSION FLOWER *Floral / Florale* ●
1997 SONG DE CHINE *Floral / Florale* ●
1999 SONOMA VALLEY *Green / Vert* ●
1970 PATCHOULI *Woody Oriental / Oriental Boisé* ●●
1970 SANDALWOOD *Woody Oriental / Oriental Boisé* ●●●
1975 HUNGARY WATER *Citrus / Hespéridé* ●●●
1984 CRABTREE & EVELYN FOR MEN *Dry Woods / Chypre Cuir* ●●●
1990 SIENNA *Mossy Woods / Chypre Boisé* ●●
1999 NOMAD *Aromatic / Fougère* ●

CREATIVE UNIVERSE
1996 TÉ ♂ *Citrus / Hespéridé* ●
1999 MARE ♂ *Water / Marine* ●●

CREED
1845/1980 FLEURS DE BULGARIE *Floral / Florale* ●●●
1850 SANTAL IMPÉRIAL ♂ *Woody Oriental / Oriental Boisé* ●●●
1862/1983 FANTASIA DE FLEURS *Floral / Florale* ●●●●
1870/1989 JASMIN IMPÉRATRICE EUGÉNIE *Floral / Florale* ●●●
1875 BOIS DE CÉDRAT ♂ *Citrus / Hespéridé* ●●●
1901 CITRUS BIGARRADE ♂ *Citrus / Hespéridé* ●●●
1933 ANGÉLIQUE ENCENS *Oriental / Oriental* ●●
1949 AMBRE CANNELLE *Soft Oriental / Oriental Doux* ●●●
1950 ORANGE SPICE ♂ *Aromatic / Fougère* ●●
1972 FLEURISSIMO *Floral / Florale* ●
1975 ZESTE MANDARINE PAMPLEMOUSSE ♂ *Citrus / Hespéridé* ●●●●
1980 INDIANA *Floral / Florale* ●●
1982 CHÈVREFEUILLE ORIGINAL ♂ *Green / Vert* ●
1987 VANISIA *Oriental / Oriental* ●●●
1993 ROYAL DELIGHT ♂ *Soft Oriental / Oriental Doux* ●●●●
1996 SPRING FLOWER *Floral / Florale* ●
1781 ROYAL ENGLISH LEATHER *Dry Woods / Chypre Cuir* ●●●
1856 ROYAL SCOTTISH LAVENDER *Floral / Florale* ●●●
1875/1999 TABAROME *Dry Woods / Chypre Cuir* ●●●●
1948 VETIVER *Mossy Woods / Chypre Boisé* ●●●
1965 EPICÉA *Aromatic / Fougère* ●●
1970 SÉLECTION VERTE *Citrus / Hespéridé* ●●
1973 ACIER ALUMINIUM *Mossy Woods / Chypre Boisé* ●●●●
1982 BAIE DE GENIÈVRE *Woody Oriental / Oriental Boisé* ●●●
1985 GREEN IRISH TWEED *Green / Vert* ●●●
1987 BOIS DU PORTUGAL *Woody Oriental / Oriental Boisé* ●●●●
1992 EROLFA *Water / Marine* ●
1994 NÉROLI SAUVAGE *Citrus / Hespéridé* ●●●●
1995 MILLÉSIME IMPÉRIAL *Water / Marine* ●●●●
1995 SILVER MOUNTAIN WATER *Water / Marine* ●●
1997 ROYAL WATER *Aromatic / Fougère* ●●●●
1999 GREEN VALLEY *Mossy Woods / Chypre Boisé* ●

CROWN
1669/1994 MARECHALE ORIGINAL *Floral / Florale* ●●●
1872 CROWN ESS BOUQUET *Citrus / Hespéridé* ●
1873 CROWN ROSE *Floral / Florale* ●●●

1874 CROWN ESTERHAZY *Citrus / Hespéridé* ●●●
1879 CROWN ALPINE LILY *Floral / Florale* ●
1882 CROWN COURT BOUQUET *Aromatic / Fougère* ●●●
1910 CROWN OF GOLD *Soft Oriental / Oriental Doux* ●●●
1919 MALABAR *Oriental / Oriental* ●●●
1921 CROWN STEPHANOTIS *Floral / Florale* ●●●
1929 MATSUKITA *Floral Oriental / Fleuri Oriental* ●●
1931 SARCANTHUS *Floral / Florale* ●●
1932 TANGLEWOOD BOUQUET *Floral Oriental / Fleuri Oriental* ●●●
1936 CROWN BOUQUET *Floral / Florale* ●●
1939 CROWN HELIOTROPE *Woody Oriental / Oriental Boisé* ●●●
1994 MARECHALE 90 *Mossy Woods / Chypre Boisé* ●●●
1873 SANDRINGHAM *Woody Oriental / Oriental Boisé* ●●●
1880 BUCKINGHAM *Aromatic / Fougère* ●●
1885 CROWN FOUGÈRE *Aromatic / Fougère* ●●●
1890 EAU DE QUININE *Citrus / Hespéridé* ●●●
1905 CROWN IMPERIAL *Citrus / Hespéridé* ●●●●
1911 EAU DE RUSSE *Oriental / Oriental* ●●
1921 CROWN SPICED LIMES *Citrus / Hespéridé* ●●●●
1925 SUMARE *Citrus / Hespéridé* ●●●●
1925 TOWN & COUNTRY *Mossy Woods / Chypre Boisé* ●●
1928 MARQUIS *Aromatic / Fougère* ●
1929 CROWN PARK ROYAL *Dry Woods / Chypre Cuir* ●●

CUSSONS
1976 IMPERIAL LEATHER *Dry Woods / Chypre Cuir* ●●●

D'ALBRET → JEAN D'ALBRET

D'ORSAY
1908/95 ETIQUETTE BLEUE ♂ *Citrus / Hespéridé* ●●
1943/95 ARÔME 3 ♂ *Floral / Florale* ●●●
1955/95 TILLEUL ♂ *Floral / Florale* ●
1997 INTOXICATION D'AMOUR *Woody Oriental / Oriental Boisé* ●●●
1998 ARÔME 3 TRADITION ♂ *Floral / Florale* ●●●●
1911/95 CHEVALIER D'ORSAY *Citrus / Hespéridé* ●●●●
1923/98 LE DANDY *Dry Woods / Chypre Cuir* ●

DALI → SALVADOR DALI

DANA
1921 TOUJOURS MOI *Oriental / Oriental* ●●●●
1932 TABU *Oriental / Oriental* ●●●●
1941 CHANTILLY *Oriental / Oriental* ●●●
1941 HEAVEN SENT *Aromatic / Fougère* ●●●
1955/97 AMBUSH *Woody Oriental / Oriental Boisé* ●●
1974 LOVE'S BABY SOFT *Soft Floral / Fleuri Aldéhydé* ●●●
1982 RAFFINÉE *Floral Oriental / Fleuri Oriental* ●●●
1984 LUTÈCE *Floral Oriental / Fleuri Oriental* ●●●●
1990 NAVY *Floral Oriental / Fleuri Oriental* ●●●●
1992 INCOGNITO *Floral Oriental / Fleuri Oriental* ●●
1994 FRENCH VANILLA *Woody Oriental / Oriental Boisé* ●●
1995 CLASSIC GARDENIA *Floral / Florale* ●●
1995 WHITE CHANTILLY *Floral / Florale* ●●
1996 DREAMS BY TABU *Floral / Florale* ●
1997 FETISH *Floral / Florale* ●
1998 SHADES BY NAVY *Floral / Florale* ●●
1936 CANOÉ *Aromatic / Fougère* ●●●
1949 ENGLISH LEATHER *Dry Woods / Chypre Cuir* ●●
1965 BRITISH STERLING *Aromatic / Fougère* ●●●
1973 MONSIEUR MUSK *Oriental / Oriental* ●●●●
1989 SILVER *Aromatic / Fougère* ●●●
1996 NAVIGATOR *Aromatic / Fougère* ●
1996 NAVY FOR MEN *Aromatic / Fougère* ●

DANICA AROMATICS
1999 I AM ENERGY *Citrus / Hespéridé* ●
1999 I AM ETERNAL *Woody Oriental / Oriental Boisé* ●●●
1999 I AM PASSION *Floral / Florale* ●
1999 I AM SERENE *Green / Vert* ●●●
1999 I AM WILD *Oriental / Oriental* ●

DANIEL DE FASSON
1990 DANIEL DE FASSON *Floral Oriental / Fleuri Oriental* ●●●
1994 TENAZ *Aromatic / Fougère* ●●●●

DANIEL HECHTER
1989 CARACTÈRE *Dry Woods / Chypre Cuir* ●●
1997 XXL *Woody Oriental / Oriental Boisé* ●
1999 DANIEL HECHTER SPORT *Aromatic / Fougère* ●

DAVIDOFF
1996 COOL WATER WOMAN *Floral / Florale* ●●
1999 GOODLIFE WOMAN *Floral Oriental / Fleuri Oriental* ●
1984 DAVIDOFF *Dry Woods / Chypre Cuir* ●●●●
1986 ZINO DAVIDOFF *Woody Oriental / Oriental Boisé* ●●●●
1988 COOL WATER *Aromatic / Fougère* ●
1990 RELAX *Woody Oriental / Oriental Boisé* ●●
1998 GOODLIFE *Aromatic / Fougère* ●●

DAVINCI
1996 XTC ♂ *Citrus / Hespéridé* ●
1997 DV8 FOR WOMEN *Floral / Florale* ●●
1991 DAVINCI CLASSICO *Dry Woods / Chypre Cuir* ●●●●
1997 DV8 FOR MEN *Aromatic / Fougère* ●
1997 SPORT 2000 *Aromatic / Fougère* ●
1999 SPORT MAXIMUM *Aromatic / Fougère* ●

DC DESIGN
1994 CHAPEAU BLEU *Mossy Woods / Chypre Boisé* ●●

DE LA MORANDIÈRE
→ MARC DE LA MORANDIÈRE

DE NICOLAÏ → PATRICIA DE NICOLAÏ

DE RUY
1998 ATREVIDA *Floral Oriental / Fleuri Oriental* ●●
1998 FUN WATER WOMAN *Water / Marine* ●●
1999 ACQUA DI FIORI *Floral / Florale* ●
1996 FUN WATER FOR MEN *Aromatic / Fougère* ●

DE VARENS → ULRIC DE VARENS

DECLÉOR
1999 AROMANTIC *Floral / Florale* ●

DÉCO
1976 BORONIA *Floral / Florale* ●●●
1981 ORIENT *Soft Oriental / Oriental Doux* ●●●
1987 ENCHANTÉ *Woody Oriental / Oriental Boisé* ●
1994 UNTAMED MUSK *Oriental / Oriental* ●●●●

DELON → ALAIN DELON
DEL POZO → J. DEL POZO

DIANA DE SILVA
1996 DIVINA *Floral / Florale* ●●

DIANA VON FURSTENBERG
1975 TATIANA *Floral / Florale* ●●●●

DIDIER CALVO-UOMO
1995 HÉROS *Woody Oriental / Oriental Boisé* ●●
1997 HÉROS SPORT *Aromatic / Fougère* ●

DIESEL
1997 DIESEL PLUS PLUS FEMININE *Floral Oriental / Fleuri Oriental* ●
1999 DIESEL ZERO PLUS FEMININE *Woody Oriental / Oriental Boisé* ●
1996 DIESEL *Woody Oriental / Oriental Boisé* ●●●
1997 DIESEL PLUS PLUS MASCULINE *Woody Oriental / Oriental Boisé* ●
1999 DIESEL ZERO PLUS MASCULINE *Woody Oriental / Oriental Boisé* ●●●

DIONNE WARWICK
1986 DIONNE *Oriental / Oriental* ●

DIOR → CHRISTIAN DIOR

DIPTYQUE
1968 L'EAU ♂ *Soft Oriental / Oriental Doux* ●●
1973 L'AUTRE ♂ *Dry Woods / Chypre Cuir* ●●●●
1975 L'EAU TROIS ♂ *Dry Woods / Chypre Cuir* ●●
1983 L'OMBRE DANS L'EAU *Floral / Florale* ●●

1986 EAU LENTE ♂ *Oriental / Oriental* ●●●
1988 EAU D'ÉLIDE ♂ *Aromatic / Fougère* ●●●
1988 OLÈNE *Floral / Florale* ●●
1990 VIRGILIO ♂ *Green / Vert* ●●
1996 PHILOSYKOS ♂ *Mossy Woods / Chypre Boisé* ●
1999 OFRÉSIA *Floral / Florale* ●

DOLCE & GABBANA
1992 DOLCE & GABBANA *Soft Floral / Fleuri Aldéhydé* ●●●●
1997 BY WOMAN *Woody Oriental / Oriental Boisé* ●●●
1999 D&G FEMININE *Soft Floral / Fleuri Aldéhydé* ●●●●
1994 DOLCE & GABBANA POUR HOMME *Aromatic / Fougère* ●●●
1998 BY MAN *Woody Oriental / Oriental Boisé* ●●
1999 D&G MASCULINE *Citrus / Hespéridé* ●●●●

DOMINGUEZ → ADOLFO DOMINGUEZ

DONNA KARAN
1992 DONNA KARAN *Dry Woods / Chypre Cuir* ●●●
1994 CASHMERE MIST *Dry Woods / Chypre Cuir* ●
1996 CHAOS* *Woody Oriental / Oriental Boisé* ●●
1999 DKNY WOMEN *Soft Floral / Fleuri Aldéhydé* ●
1994 DK MEN* *Dry Woods / Chypre Cuir* ●●
1995 DK MEN UNLEADED* *Dry Woods / Chypre Cuir* ●
2000 DKNY MEN *Aromatic / Fougère* ●

DUNHILL
1934 DUNHILL *Dry Woods / Chypre Cuir* ●●●
1985 DUNHILL EDITION *Aromatic / Fougère* ●●
1996 D *Aromatic / Fougère* ●

E.COUDRAY
1922 NOHIBA (TULIPE NOIRE) *Soft Oriental / Oriental Doux* ●●●
1935 VANILLE CANNELLE *Oriental / Oriental* ●●●
1946 CAMÉLIA IRIS (BLEU) *Soft Floral / Fleuri Aldéhydé* ●
1950 GIVRINE (SICILE) ♂ *Citrus / Hespéridé* ●●●
1983 JACINTHE ROSE (ROMANTICA) *Floral / Florale* ●
1990 VANILLE COCO *Woody Oriental / Oriental Boisé* ●
1995 MIEL ORANGE *Citrus / Hespéridé* ●●●●
1998 FÉTICHE *Floral Oriental / Fleuri Oriental* ●●●

EDDIE BAUER
1996 BALANCE *Floral / Florale* ●

EDGAR DE BERCHELAI
1997 DE BERCHELAI *Floral / Florale* ●●

ELIZABETH ARDEN
1934/89 BLUE GRASS *Floral / Florale* ●●●●
1986 EAU FRAÎCHE *Floral / Florale* ●
1989 RED DOOR *Floral / Florale* ●●●●
1993 SUNFLOWERS *Water / Marine* ●●●
1994 TRUE LOVE *Soft Floral / Fleuri Aldéhydé* ●
1996 5th AVENUE *Floral / Florale* ●
1998 SPLENDOR *Floral / Florale* ●
1999 GREEN TEA *Citrus / Hespéridé* ●

ELIZABETH TAYLOR
1987 PASSION *Woody Oriental / Oriental Boisé* ●●●
1991 WHITE DIAMONDS *Soft Floral / Fleuri Aldéhydé* ●●
1993 DIAMONDS & EMERALDS* *Floral / Florale* ●●
1993 DIAMONDS & RUBIES* *Woody Oriental / Oriental Boisé* ●●●
1993 DIAMONDS & SAPPHIRES* *Floral / Florale* ●
1996 BLACK PEARLS* *Floral Oriental / Fleuri Oriental* ●
1989 PASSION FOR MEN *Woody Oriental / Oriental Boisé* ●●●

ELYSIOS
1997 ELYSEOS FEMME *Floral Oriental / Fleuri Oriental* ●
1997 ELYSEOS HOMME *Dry Woods / Chypre Cuir* ●●●●

ENRICO COVERI
1987 ENRICO COVERI *Soft Oriental / Oriental Doux* ●●●
1993 FIRENZE *Soft Floral / Fleuri Aldéhydé* ●●

ERIC TABARLY
1998 PEN DUICK *Aromatic / Fougère* ●

ERMENEGILDO ZEGNA
1992 ZEGNA *Aromatic / Fougère* ●●

EROX / HPS
1993 REALM WOMEN *Soft Oriental / Oriental Doux* ●
1993 REALM MEN *Woody Oriental / Oriental Boisé* ●●

ESCADA-MARGARETHA LEY
1990 ESCADA *Floral Oriental / Fleuri Oriental* ●●●
1995 ACTE 2 *Soft Floral / Fleuri Aldéhydé* ●●
1996 COUNTRY WEEKEND ♂ *Aromatic / Fougère* ●●
1996 FEELING FREE *Floral / Florale* ●
1996 SPORT SPIRIT ♂ *Citrus / Hespéridé* ●
1997 ESCADA COLLECTION *Woody Oriental / Oriental Boisé* ●
1997 ESCADA EN FLEURS *Floral / Florale* ●
1999 LOVING BOUQUET Ⓛ *Floral / Florale* ●
1993 ESCADA POUR HOMME *Woody Oriental / Oriental Boisé* ●●
1997 SILVER LIGHT *Citrus / Hespéridé* ●●
1999 CASUAL FRIDAY *Woody Oriental / Oriental Boisé* ●

ESTÉE LAUDER
1953 YOUTH-DEW *Soft Oriental / Oriental Doux* ●●●
1968 ESTÉE *Floral / Florale* ●●●●
1969 AZURÉE *Dry Woods / Chypre Cuir* ●●●
1972 ALIAGE / ALLIAGE *Green / Vert* ●●●
1973 PRIVATE COLLECTION *Green / Vert* ●●●●
1978 CINNABAR *Soft Oriental / Oriental Doux* ●●●
1978 WHITE LINEN *Soft Floral / Fleuri Aldéhydé* ●●
1985 BEAUTIFUL *Floral / Florale* ●●
1988 KNOWING *Mossy Woods / Chypre Boisé* ●●●
1991 SPELLBOUND *Floral Oriental / Fleuri Oriental* ●●●
1992 TUSCANY PER DONNA *Woody Oriental / Oriental Boisé* ●
1995 PLEASURES *Floral / Florale* ●
1996 WHITE LINEN BREEZE *Soft Floral / Fleuri Aldéhydé* ●
1998 DAZZLING GOLD *Floral / Florale* ●●
1998 DAZZLING SILVER *Soft Floral / Fleuri Aldéhydé* ●●
1987 LAUDER FOR MEN *Aromatic / Fougère* ●●
1987 METROPOLIS *Mossy Woods / Chypre Boisé* ●●
1997 PLEASURES FOR MEN *Aromatic / Fougère* ●

ETIENNE AIGNER
1986 EXPLOSIVE* *Mossy Woods / Chypre Boisé* ●●
1991 PRIVATE NUMBER FOR WOMEN* *Floral / Florale* ●●
1997 CLEAR DAY *Floral / Florale* ●●
1997 X LIMITED ♂ *Citrus / Hespéridé* ●
1999 CLEAR DAY LIGHT *Floral / Florale* ●
1975 ETIENNE AIGNER N° 1* *Dry Woods / Chypre Cuir* ●●●
1976 ETIENNE AIGNER N° 2 *Aromatic / Fougère* ●●●●
1992 PRIVATE NUMBER FOR MEN* *Mossy Woods / Chypre Boisé* ●●
1994 STATEMENT FOR MEN *Aromatic / Fougère* ●
1998 CLEAR DAY FOR MEN *Aromatic / Fougère* ●

ETRO
1989 HELIOTROPE *Floral Oriental / Fleuri Oriental* ●●●
1989 LEMON SORBET ♂ *Aromatic / Fougère* ●
1989 PALAIS JAMAIS ♂ *Dry Woods / Chypre Cuir* ●●●●
1989 PATCHOULY ♂ *Woody Oriental / Oriental Boisé* ●●●
1989 ROYAL PAVILLON *Floral / Florale* ●●
1996 MAGOT *Oriental / Oriental* ●
1996 VICOLO FIORI *Floral Oriental / Fleuri Oriental* ●
1997 SHAAL NUR ♂ *Soft Oriental / Oriental Doux* ●●●●
1989 SANDALO *Woody Oriental / Oriental Boisé* ●●●●
1989 VETIVER *Dry Woods / Chypre Cuir* ●●●

ETTORE BUGATTI
1992/99 BUGATTI *Aromatic / Fougère* ●

EUROITALIA
1993 JOSEPH ABBOUD *Aromatic / Fougère* ●●

EVYAN
1945 WHITE SHOULDERS *Floral / Florale* ●●●

EVYAN / LTL
1965/96 THE BARON *Aromatic / Fougère* ●●●

FABERGÉ
1938 APHRODISIA* *Mossy Woods / Chypre Boisé* ●●
1938 TIGRESS* *Floral Oriental / Fleuri Oriental* ●●●
1944 WOODHUE* *Woody Oriental / Oriental Boisé* ●●●
1983 AUDACE *Mossy Woods / Chypre Boisé* ●●●
1996 FABERGÉ IMPERIAL *Floral / Florale* ●●●●
1997 FUSION *Citrus / Hespéridé* ●
1964 BRUT *Aromatic / Fougère* ●●●
1994 BRUT ACTIF BLUE *Aromatic / Fougère* ●
1997 BRUT INSTINCT *Aromatic / Fougère* ●●

FAÇONNABLE
1996 FACE À FACE FEMME *Floral / Florale* ●
1994 FAÇONNABLE *Aromatic / Fougère* ●
1996 FACE À FACE HOMME *Aromatic / Fougère* ●

FASHION FAIR
1977 FASHION FAIR N° 1 *Floral / Florale* ●●
1985 EUNECE *Woody Oriental / Oriental Boisé* ●●●
1993 ZAHRA *Floral Oriental / Fleuri Oriental* ●●
1975 MR J *Aromatic / Fougère* ●●

FATH → JACQUES FATH

FENDI
1985 FENDI *Woody Oriental / Oriental Boisé* ●●●●
1992 ASJA *Soft Oriental / Oriental Doux* ●●●
1996 FANTASIA *Floral / Florale* ●●
1998 THEOREMA *Soft Oriental / Oriental Doux* ●●●
1999 THEOREMA ESPRIT D'ÉTÉ *Soft Oriental / Oriental Doux* ●●
1988 FENDI UOMO *Dry Woods / Chypre Cuir* ●●●●
1996 LIFE ESSENCE *Mossy Woods / Chypre Boisé* ●●

FERRAGAMO → SALVATORE FERRAGAMO

FERRARI
1995 FERRARI DONNA *Floral / Florale* ●●
1996 FERRARI *Woody Oriental / Oriental Boisé* ●
1998 FERRARI COLOGNE WATER *Citrus / Hespéridé* ●●●
1999 FERRARI BLACK *Mossy Woods / Chypre Boisé* ●●

FERRÉ → GIANFRANCO FERRÉ

FFC - FINE FRAGRANCES & COSMETICS
1924/92 TWEED *Floral / Florale* ●●●●
1976 CHIQUE *Mossy Woods / Chypre Boisé* ●●●●
1979 PANACHE *Soft Floral / Fleuri Aldéhydé* ●●
1984 LACE *Mossy Woods / Chypre Boisé* ●
1985 WHITE SATIN *Soft Floral / Fleuri Aldéhydé* ●●

FILA
1997 EMOZIONI FOR WOMAN *Floral / Florale* ●
1997 EMOZIONI FOR MAN *Aromatic / Fougère* ●

FIORUCCI
1999 FIORUCCI *Floral / Florale* ●●

FLORBATH
1978 NICKI LAUDA *Aromatic / Fougère* ●●

FLORI ROBERTS
1996 PATTI LaBELLE *Floral Oriental / Fleuri Oriental* ●

FLORIS
1786 STEPHANOTIS *Floral / Florale* ●●●●
1828 LAVENDER ♂ *Floral / Florale* ●●●
1830/1999 MALMAISON *Floral / Florale* ●●●●
1832 LIMES ♂ *Citrus / Hespéridé* ●●●●
1847 LILY OF THE VALLEY *Floral / Florale* ●
1901/84 EDWARDIAN BOUQUET *Floral / Florale* ●
1910 SPECIAL N° 127 ♂ *Citrus / Hespéridé* ●●●
1978 FLORISSA *Soft Floral / Fleuri Aldéhydé* ●●
1990 ZINNIA *Floral / Florale* ●
1993 SERINGA *Floral / Florale* ●
1996 BOUVARDIA* *Floral Oriental / Fleuri Oriental* ●●●
1997 GARDENIA *Floral / Florale* ●●
2000 CHINA ROSE *Floral Oriental / Fleuri Oriental* ●●●●

2000 FLEUR *Floral / Florale* ●
1950 N° 89 *Aromatic / Fougère* ●●●
1980 ELITE *Citrus / Hespéridé* ●●●●
1993 J.F. *Aromatic / Fougère* ●

FRAGONARD
1995 SOLEIL *Floral / Florale* ●●
1996 SORENZA *Floral / Florale* ●●●
1999 GRAIN DE SOLEIL *Woody Oriental / Oriental Boisé* ●●●
1932 ZIZANIE* *Woody Oriental / Oriental Boisé* ●●●
1999 SIESTE *Dry Woods / Chypre Cuir* ●●●

FRAGRANCE INTERNATIONAL
1999 KISS & TELL *Floral / Florale* ●

FRAGRANCES OF IRELAND
1998 INIS ♂ *Water / Marine* ●
1999 ETERNAL ROSE *Floral / Florale* ●●

FRANCESCO SMALTO
1993 SMALTO DONNA* *Woody Oriental / Oriental Boisé* ●●●
1987/98 SMALTO *Mossy Woods / Chypre Boisé* ●●
1992 MOLTO SMALTO* *Aromatic / Fougère* ●

FRANCES DENNEY
1952 HOPE *Soft Floral / Fleuri Aldéhydé* ●●●●
1965 INTERLUDE *Oriental / Oriental* ●●●

FRED HAYMAN
1989 273 FOR WOMEN *Floral / Florale* ●●●
1991 WITH LOVE* *Woody Oriental / Oriental Boisé* ●
1993 TOUCH FOR WOMEN *Floral / Florale* ●●
1998 HOLLYWOOD FOR WOMEN *Woody Oriental / Oriental Boisé* ●●
1990 273 FOR MEN *Dry Woods / Chypre Cuir* ●●
1995 TOUCH FOR MEN* *Aromatic / Fougère* ●●●
1998 HOLLYWOOD FOR MEN *Aromatic / Fougère* ●●

FRENCH CONNECTION
1997 FRENCH CONNECTION *Citrus / Hesperide* ●

GABRIELA SABATINI
1989 GABRIELA SABATINI *Floral Oriental / Fleuri Oriental* ●●
1992 MAGNETIC *Floral Oriental / Fleuri Oriental* ●
1994 CASCAYA *Floral Oriental / Fleuri Oriental* ●●
1997 BOLERO *Floral / Florale* ●●
1998 CASCAYA SUMMER *Floral / Florale* ●
1999 WILD WIND *Water / Marine* ●●
1999 WILD WIND FOR MEN *Aromatic / Fougère* ●

GAI MATTIOLO-ICR
1997 GAI MATTIOLO *Floral Oriental / Fleuri Oriental* ●
1998 GAI MATTIOLO UOMO *Citrus / Hespéridé* ●

GALANOS
1979 GALANOS DE SERENE *Soft Oriental / Oriental Doux* ●●●
1979/96 GALANOS *Soft Floral / Fleuri Aldéhydé* ●●●

GALE HAYMAN
1990 BEVERLY HILLS *Woody Oriental / Oriental Boisé* ●
1993 "DELICIOUS" *Soft Floral / Fleuri Aldéhydé* ●●●●
1996 "DELICIOUS" FEELINGS *Floral / Florale* ●
1998 SUNSET BOULEVARD *Floral Oriental / Fleuri Oriental* ●●
1999 GLAMOUR *Floral Oriental / Fleuri Oriental* ●●●
1999 STYLE *Floral Oriental / Fleuri Oriental* ●
1997 GALE HAYMAN MAN *Aromatic / Fougère* ●●

GANDH SUGANDH
1999 URVASHI *Floral Oriental / Fleuri Oriental* ●●

GATTINONI
1998 GATTINONI COUTURE *Woody Oriental / Oriental Boisé* ●
1999 GATTINONI À PORTER *Floral / Florale* ●●

GAULTIER → JEAN PAUL GAULTIER

GEIR NESS
1995 LAILA *Floral / Florale* ●

GENDARME
1996 CARRIÈRE *Citrus / Hespéridé* ●●
1991 GENDARME *Citrus / Hespéridé* ●●●●
1995 GRABAZZI *Soft Oriental / Oriental Doux* ●●●

GENNY
1987 GENNY* (Original) *Dry Woods / Chypre Cuir* ●
1987/98 GENNY *Floral / Florale* ●●
1993 GENNY SHINE* *Floral Oriental / Fleuri Oriental* ●●

GEOFFREY BEENE
1998 GEOFFREY BEENE *Floral / Florale* ●●
1976 GREY FLANNEL *Mossy Woods / Chypre Boisé* ●
1987 BOWLING GREEN *Aromatic / Fougère* ●●
1996 EAU DE GREY FLANNEL *Mossy Woods / Chypre Boisé* ●

GEORGES MARCIANO
1990 GUESS* *Woody Oriental / Oriental Boisé* ●●
1991 GUESS FOR MEN* *Aromatic / Fougère* ●●●●

GERANI
1998 GERANI *Woody Oriental / Oriental Boisé* ●
1999 GERANI UOMO *Woody Oriental / Oriental Boisé* ●

GIANFRANCO FERRÉ
1984 GIANFRANCO FERRÉ *Floral / Florale* ●
1991 FERRÉ BY FERRÉ *Soft Floral / Fleuri Aldéhydé* ●●●
1995 GIEFFEFFE ♂ *Citrus / Hespéridé* ●
1997 GFF DONNA *Floral / Florale* ●●
1998 GIANFRANCO FERRÉ 20 *Floral / Florale* ●●●
1986 FERRÉ FOR MAN *Woody Oriental / Oriental Boisé* ●●●
1997 GFF UOMO *Aromatic / Fougère* ●
1999 PONTACCIO 21 *Dry Woods / Chypre Cuir* ●●

GIAN MARCO VENTURI
1999 GMV DONNA *Floral Oriental / Fleuri Oriental* ●●
1997 GMV UOMO *Aromatic / Fougère* ●
1998 GMV ENERGY *Aromatic / Fougère* ●

GIGLI → ROMEO GIGLI

GILLES CANTUEL
1985 CRÉATURE *Soft Oriental / Oriental Doux* ●●●
1992 FOLIE DE CRÉATURE *Floral / Florale* ●●●●
1994 MOOVING *Aromatic / Fougère* ●●●
1996 EAU DE MOOVING *Floral / Florale* ●●
1997 CRÉATURE D'ANGES *Floral / Florale* ●●
1998 ARSENAL FOR WOMAN *Floral Oriental / Fleuri Oriental* ●●
1999 BABYLON *Soft Floral / Fleuri Aldéhydé* ●●●●
1999 FLOWERS *Floral / Florale* ●
1996 ARSENAL *Woody Oriental / Oriental Boisé* ●

GIORGIO ARMANI
1982 ARMANI *Mossy Woods / Chypre Boisé* ●
1992 GIÒ *Floral / Florale* ●●●●
1995 ACQUA DI GIÒ *Floral / Florale* ●
1998 EMPORIO ARMANI SHE / ELLE *Floral Oriental / Fleuri Oriental* ●●●
1999 MANIA *Woody Oriental / Oriental Boisé* ●●●
1984 ARMANI POUR HOMME *Citrus / Hespéridé* ●●●●
1996 ACQUA DI GIÒ POUR HOMME *Water / Marine* ●●
1998 EMPORIO ARMANI HE / LUI *Mossy Woods / Chypre Boisé* ●●

GIORGIO BEVERLY HILLS
1981 GIORGIO *Floral / Florale* ●●
1989 RED *Mossy Woods / Chypre Boisé* ●●
1992 WINGS *Floral / Florale* ●●●●
1996 GIORGIO AIRE* *Soft Floral / Fleuri Aldéhydé* ●
1996 OCEAN DREAM *Floral / Florale* ●
1996 RED 2* *Floral Oriental / Fleuri Oriental* ●
1998 GIORGIO HOLIDAY ⓛ *Floral / Florale* ●●
1999 G *Soft Floral / Fleuri Aldéhydé* ●
1984 GIORGIO MEN* *Mossy Woods / Chypre Boisé* ●●●●
1990 RED FOR MEN *Aromatic / Fougère* ●●
1994 WINGS FOR MEN *Aromatic / Fougère* ●

GIVENCHY
1957 LE DE *Floral / Florale* ●●●
1957 L'INTERDIT *Soft Floral / Fleuri Aldéhydé* ●●●
1970 GIVENCHY III *Mossy Woods / Chypre Boisé* ●
1980 EAU DE GIVENCHY *Floral / Florale* ●
1984 YSATIS *Woody Oriental / Oriental Boisé* ●
1991 AMARIGE *Floral Oriental / Fleuri Oriental* ●●
1994 FLEUR D'INTERDIT *Floral / Florale* ●
1996 ORGANZA *Woody Oriental / Oriental Boisé* ●●
1998 EXTRAVAGANCE D'AMARIGE *Floral / Florale* ●
1999 ORGANZA INDÉCENCE *Woody Oriental / Oriental Boisé* ●●●●
1959 MONSIEUR DE GIVENCHY *Citrus / Hespéridé* ●●●
1974 GIVENCHY GENTLEMAN *Mossy Woods / Chypre Boisé* ●●●●
1986 XERYUS *Aromatic / Fougère* ●●
1993 INSENSÉ *Floral / Florale* ●●
1994 INSENSÉ ULTRAMARINE *Aromatic / Fougère* ●
1995 XERYUS ROUGE *Woody Oriental / Oriental Boisé* ●●
1998 π *Woody Oriental / Oriental Boisé* ●●●

GLOBE
1998 MYSTERY AUSTRALIA WOMAN *Woody Oriental / Oriental Boisé* ●
1998 MYSTERY AUSTRALIA MAN *Aromatic / Fougère* ●

GLORIA VANDERBILT
1982 VANDERBILT *Floral Oriental / Fleuri Oriental* ●●●
1994 V *Soft Floral / Fleuri Aldéhydé* ●●
1996 HONEYMOON *Woody Oriental / Oriental Boisé* ●●
1999 RÊVERIE *Floral Oriental / Fleuri Oriental* ●●●

GOLF ELEGANCE
1990 MATCH PLAY *Aromatic / Fougère* ●

GOUTAL → ANNICK GOUTAL

GRANITE
1992 GRANITE ORIGINAL *Aromatic / Fougère* ●
1996 GRANITE BLUE *Aromatic / Fougère* ●

GRÈS
1959 CABOCHARD *Dry Woods / Chypre Cuir* ●●●
1990 CABOTINE DE GRÈS *Floral / Florale* ●●
1996 PASTEL DE CABOTINE *Floral / Florale* ●
1997 FOLIE DOUCE *Floral / Florale* ●●
1999 GRAIN DE FOLIE *Green / Vert* ●●
1996 HOMME DE GRÈS *Dry Woods / Chypre Cuir* ●●●●

GUCCI
1975 GUCCI N° 1* *Soft Floral / Fleuri Aldéhydé* ●●
1982/93 EAU DE GUCCI* *Floral / Florale* ●●
1985 GUCCI N° 3* *Mossy Woods / Chypre Boisé* ●●
1991 L'ARTE DI GUCCI* *Mossy Woods / Chypre Boisé* ●●●
1995 ACCENTI *Floral Oriental / Fleuri Oriental* ●
1997 ENVY *Floral / Florale* ●
1999 GUCCI RUSH *Woody Oriental / Oriental Boisé* ●●
1988 GUCCI NOBILE* *Aromatic / Fougère* ●●
1998 ENVY FOR MEN *Woody Oriental / Oriental Boisé* ●

GUÉPARD
1997 GUÉPARD *Mossy Woods / Chypre Boisé* ●●●
1998 GUÉPARD HOMME *Mossy Woods / Chypre Boisé* ●●

GUERLAIN
1853 EAU IMPÉRIALE ♂ *Citrus / Hespéridé* ●●●
1889 JICKY ♂ *Aromatic / Fougère* ●●●
1894 EAU DU COQ ♂ *Citrus / Hespéridé* ●●●
1906 APRÈS L'ONDÉE *Floral Oriental / Fleuri Oriental* ●
1912 L'HEURE BLEUE *Floral Oriental / Fleuri Oriental* ●●●
1919 MITSOUKO *Mossy Woods / Chypre Boisé* ●●●
1920 EAU DE FLEURS DE CÉDRAT ♂ *Citrus / Hespéridé* ●●●
1925 SHALIMAR *Oriental / Oriental* ●●●●
1929 LIÙ *Soft Floral / Fleuri Aldéhydé* ●●●
1933 VOL DE NUIT *Woody Oriental / Oriental Boisé* ●●
1962 CHANT D'ARÔMES *Mossy Woods / Chypre Boisé* ●●
1969 CHAMADE *Floral Oriental / Fleuri Oriental* ●●
1974 EAU DE GUERLAIN ♂ *Citrus / Hespéridé* ●●●
1975 PARURE *Mossy Woods / Chypre Boisé* ●●●
1979 NAHÉMA *Floral Oriental / Fleuri Oriental* ●●●●
1983 JARDINS DE BAGATELLE *Floral / Florale* ●●●●
1989 SAMSARA *Woody Oriental / Oriental Boisé* ●●●

1995 UN AIR DE SAMSARA *Woody Oriental / Oriental Boisé* ●
1904/96/98 CHAMPS-ELYSÉES *Floral / Florale* ●
1999 GUET-APENS Ⓛ *Woody Oriental / Oriental Boisé* ●
1999 HERBA FRESCA ♂ *Green / Vert* ●●
1999 LAVANDE VELOURS ♂ *Floral / Florale* ●●●
1999 PAMPLELUNE ♂ *Citrus / Hespéridé* ●●●●
1999 ROSA MAGNIFICA *Floral / Florale* ●●
1999 YLANG & VANILLE *Floral / Florale* ●●●
1904 MOUCHOIR DE MONSIEUR *Aromatic / Fougère* ●●●
1959 VETIVER *Mossy Woods / Chypre Boisé* ●●●
1965 HABIT ROUGE *Oriental / Oriental* ●●●
1985 DERBY *Dry Woods / Chypre Cuir* ●●●●
1992 HÉRITAGE *Woody Oriental / Oriental Boisé* ●●
1998 CORIOLAN *Mossy Woods / Chypre Boisé* ●●
1999 CHAMADE POUR HOMME Ⓛ *Mossy Woods / Chypre Boisé* ●

GUY LAROCHE
1966 FIDJI *Floral / Florale* ●
1977 J'AI OSÉ *Soft Oriental / Oriental Doux* ●●●
1982 DRAKKAR NOIR *Aromatic / Fougère* ●●
1993 HORIZON *Aromatic / Fougère* ●
1999 DRAKKAR DYNAMIK *Aromatic / Fougère* ●

HALSTON
1975 HALSTON *Mossy Woods / Chypre Boisé* ●
1993 CATALYST *Floral / Florale* ●
1998 SHEER HALSTON *Floral Oriental / Fleuri Oriental* ●
1976 HALSTON 1-12 *Green / Vert* ●●●
1976 HALSTON Z-14 *Mossy Woods / Chypre Boisé* ●●
1994 CATALYST FOR MEN *Woody Oriental / Oriental Boisé* ●●
1998 HALSTON Z *Mossy Woods / Chypre Boisé* ●●

HANAE MORI
1968/95 HANAE MORI *Woody Oriental / Oriental Boisé* ●●
1998 HANAE MORI HAUTE COUTURE *Soft Floral / Fleuri Aldéhydé* ●
1997 H.M. *Woody Oriental / Oriental Boisé* ●

HARLEY-DAVIDSON
1999 DESTINY WOMAN *Woody Oriental / Oriental Boisé* ●
1994 LEGENDARY *Dry Woods / Chypre Cuir* ●●
1999 DESTINY *Mossy Woods / Chypre Boisé* ●●●

H&BF - HEALTH & BEAUTY FOCUS
1975 BLASÉ *Soft Floral / Fleuri Aldéhydé* ●●●●
1983 LE JARDIN *Floral / Florale* ●
1987 LE JARDIN D'AMOUR *Floral Oriental / Fleuri Oriental* ●●●●
1976 MANDATE *Aromatic / Fougère* ●●
1988 RAPPORT *Aromatic / Fougère* ●●

HECHTER → DANIEL HECHTER

HENRI D'ORLÉANS
1997 ROYALISSIME *Soft Floral / Fleuri Aldéhydé* ●●

HENRY DUNAY
1998 SABI *Green / Vert* ●●●●

HERMÈS
1951 EAU D'HERMÈS ♂ *Dry Woods / Chypre Cuir* ●●●
1961/92 CALÈCHE *Mossy Woods / Chypre Boisé* ●●●
1974/89 AMAZONE *Floral / Florale* ●●
1979 EAU D'ORANGE VERTE ♂ *Citrus / Hespéridé* ●●●●
1984 PARFUM D'HERMÈS *Soft Oriental / Oriental Doux* ●●
1995 24, FAUBOURG *Floral / Florale* ●●
1999 HIRIS *Floral / Florale* ●
1970 ÉQUIPAGE *Aromatic / Fougère* ●●●●
1986 BEL AMI *Dry Woods / Chypre Cuir* ●●●●
1998 ROCABAR *Dry Woods / Chypre Cuir* ●●●●

HERRERA → CAROLINA HERRERA

HERVÉ LÉGER
1999 HERVÉ LÉGER *Floral Oriental / Fleuri Oriental* ●●●

HILFIGER → TOMMY HILFIGER

HOLZMAN & STEPHANIE
1987 JE T'AIME *Floral Oriental / Fleuri Oriental* ●●●
1987 MISUKI *Oriental / Oriental* ●●●
1989 LA PARISIENNE *Soft Floral / Fleuri Aldéhydé* ●●
1990 FASCINATION *Floral / Florale* ●●
2000 TRÈS CHIC *Soft Oriental / Oriental Doux* ●

HOPE DIAMOND COLLECTION
1999 FABLE *Woody Oriental / Oriental Boisé* ●●●

HOUBIGANT / CLAIRE
1912/87 QUELQUES FLEURS *Floral / Florale* ●●●
1988 DEMI-JOUR* *Soft Floral / Fleuri Aldéhydé* ●●●●
1996 QUELQUES VIOLETTES *Floral / Florale* ●●●●
1997 QUELQUES ROSES *Floral / Florale* ●●●
1882 FOUGÈRE ROYALE* *Aromatic / Fougère* ●●●
1991 DUC DE VERVINS *Aromatic / Fougère* ●●

HOUBIGANT / DANA → DANA

HUGO BOSS
1997 HUGO WOMAN *Floral / Florale* ●●
1985 BOSS NUMBER ONE *Aromatic / Fougère* ●●
1987 BOSS SPORT* *Aromatic / Fougère* ●●
1989 BOSS SPIRIT* *Dry Woods / Chypre Cuir* ●●
1993 ELEMENTS *Aromatic / Fougère* ●
1995 HUGO *Aromatic / Fougère* ●
1996 ELEMENTS AQUA *Aromatic / Fougère* ●●
1998 BOSS *Woody Oriental / Oriental Boisé* ●●
1999 HUGO DARK BLUE *Mossy Woods / Chypre Boisé* ●

ICEBERG
1989 ICEBERG *Floral / Florale* ●
1994 ICEBERG TWICE *Floral / Florale* ●
1997 ICEBERG UNIVERSE FEMME *Floral Oriental / Fleuri Oriental* ●●●
1998 ICEBERG TWICE ICE *Citrus / Hespéridé* ●●
1991 ICEBERG HOMME *Citrus / Hespéridé* ●●●●
1995 ICEBERG TWICE HOMME *Aromatic / Fougère* ●
1997 ICEBERG UNIVERSE HOMME *Woody Oriental / Oriental Boisé* ●

IMPERIALE
1983 MING *Woody Oriental / Oriental Boisé* ●●●
1989 SHANGRI-LA *Floral / Florale* ●●

INÈS DE LA FRESSANGE
1999 INÈS DE LA FRESSANGE *Floral / Fleuri* ●

INFINITIF
1994 INFINITIF *Mossy Woods / Chypre Boisé* ●●●
1996 EAU D'INFINITIF *Floral / Florale* ●●

INNOXA
1970 GINGHAM *Aromatic / Fougère* ●●●

ISSEY MIYAKE
1992 L'EAU D'ISSEY *Water / Marine* ●●
1998 LE FEU D'ISSEY *Woody Oriental / Oriental Boisé* ●●●
1994 L'EAU D'ISSEY POUR HOMME *Water / Marine* ●●●

ITALART
1989 MASERATI *Aromatic / Fougère* ●●

IVANA TRUMP
1995 IVANA *Floral / Florale* ●●●●

J. DEL POZO
1992 DUENDE *Water / Marine* ●
1995 ESENCIA DE DUENDE *Floral / Florale* ●
1997 HALLOWEEN *Floral / Florale* ●●
1994 QUASAR *Aromatic / Fougère* ●
1999 ADVENTURE QUASAR *Aromatic / Fougère* ●

J FRAGRANCES
1997 PERSUASION *Floral / Florale* ●●

JACOMO
1978 SILENCES *Green / Vert* ●●●●

1985 COEUR DE PARFUM* *Dry Woods / Chypre Cuir* ●●
1991 ANTHRACITE *Floral Oriental / Fleuri Oriental* ●
1996 PERLE DE SILENCES *Soft Oriental / Oriental Doux* ●
1998 PARADOX *Floral Oriental / Fleuri Oriental* ●
1980 JACOMO DE JACOMO *Woody Oriental / Oriental Boisé* ●●
1991 ANTHRACITE POUR L'HOMME *Aromatic / Fougère* ●●
1996 AMBRO DE JACOMO *Woody Oriental / Oriental Boisé* ●●●
1999 PARADOX FOR MEN *Woody Oriental / Oriental Boisé* ●

JACLYN SMITH
1989 CALIFORNIA *Soft Floral / Fleuri Aldéhydé* ●●●●
1990 CALIFORNIA FOR MEN *Aromatic / Fougère* ●●

JACQUES BOGART
1975 BOGART *Aromatic / Fougère* ●●
1980 ONE MAN SHOW *Dry Woods / Chypre Cuir* ●●●●
1988 FURYO* *Woody Oriental / Oriental Boisé* ●●●●
1992 WITNESS* *Woody Oriental / Oriental Boisé* ●●
1993 EAU FRESH *Aromatic / Fougère* ●
1998 FORCE MAJEURE *Woody Oriental / Oriental Boisé* ●●

JACQUES FATH
1953/93 FATH DE FATH *Oriental / Oriental* ●●
1996 EAU DE FATH *Floral / Florale* ●
1999 YIN *Floral / Florale* ●●
1947/67/93 GREEN WATER *Citrus / Hespéridé* ●●
1998 POUR L'HOMME *Woody Oriental / Oriental Boisé* ●●
1999 YANG *Woody Oriental / Oriental Boisé* ●

JACQUES SAINT PRÈS
1983 INDRA *Floral / Florale* ●

JAGUAR
1993 MISS JAGUAR *Floral / Florale* ●●
1998 ESSENTIALLY JAGUAR *Floral Oriental / Fleuri Oriental* ●●
1988 JAGUAR *Aromatic / Fougère* ●●●●
1995 JAGUAR MARK II *Woody Oriental / Oriental Boisé* ●●
1998 JAGUAR SPECIAL EDITION *Aromatic / Fougère* ●

JAMES BOND
1997 BOND *Oriental / Oriental* ●

JAN MORAN
1996 FABULOUS *Floral Oriental / Fleuri Oriental* ●●●

JEAN BARTHET
1988 BIBI *Woody Oriental / Oriental Boisé* ●

JEAN-CHARLES BROSSEAU
1981 OMBRE ROSE *Floral Oriental / Fleuri Oriental* ●●●●
1987 OMBRE BLEUE* *Floral / Florale* ●●●●
1994 OMBRE D'OR* *Soft Floral / Fleuri Aldéhydé* ●
1997 OMBRE ROSE FRAÎCHE *Floral / Florale* ●

JEAN-CLAUDE JITROIS
1989 JITROIS *Dry Woods / Chypre Cuir* ●●

JEAN COUTURIER
1973 CORIANDRE *Mossy Woods / Chypre Boisé* ●●●●
1983 KÉORA *Oriental / Oriental* ●●●●
1996 EAU DE CORIANDRE *Floral / Florale* ●
1997 MARJOLAINE *Floral / Florale* ●●

JEAN D'ALBRET
1947 ÉCUSSON *Soft Floral / Fleuri Aldéhydé* ●●●
1961/96 MESSIRE *Citrus / Hespéridé* ●●●

JEAN DESPREZ
1962/95 BAL À VERSAILLES *Floral Oriental / Fleuri Oriental* ●●●
1989 REVOLUTION À VERSAILLES* *Floral Oriental / Fleuri Oriental* ●●
1980 VERSAILLES *Oriental / Oriental* ●●

JEAN-JACQUES DIENER
1998 JACQUELINE *Oriental / Oriental* ●●

JEAN-LOUIS SCHERRER
1979 JEAN-LOUIS SCHERRER *Green / Vert* ●●●●

1986 SCHERRER 2 *Floral Oriental / Fleuri Oriental* ●●
1994 NUITS INDIENNES *Oriental / Oriental* ●●●

JEAN PAUL GAULTIER
1993 JEAN PAUL GAULTIER *Floral Oriental / Fleuri Oriental* ●●
1999 FRAGILE *Floral / Florale* ●●●●
1995 LE MÂLE *Woody Oriental / Oriental Boisé* ●●

JEAN PATOU
1925 ADIEU SAGESSE *Floral / Florale* ●●
1925 AMOUR AMOUR *Floral / Florale* ●●●●
1925 QUE SAIS-JE? *Mossy Woods / Chypre Boisé* ●●●
1927 CHALDÉE *Floral Oriental / Fleuri Oriental* ●●●
1929 MOMENT SUPRÊME *Floral / Florale* ●●●●
1930 COCKTAIL *Mossy Woods / Chypre Boisé* ●
1930 JOY *Floral / Florale* ●●●
1933 DIVINE FOLIE *Floral Oriental / Fleuri Oriental* ●●●
1935 NORMANDIE *Soft Oriental / Oriental Doux* ●●●
1936 VACANCES *Green / Vert* ●●●
1938 COLONY *Mossy Woods / Chypre Boisé* ●●
1946 L'HEURE ATTENDUE *Woody Oriental / Oriental Boisé* ●●●
1964 CÂLINE *Soft Floral / Fleuri Aldéhydé* ●●
1972 1000 *Floral / Florale* ●●●●
1976 EAU DE PATOU *Citrus / Hespéridé* ●●●
1987 MA LIBERTÉ* *Aromatic / Fougère* ●●●
1992 SUBLIME *Soft Oriental / Oriental Doux* ●●●
1998 PATOU FOR EVER *Floral / Florale* ●●
1998 UN AMOUR DE PATOU *Floral / Florale* ●
1980 PATOU POUR HOMME *Woody Oriental / Oriental Boisé* ●●●
1994 PATOU POUR HOMME PRIVÉ *Aromatic / Fougère* ●●●
1995 VOYAGEUR *Mossy Woods / Chypre Boisé* ●

JESSICA McCLINTOCK
1987 JESSICA McCLINTOCK *Floral / Florale* ●
1995 JESS *Floral / Florale* ●●●●
1992 SCOTT McCLINTOCK *Soft Oriental / Oriental Doux* ●

JIL SANDER
1980 JIL SANDER WOMAN PURE* *Soft Floral / Fleuri Aldéhydé* ●
1981 JIL SANDER BATH & BEAUTY *Mossy Woods / Chypre Boisé* ●●●
1982 JIL SANDER WOMAN II* *Mossy Woods / Chypre Boisé* ●●
1986 JIL SANDER WOMAN III *Dry Woods / Chypre Cuir* ●●
1989 JIL SANDER SUN *Floral Oriental / Fleuri Oriental* ●●●
1990 JIL SANDER N° 4 *Floral Oriental / Fleuri Oriental* ●
1997 JIL *Woody Oriental / Oriental Boisé* ●
1981 JIL SANDER MAN PURE *Dry Woods / Chypre Cuir* ●●●●
1987 JIL SANDER MAN III* *Aromatic / Fougère* ●●
1989 JIL SANDER FEELING MAN *Soft Oriental / Oriental Doux* ●
1993 BACKGROUND *Woody Oriental / Oriental Boisé* ●●
1999 SANDER FOR MEN *Aromatic / Fougère* ●●

JIN ABE
1998 JIN ABE *Floral Oriental / Fleuri Oriental* ●●

JIVAGO
1994 JIVAGO 24k WOMEN *Floral / Florale* ●●●●
1998 JIVAGO 7 NOTES *Floral Oriental / Fleuri Oriental* ●●
1999 MILLENNIUM HOPE WOMAN *Floral / Florale* ●●
1995 JIVAGO 24k MEN *Aromatic / Fougère* ●
1998 JIVAGO 7 ELEMENTS *Woody Oriental / Oriental Boisé* ●●
1999 MILLENNIUM HOPE MAN *Aromatic / Fougère* ●

JO MALONE
1990 NUTMEG & GINGER ♂ *Woody Oriental / Oriental Boisé* ●●
1991 LIME, BASIL & MANDARIN ♂ *Citrus / Hespéridé* ●●●●
1991 TUBEROSE *Floral / Florale* ●●●●
1992 GRAPEFRUIT ♂ *Citrus / Hespéridé* ●●
1995 AMBER & LAVENDER ♂ *Woody Oriental / Oriental Boisé* ●●●
1995 FLEURS DE LA FORÊT *Mossy Woods / Chypre Boisé* ●●●
1995 FRENCH LIME BLOSSOM *Floral / Florale* ●
1995 GARDENIA *Floral / Florale* ●●
1995 VERBENAS OF PROVENCE ♂ *Citrus / Hespéridé* ●●●
1995 VETYVER ♂ *Mossy Woods / Chypre Boisé* ●●
1995 WILD MUGUET *Floral / Florale* ●
1996 HONEYSUCKLE & JASMINE *Floral / Florale* ●●
1996 RED ROSES *Floral / Florale* ●●●

JONES NEW YORK
1996 JONES NEW YORK   *Green / Vert* ●●

JOOP!
1987 JOOP!   *Woody Oriental / Oriental Boisé* ●●●●
1988 JOOP! LE BAIN   *Floral Oriental / Fleuri Oriental* ●●●●
1990 JOOP! NUIT D'ÉTÉ   *Woody Oriental / Oriental Boisé* ●●●
1991 JOOP! BERLIN   *Soft Floral / Fleuri Aldéhydé* ●
1996 ALL ABOUT EVE   *Woody Oriental / Oriental Boisé* ●●
1999 ROCOCO   *Woody Oriental / Oriental Boisé* ●●●
1989 JOOP! HOMME   *Woody Oriental / Oriental Boisé* ●●●
1992 NIGHTFLIGHT   *Aromatic / Fougère* ●
1997 WHAT ABOUT ADAM   *Aromatic / Fougère* ●

JOSEPH
1997 JOSEPH DE JOUR   *Soft Floral / Fleuri Aldéhydé* ●

JOURDAN → CHARLES JOURDAN

JOVAN
1972 JOVAN MUSK   *Soft Floral / Fleuri Aldéhydé* ●●●●
1976 WOMAN*   *Woody Oriental / Oriental Boisé* ●●●
1985 JOVAN EVENING MUSK*   *Soft Floral / Fleuri Aldéhydé* ●●●
1986 ISLAND GARDENIA   *Floral / Florale* ●●
1992 JOVAN WHITE MUSK   *Soft Oriental / Oriental Doux* ●
1996 JOVAN FRESH MUSK   *Floral / Florale* ●
1973 JOVAN MUSK FOR MEN   *Soft Floral / Fleuri Aldéhydé* ●●●●
1975 MONSIEUR JOVAN*   *Dry Woods / Chypre Cuir* ●●●●
1976 SEX APPEAL FOR MEN*   *Woody Oriental / Oriental Boisé* ●●●
1985 JOVAN EVENING MUSK FOR MEN*   *Soft Oriental / Oriental Doux* ●●
1992 JOVAN WHITE MUSK FOR MEN   *Woody Oriental / Oriental Boisé* ●
1998 GINSENG N.R.G   *Woody Oriental / Oriental Boisé* ●●

JULIO IGLESIAS
1989 ONLY   *Woody Oriental / Oriental Boisé* ●●●
1994 ONLY CRAZY   *Floral Oriental / Fleuri Oriental* ●●●●
1991 ONLY FOR MEN   *Aromatic / Fougère* ●●●

JUVENA
1994 DISCOVER   *Aromatic / Fougère* ●●

KARE
1994 EAU DE MURANO   *Floral / Florale* ●●●

KARL MORAN
1997 STREET GAMES   *Aromatic / Fougère* ●

KENZO
1988 KENZO   *Floral / Florale* ●●
1993 PARFUM D'ÉTÉ   *Floral / Florale* ●
1994 KASHÂYA   *Floral Oriental / Fleuri Oriental* ●
1996 L'EAU PAR KENZO   *Floral / Florale* ●
1996 JUNGLE: L'ÉLÉPHANT   *Soft Oriental / Oriental Doux* ●●●
1997 JUNGLE: LE TIGRE   *Floral Oriental / Fleuri Oriental* ●
1997 LE MONDE EST BEAU   *Floral / Florale* ●
1991 KENZO POUR HOMME   *Water / Marine* ●
1998 JUNGLE POUR HOMME   *Woody Oriental / Oriental Boisé* ●●
1999 L'EAU PAR KENZO POUR HOMME   *Citrus / Hespéridé* ●●

KERN → OTTO KERN

KESLING
1991 BE BOP   *Floral / Florale* ●●
1993 MISS BE BOP   *Floral / Florale* ●●●●
1994 FORMIDABLE   *Floral Oriental / Fleuri Oriental* ●●●
1997 C'EST MAGIQUE   *Floral / Florale* ●●
1997 SINAÏ   *Floral Oriental / Fleuri Oriental* ●
1998 ROUGE FORMIDABLE   *Soft Floral / Fleuri Aldéhydé* ●●
1992 BE BOP POUR HOMME   *Aromatic / Fougère* ●●
1995 BE BOP MAN   *Dry Woods / Chypre Cuir* ●
1995 FORMIDABLE HOMME   *Aromatic / Fougère* ●●
1997 C'EST MAGIQUE HOMME   *Aromatic / Fougère* ●●
1998 BLEU FORMIDABLE   *Aromatic / Fougère* ●

KIRI TE KANAWA
1999 KIRI   *Woody Oriental / Oriental Boisé* ●●●

KITON → PALLADIO
KLEIN → CALVIN KLEIN

KNIZE
1924 KNIZE TEN   *Dry Woods / Chypre Cuir* ●●●

KOOKAÏ
1993 KOOKAÏ OUI-NON   *Floral / Florale* ●●
1996 L'EAU DE KOOKAÏ   *Citrus / Hespéridé* ●

KRAFT INTERNATIONAL
1998 REBEL ... JAMES DEAN   *Aromatic / Fougère* ●

KRISTEL SAINT MARTIN
1995 PARFUM D'OR   *Mossy Woods / Chypre Boisé* ●●
1996 DIAMANT D'OR   *Floral Oriental / Fleuri Oriental* ●●
1996 RUBIS D'OR   *Floral Oriental / Fleuri Oriental* ●
1995 PARFUM D'HOMME   *Aromatic / Fougère* ●●

KRIZIA
1981 K de KRIZIA   *Soft Floral / Fleuri Aldéhydé* ●●
1986 TEATRO ALLA SCALA*   *Soft Oriental / Oriental Doux* ●●●
1989 MOODS   *Floral / Florale* ●●
1991 KRAZY KRIZIA*   *Oriental / Oriental* ●●
1995 FIORI DI KRIZIA   *Floral / Florale* ●
1998 SPAZIO KRIZIA DONNA   *Floral Oriental / Fleuri Oriental* ●●●
1999 EASY KRIZIA   *Mossy Woods / Chypre Boisé* ●
1984 KRIZIA UOMO   *Dry Woods / Chypre Cuir* ●●●●
1989 MOODS UOMO   *Woody Oriental / Oriental Boisé* ●●●
1993 SPAZIO KRIZIA UOMO   *Dry Woods / Chypre Cuir* ●

L'ARTISAN PARFUMEUR
1978 L'EAU D'AMBRE   *Oriental / Oriental* ●●●
1978 MÛRE ET MUSC   *Citrus / Hespéridé* ●●●●
1978 VANILIA   *Oriental / Oriental* ●
1992 MIMOSA POUR MOI   *Floral / Florale* ●●
1993 L'EAU DE L'ARTISAN ♂   *Citrus / Hespéridé* ●●●
1993 MÛRE ET MUSC EXTRÊME   *Citrus / Hespéridé* ●●●●
1993 VOLEUR DE ROSES ♂   *Dry Woods / Chypre Cuir* ●
1994 BOUTON D'OR   *Floral / Florale* ●
1994 PREMIER FIGUIER   *Mossy Woods / Chypre Boisé* ●
1996 DRÔLE DE ROSE   *Soft Floral / Fleuri Aldéhydé* ●●
1996 THÉ POUR UN ÉTÉ ♂   *Citrus / Hespéridé* ●
1999 DZING!   *Dry Woods / Chypre Cuir* ●●●●
1999 LA CHASSE AUX PAPILLONS   *Floral / Florale* ●●
1999 PASSAGE D'ENFER   *Dry Woods / Chypre Cuir* ●●
1978 SANTAL   *Dry Woods / Chypre Cuir* ●●●
1978 VETIVER   *Dry Woods / Chypre Cuir* ●
1982 EAU DU NAVIGATEUR   *Dry Woods / Chypre Cuir* ●●●●
1997 MÉCHANT LOUP   *Dry Woods / Chypre Cuir* ●●●●

L'OCCITANE
1996/99 CANNELLE ORANGE ♂   *Citrus / Hespéridé* ●
1996/99 FLEUR DE LOTUS   *Water / Marine* ●●
1999 CASSISSIER   *Floral / Florale* ●
1999 CÉDRAT POMELO ♂   *Citrus / Hespéridé* ●●
1999 FEUILLE D'HERBE FLORALE FRUITÉE   *Mossy Woods / Chypre Boisé* ●
1999 FEUILLE D'HERBE FRAÎCHE EPICÉE   *Woody Oriental / Oriental Boisé* ●●●●
1999 FEUILLE D'HERBE FRAÎCHE HERBACÉE   *Green / Vert* ●
1999 FEUILLE DE VERVEINE ♂   *Citrus / Hespéridé* ●
1999 JASMIN MANDARINE   *Soft Floral / Fleuri Aldéhydé* ●●●
1999 MENTHE FROISSÉE   *Green / Vert* ●
1999 ROSE NÉROLI   *Floral / Florale* ●●●
1999 THÉ VERT ♂   *Citrus / Hespéridé* ●●
1999 TILLEUL CHÈVREFEUILLE   *Soft Floral / Fleuri Aldéhydé* ●
1999 VANILLE ♂   *Soft Oriental / Oriental Doux* ●
1990 EAU DE COLOGNE EXTRA FINE   *Citrus / Hespéridé* ●●●●
1991 EAU DES 4 VOLEURS   *Aromatic / Fougère* ●
1994 EAU DU CONTADOUR   *Aromatic / Fougère* ●●●
1999 EAU DU BADIAN   *Citrus / Hespéridé* ●●
1999 LAVANDE   *Aromatic / Fougère* ●●●●

LA PERLA
1987 LA PERLA   *Dry Woods / Chypre Cuir* ●●●
1995 IO   *Mossy Woods / Chypre Boisé* ●●
1998 PARFUM PRIVÉ   *Mossy Woods / Chypre Boisé* ●●●
1991 GRIGIO PERLA   *Aromatic / Fougère* ●

LA PRAIRIE
1993 LA PRAIRIE   *Floral / Florale* ●●●●

LE GALION
1937 SORTILÈGE*   *Soft Floral / Fleuri Aldéhydé* ●●●●

LE JARDIN RETROUVÉ
1977 CHÈVREFEUILLE   *Floral / Florale* ●●
1977 JASMIN   *Floral / Florale* ●●●
1978 VERVEINE ♂   *Citrus / Hespéridé* ●●●
1980 TUBÉREUSE   *Floral / Florale* ●●●●
1989 LYS   *Floral / Florale* ●●
1989 ROSE THÉ   *Floral / Florale* ●●●
1977 EAU DE CUIR DE RUSSIE   *Dry Woods / Chypre Cuir* ●●
1977 EAU DE SANDALWOOD   *Woody Oriental / Oriental Boisé* ●●●
1977 EAU DE VÉTYVER   *Mossy Woods / Chypre Boisé* ●●
1980 EAU POUR HOMME   *Aromatic / Fougère* ●●

LES COPAINS
1988/97 LES COPAINS   *Floral Oriental / Fleuri Oriental* ●
1999 EAU MARINE   *Floral / Florale* ●
1998 LES COPAINS L'HOMME   *Mossy Woods / Chypre Boisé* ●●

LES FLORALIES
1994 SENSES   *Floral / Florale* ●●●●
1995 ZOE   *Floral Oriental / Fleuri Oriental* ●
1993 INSTINCT   *Aromatic / Fougère* ●●

LES SENTEURS
1991 APOGÉE   *Mossy Woods / Chypre Boisé* ●●●

LACOSTE
1999 LACOSTE FOR WOMEN   *Floral / Florale* ●
1984 LACOSTE   *Aromatic / Fougère* ●●
1991 LAND   *Woody Oriental / Oriental Boisé* ●
1996 BOOSTER   *Citrus / Hespéridé* ●●
1999 LACOSTE 2000   *Aromatic / Fougère* ●

LAGERFELD
1982 KL   *Soft Oriental / Oriental Doux* ●
1994 SUN MOON STARS   *Floral Oriental / Fleuri Oriental* ●
1978 LAGERFELD   *Woody Oriental / Oriental Boisé* ●●●
1986 KL HOMME*   *Oriental / Oriental* ●●●
1990 PHOTO   *Aromatic / Fougère* ●●
1997 JAKO   *Woody Oriental / Oriental Boisé* ●●

LALIQUE
1992 LALIQUE   *Floral Oriental / Fleuri Oriental* ●●
1995 NILANG   *Floral Oriental / Fleuri Oriental* ●
1997 CLAIRE DE NILANG   *Floral / Florale* ●
1999 LE BAISER   *Floral / Florale* ●●
1997 LALIQUE POUR HOMME   *Woody Oriental / Oriental Boisé* ●●

LANCASTER
1977 EAU DE LANCASTER   *Citrus / Hespéridé* ●●●
1987 LANCASTER BODY & BATH   *Oriental / Oriental* ●
1997 SUNWATER   *Floral / Florale* ●

LANCETTI
1995 LANCETTI MADAME   *Mossy Woods / Chypre Boisé* ●●●
1997 LANCETTI EAU DE JOIE   *Floral / Florale* ●●
1998 LANCETTI   *Soft Floral / Fleuri Aldéhydé* ●●●
1995 LANCETTI MONSIEUR   *Dry Woods / Chypre Cuir* ●●●
1999 LANCETTI POUR HOMME   *Aromatic / Fougère* ●●

LANCÔME
1967 CLIMAT   *Soft Floral / Fleuri Aldéhydé* ●●●●
1969 Ô de LANCÔME   *Citrus / Hespéridé* ●●●
1978 MAGIE NOIRE   *Woody Oriental / Oriental Boisé* ●●
1990 TRÉSOR   *Floral Oriental / Fleuri Oriental* ●●
1995 POÊME   *Floral Oriental / Fleuri Oriental* ●●●
1998 Ô OUI   *Floral / Florale* ●
1999 2000 ET UNE RÔSE ⓛ   *Floral / Florale* ●●●
1999 AROMATONIC   *Citrus / Hespéridé* ●
1982 TROPHÈE LANCÔME   *Citrus / Hespéridé* ●●●●
1996 Ô POUR HOMME   *Green / Vert* ●●

LANVIN
1927/93 ARPÈGE   *Soft Floral / Fleuri Aldéhydé* ●●●●
1997 LANVIN L'HOMME   *Aromatic / Fougère* ●

LAPIDUS → TED LAPIDUS
LAUDER → ESTÉE LAUDER

LAURA ASHLEY
1989 LAURA ASHLEY Nº 1   *Soft Floral / Fleuri Aldéhydé* ●
1991 DILYS   *Floral / Florale* ●●●●
1995 L'EAU   *Citrus / Hespéridé* ●●

LAURA BIAGIOTTI
1988 ROMA   *Oriental / Oriental* ●●
1992 VENEZIA   *Woody Oriental / Oriental Boisé* ●●●
1994 LAURA   *Floral / Florale* ●
1995 VENEZIA PASTELLO*   *Soft Floral / Fleuri Aldéhydé* ●
1996 SOTTO VOCE   *Woody Oriental / Oriental Boisé* ●●●
1999 TEMPORE DONNA   *Woody Oriental / Oriental Boisé* ●●
1994 ROMA UOMO   *Woody Oriental / Oriental Boisé* ●●
1995 VENEZIA UOMO   *Woody Oriental / Oriental Boisé* ●●
1999 TEMPORE UOMO   *Woody Oriental / Oriental Boisé* ●

LAUREN → RALPH LAUREN

LENTHERIC / FFC
→ FINE FRAGRANCES & COSMETICS

LÉONARD
1970/93 FASHION   *Floral Oriental / Fleuri Oriental* ●●
1974 EAU FRAÎCHE   *Citrus / Hespéridé* ●●●
1977 TAMANGO   *Soft Floral / Fleuri Aldéhydé* ●●
1983 BALAHÉ   *Floral Oriental / Fleuri Oriental* ●●●
1989 LÉONARD DE LÉONARD*   *Soft Floral / Fleuri Aldéhydé* ●
1996 MISS BALAHÉ   *Floral / Florale* ●●
1998 FABULEUSE   *Floral / Florale* ●
1980 LÉONARD POUR HOMME*   *Dry Woods / Chypre Cuir* ●●●●
1992 MONSIEUR LÉONARD   *Aromatic / Fougère* ●●●●

LILIAN BARONY
1994 L'EAU LILIAN   *Water / Marine* ●●
1998 SUMMER SPLASH   *Citrus / Hespéridé* ●

LILLIE RUBIN
1992 LILLIE RUBIN   *Floral / Florale* ●

LIZ CLAIBORNE
1986 LIZ CLAIBORNE   *Floral / Florale* ●
1990 REALITIES*   *Floral / Florale* ●●
1993 VIVID   *Floral / Florale* ●●●●
1996 CURVE FOR WOMEN   *Floral / Florale* ●
1997 LIZSPORT   *Floral / Florale* ●
1999 CANDIE'S   *Floral / Florale* ●●●
1989 CLAIBORNE FOR MEN*   *Citrus / Hespéridé* ●
1996 CURVE FOR MEN   *Aromatic / Fougère* ●
1997 CLAIBORNE SPORT   *Aromatic / Fougère* ●
1999 CANDIE'S MEN   *Aromatic / Fougère* ●

LLEWELYN
1998 STARDUST   *Floral Oriental / Fleuri Oriental* ●●

LOEWE
1972/88 L de LOEWE   *Floral / Florale* ●●
1985 AIRE LOEWE   *Green / Vert* ●●●
1991 GALA LOEWE   *Floral Oriental / Fleuri Oriental* ●●
1994 AURA LOEWE   *Floral Oriental / Fleuri Oriental* ●
1996 GALA DE DIA   *Floral / Florale* ●
1974 LOEWE POUR HOMME   *Aromatic / Fougère* ●●
1987 ESENCIA LOEWE   *Dry Woods / Chypre Cuir* ●●

LOLITA LEMPICKA
1997 LOLITA LEMPICKA   *Woody Oriental / Oriental Boisé* ●

LOMANI
1996 NETWORK ♂   *Citrus / Hespéridé* ●
1996 SOLYTIS   *Floral Oriental / Fleuri Oriental* ●●
1998 CRUISER FOR WOMEN   *Floral / Florale* ●●●●

1999 DUÉ 2 DAY   *Floral / Florale* ●
1999 DUÉ 2 NIGHT   *Floral / Florale* ●●
1999 HIGH TECH WOMEN   *Floral / Florale* ●
1987 LOMANI   *Aromatic / Fougère* ●●
1993 EL PASO   *Aromatic / Fougère* ●●
1994 DEEP BLUE   *Aromatic / Fougère* ●
1998 CRUISER FOR MEN   *Aromatic / Fougère* ●●
1999 HIGH TECH MEN   *Mossy Woods / Chypre Boisé* ●●
1999 VOLCANO HOMME   *Aromatic / Fougère* ●

LORESTE
1993 LORESTE FEMME   *Floral Oriental / Fleuri Oriental* ●●
1997 BLUE DREAM   *Floral / Florale* ●●
1987 LORESTE   *Aromatic / Fougère* ●●

LORIS AZZARO
1975 AZZARO   *Mossy Woods / Chypre Boisé* ●●●
1984 AZZARO 9   *Floral / Florale* ●●●●
1993 OH LA LA   *Soft Oriental / Oriental Doux* ●●
1995 EAU BELLE   *Citrus / Hespéridé* ●
1999 AZZURA   *Floral / Florale* ●
1978 AZZARO POUR HOMME   *Aromatic / Fougère* ●
1989 ACTEUR   *Dry Woods / Chypre Cuir* ●●
1996 CHROME   *Citrus / Hespéridé* ●●

LOUIS FÉRAUD
1997 LOVE STORY   *Floral Oriental / Fleuri Oriental* ●●●●

LOUIS FRÈRES
1966 JUSTINE   *Soft Floral / Fleuri Aldéhydé* ●●●●

L.T. PIVER
1889 / 1926 RÊVE D'OR   *Soft Floral / Fleuri Aldéhydé* ●●●●
1905 / 91 FLORAMYE   *Mossy Woods / Chypre Boisé* ●●
1907 POMPEÏA   *Dry Woods / Chypre Cuir* ●●●
1939 CUIR DE RUSSIE ♂   *Dry Woods / Chypre Cuir* ●●●
1998 CLARTÉ   *Floral / Florale* ●●
1998 INCLINATION   *Floral / Florale* ●
1850 EAU DES PRINCES   *Citrus / Hespéridé* ●●●
1991 LAVANDE DES PRINCES   *Floral / Florale* ●●●●
1991 VÉTYVER   *Mossy Woods / Chypre Boisé* ●●●
1995 EAU POUR HOMME   *Citrus / Hespéridé* ●●●●

LUCKY BRAND
1997 LUCKY BRAND WOMEN'S   *Floral / Florale* ●
1997 LUCKY BRAND MEN'S   *Aromatic / Fougère* ●

LUCIANO SOPRANI
1994 SOPRANI 2   *Woody Oriental / Oriental Boisé* ●
1999 PEOPLE DONNA   *Floral / Florale* ●
1994 SOPRANI ACTIVE MAN   *Aromatic / Fougère* ●●
1999 PEOPLE UOMO   *Woody Oriental / Oriental Boisé* ●

LUCIEN LELONG
1935 / 97 INDISCRET   *Green / Vert* ●●
1999 LELONG POUR FEMME   *Woody Oriental / Oriental Boisé* ●●●

McEVOY → TRISH McEVOY

MAC
1999 ASPHALT FLOWER   *Floral / Florale* ●●●●
1999 HYPERSOUK   *Soft Oriental / Oriental Doux* ●●●
1999 SYNTHETIC NIRVANA   *Woody Oriental / Oriental Boisé* ●●

MACKIE → BOB MACKIE

MADELEINE DE RAUCH
1998 BELLE DE RAUCH   *Floral / Florale* ●●●
1998 MAN DE RAUCH   *Woody Oriental / Oriental Boisé* ●●●●

MADELEINE MONO
1978 MADELEINE   *Floral / Florale* ●●●●

MADELEINE VIONNET
1925 / 96 MADELEINE VIONNET   *Floral Oriental / Fleuri Oriental* ●●●
1998 MV   *Floral / Florale* ●

MAGIC HELVETIA
1994 LA BASE FOR HER   *Floral / Florale* ●●
1994 LA BASE FOR HIM   *Dry Woods / Chypre Cuir* ●●●●

MAÎTRE PARFUMEUR ET GANTIER
1988 AMBRE PRÉCIEUX ♂   *Oriental / Oriental* ●●●●
1988 EAU DE MÛRE   *Citrus / Hespéridé* ●●●
1988 EAU DU GANTIER ♂   *Citrus / Hespéridé* ●●●
1988 FLEUR D'IRIS   *Soft Floral / Fleuri Aldéhydé* ●●●
1988 FLEURS DES COMORES   *Mossy Woods / Chypre Boisé* ●●
1988 FRAÎCHE PASSIFLORE   *Citrus / Hespéridé* ●●
1988 FRAÎCHEUR MUSKISSIME ♂   *Citrus / Hespéridé* ●●●●
1988 FREEZIA D'OR   *Floral / Florale* ●●●●
1988 JARDIN BLANC   *Floral / Florale* ●●
1988 JASMIN   *Floral / Florale* ●●●
1988 OR DES INDES   *Oriental / Oriental* ●●●
1988 RACINE ♂   *Mossy Woods / Chypre Boisé* ●●
1988 ROSE MUSKISSIME   *Floral / Florale* ●●
1988 ROSE OPULENTE   *Floral / Florale* ●●●
1988 SANGUINE MUSKISSIME ♂   *Citrus / Hespéridé* ●
1988 SOIE ROUGE   *Dry Woods / Chypre Cuir* ●●
1988 TUBÉREUSE   *Floral / Florale* ●●●●
1988 VOCALISE   *Citrus / Hespéridé* ●●
1992 SECRETE DATURA   *Oriental / Oriental* ●●●●
1997 CAMÉLIA CHINOIS   *Green / Vert* ●●●●
1998 GRAIN DE PLAISIR ♂   *Mossy Woods / Chypre Boisé* ●
1988 EAU DES ÎLES   *Dry Woods / Chypre Cuir* ●●●●
1988 GARRIGUE   *Aromatic / Fougère* ●●
1988 IRIS BLEU GRIS   *Mossy Woods / Chypre Boisé* ●
1988 JARDIN DU NIL   *Floral / Florale* ●●
1988 PARFUM D'HABIT   *Dry Woods / Chypre Cuir* ●●●●
1988 ROUTE DU VÉTIVER   *Mossy Woods / Chypre Boisé* ●●●
1988 SANTAL NOBLE   *Mossy Woods / Chypre Boisé* ●●●●
1988 SECRET MÉLANGE   *Aromatic / Fougère* ●
1990 POUR LE JEUNE HOMME   *Citrus / Hespéridé* ●
1991 CENTAURE   *Aromatic / Fougère* ●●●
1994 FRAÎCHE BADIANE   *Mossy Woods / Chypre Boisé* ●●

MARBERT
1987 MARBERT WOMAN   *Oriental / Oriental* ●●●
1993 SCARF   *Woody Oriental / Oriental Boisé* ●●
1995 SUN SPIRIT*   *Floral / Florale* ●●
1996 SCARF TAORMINA   *Floral / Florale* ●●
1999 MARBERT WOMAN RED   *Floral / Florale* ●
1977 MARBERT MAN   *Aromatic / Fougère* ●●
1986 MARBERT GENTLEMAN*   *Mossy Woods / Chypre Boisé* ●●
1988 MARBERT HOMME*   *Dry Woods / Chypre Cuir* ●●
1989 MARBERT MAN PURE   *Mossy Woods / Chypre Boisé* ●
1997 TYCOON   *Woody Oriental / Oriental Boisé* ●●
1998 MARBERT MAN TOO   *Aromatic / Fougère* ●

MARC DE LA MORANDIÈRE
1987 / 94 BLEU DE CHINE   *Soft Oriental / Oriental Doux* ●●●●
1991 SISSI   *Floral / Florale* ●●●
1994 NUAGE D'OR   *Soft Floral / Fleuri Aldéhydé* ●●●●
1994 NUAGES D'EAU   *Floral / Florale* ●●
1994 THIARA   *Floral Oriental / Fleuri Oriental* ●●●
1996 MELODIE D'AMOUR   *Floral / Florale* ●
1999 AYAKO   *Oriental / Oriental* ●
1999 LA PLAGE   *Woody Oriental / Oriental Boisé* ●
1989 GENGIS KHAN   *Woody Oriental / Oriental Boisé* ●
1992 M pour MONSIEUR   *Aromatic / Fougère* ●
1998 M de M   *Soft Oriental / Oriental Doux* ●●

MARCELLA BORGHESE
1978 DI BORGHESE*   *Green / Vert* ●●●
1993 IL BACIO   *Floral / Florale* ●
1993 PROFUMO DI MONTECATINI ♂   *Water / Marine* ●●●

MARIELLA BURANI
1992 MARIELLA BURANI   *Soft Floral / Fleuri Aldéhydé* ●●
1996 MARIELLA   *Soft Oriental / Oriental Doux* ●
1999 AMULETI   *Floral / Florale* ●

MARILYN MIGLIN
1978 PHEROMONE   *Green / Vert* ●●●●
1990 DESTINY   *Floral / Florale* ●

1998 MYSTIC   *Floral / Florale* ●●
1999 PHEROMONE FOR MEN   *Dry Woods / Chypre Cuir* ●●

MARINA DE BOURBON
1994 MARINA DE BOURBON   *Woody Oriental / Oriental Boisé* ●
1998 MON BOUQUET   *Floral / Florale* ●
1999 À LA FRANÇAISE   *Floral / Florale* ●●
1997 M de BOURBON   *Aromatic / Fougère* ●●
1999 BOURBON HOMME   *Mossy Woods / Chypre Boisé* ●●●●

MARK BIRLEY
1996 MARK BIRLEY FOR MEN   *Dry Woods / Chypre Cuir* ●●

MARK CROSS
1997 EMBRACE*   *Soft Floral / Fleuri Aldéhydé* ●●●

MARY McFADDEN
1996 ALABASTER   *Soft Floral / Fleuri Aldéhydé* ●
1996 GOLD   *Woody Oriental / Oriental Boisé* ●

MÄURER & WIRTZ
1960 NONCHALANCE   *Soft Floral / Fleuri Aldéhydé* ●●●
1992 BETTY BARCLAY*   *Floral Oriental / Fleuri Oriental* ●●
1994 SKARLETT   *Woody Oriental / Oriental Boisé* ●●●
1995 VOICE BY BETTY BARCLAY   *Floral Oriental / Fleuri Oriental* ●●●
1996 SKARLETT SECRETS   *Woody Oriental / Oriental Boisé* ●●
1997 CYBERSP@CE ♂   *Water / Marine* ●
1997 ERUPTION WOMAN   *Floral Oriental / Fleuri Oriental* ●●
1998 BETTY BARCLAY WOMAN   *Floral / Florale* ●
1999 BETTY BARCLAY WOMAN N° 2   *Floral Oriental / Fleuri Oriental* ●
1999 ÉLÀ NONCHALANCE   *Floral / Florale* ●●
1999 FREE WORLD WOMAN   *Floral / Florale* ●
1959 TABAC ORIGINAL (EdC)   *Soft Floral / Fleuri Aldéhydé* ●●
1959 TABAC ORIGINAL (Aftershave)   *Aromatic / Fougère* ●●
1991 TABAC EXTREME   *Aromatic / Fougère* ●●
1996 CULTURE by TABAC   *Aromatic / Fougère* ●●
1997 ERUPTION MAN   *Woody Oriental / Oriental Boisé* ●●
1998 X   *Woody Oriental / Oriental Boisé* ●
1999 CULTURE by TABAC BLUE   *Aromatic / Fougère* ●
1999 FREE WORLD MAN   *Aromatic / Fougère* ●

MAX FACTOR / H&BF
→ HEALTH & BEAUTY FOCUS

MAXIM'S
1984 MAXIM'S DE PARIS   *Floral Oriental / Fleuri Oriental* ●
1988 MAXIM'S POUR HOMME   *Woody Oriental / Oriental Boisé* ●●●●
1998 ORPHÉE   *Aromatic / Fougère* ●●

MCM
1985 MCM OBELISK*   *Oriental / Oriental* ●
1989 MCM BLUE PARADISE*   *Floral / Florale* ●●
1991 MCM 1900*   *Floral Oriental / Fleuri Oriental* ●●●
1996 VERY M.C. ♂   *Citrus / Hespéridé* ●
1998 BLACK SILVER ♂   *Aromatic / Fougère* ●●
1999 MCM   *Floral / Florale* ●●
1986 MCM SUCCESS*   *Mossy Woods / Chypre Boisé* ●●●●
1993 MCM 24 MORNING*   *Aromatic / Fougère* ●
1993 MCM 24 EVENING*   *Woody Oriental / Oriental Boisé* ●●●

MEM / DANA → DANA

MENNEN
1931 MENNEN SKIN BRACER   *Aromatic / Fougère* ●●●

MICHEL GERMAIN
1994 SÉXUAL   *Floral Oriental / Fleuri Oriental* ●
1999 DEAUVILLE   *Soft Floral / Fleuri Aldéhydé* ●●
1996 SÉXUAL POUR HOMME   *Woody Oriental / Oriental Boisé* ●
1999 DEAUVILLE POUR HOMME   *Aromatic / Fougère* ●

MICHEL JORDI
1999 THE SPIRIT OF SWITZERLAND   *Floral / Florale* ●

MIGLIN → MARILYN MIGLIN

MIKHAIL BARYSHNIKOV
1989 MISHA   *Mossy Woods / Chypre Boisé* ●●●●
1995 BARYSHNIKOV POUR FEMME   *Floral / Florale* ●●●
1991 BARYSHNIKOV   *Aromatic / Fougère* ●●
1996 BARYSHNIKOV SPORT   *Aromatic / Fougère* ●

MILA SCHÖN
1981 MILA SCHÖN   *Mossy Woods / Chypre Boisé* ●●●
1997 SCHÖN   *Floral / Florale* ●●
1986 MILA SCHÖN UOMO   *Green / Vert* ●●●●

MILLER → NICOLE MILLER

MIRA TAKLA
1990 VALLÉE DES ROIS   *Floral Oriental / Fleuri Oriental* ●●●

MISSONI
1981 MISSONI   *Mossy Woods / Chypre Boisé* ●●●●
1987 ARIA MISSONI   *Floral / Florale* ●●
1990 MOLTO MISSONI   *Oriental / Oriental* ●●●●
1994 NOI MISSONI   *Citrus / Hespéridé* ●●
1983 MISSONI UOMO   *Dry Woods / Chypre Cuir* ●●●
1990 MISSONI SPORT   *Citrus / Hespéridé* ●●●●
1994 OLYMPIOS   *Aromatic / Fougère* ●
1997 NOI UOMINI   *Citrus / Hespéridé* ●

MIYAKE → ISSEY MIYAKE

MOLINARD
1900/93 ORVAL   *Floral / Florale* ●●●
1921 HABANITA   *Woody Oriental / Oriental Boisé* ●●●●
1925/96 LAVANDE   *Floral / Florale* ●●●●
1929/93 ÎLES D'OR   *Floral / Florale* ●
1949 EAU FRANCE ♂   *Citrus / Hespéridé* ●●●
1955/93 NIRMALA*   *Woody Oriental / Oriental Boisé* ●
1979 MOLINARD DE MOLINARD   *Floral / Florale* ●●
1992 EAU FRAÎCHE ♂   *Citrus / Hespéridé* ●●
1993 AMBRE   *Oriental / Oriental* ●●●
1993 CHÈVREFEUILLE   *Floral / Florale* ●●
1993 CITRON VERT ♂   *Citrus / Hespéridé* ●
1993 CLÉMENTINE   *Citrus / Hespéridé* ●●●
1993 MÛRE   *Citrus / Hespéridé* ●●●●
1993 OEILLET   *Floral / Florale* ●●●●
1993 ORANGE-CANNELLE   *Soft Oriental / Oriental Doux* ●●
1993 PATCHOULI ♂   *Mossy Woods / Chypre Boisé* ●●●
1993 VANILLE   *Oriental / Oriental* ●●●
1994 JASMIN   *Floral / Florale* ●●
1994 MIMOSA   *Floral / Florale* ●●
1994 MISS HABANITA   *Floral / Florale* ●
1994 MUGUET / LILY OF THE VALLEY   *Floral / Florale* ●
1994 ROSE   *Floral / Florale* ●●●
1994 VIOLETTE   *Floral / Florale* ●●●●
1995 EAU LES COEURS   *Floral / Florale* ●●
1995 MUSC   *Woody Oriental / Oriental Boisé* ●●●
1997 ÉCOUTE-MOI   *Floral / Florale* ●●●●
1998 VANILLE FLEURIE   *Floral / Florale* ●●●
1998 VANILLE FRAÎCHEUR   *Oriental / Oriental* ●●
1998 VANILLE FRUITÉE   *Oriental / Oriental* ●●
1998 VANILLE MARINE   *Water / Marine* ●●●●
1998 VANILLE PATCHOULI   *Woody Oriental / Oriental Boisé* ●●●
1999 BASILIC FLEUR D'ORANGER   *Floral / Florale* ●●●●
1999 BULLES DE FRAÎCHEUR   *Citrus / Hespéridé* ●
1999 CARAMEL PAIN D'ÉPICE   *Soft Oriental / Oriental Doux* ●●
1999 CHOCOLAT MENTHE   *Oriental / Oriental* ●●
1999 FLEUR DE FIGUIER   *Mossy Woods / Chypre Boisé* ●
1999 ORANGE CAFÉ   *Citrus / Hespéridé* ●●●●
1999 POMME CANNELLE   *Mossy Woods / Chypre Boisé* ●●
1999 ROSE SANTAL   *Floral / Florale* ●●●
1935/93 MADRIGAL   *Mossy Woods / Chypre Boisé* ●●
1949 VERVEINE   *Citrus / Hespéridé* ●●●
1977/94 RAFALE   *Aromatic / Fougère* ●●
1984 VETYVER   *Mossy Woods / Chypre Boisé* ●●●
1989 TECK   *Dry Woods / Chypre Cuir* ●●●
1995 BOIS PRÉCIEUX   *Mossy Woods / Chypre Boisé* ●●●●
1996 MOLINARD HOMME I   *Aromatic / Fougère* ●●
1996 MOLINARD HOMME II   *Woody Oriental / Oriental Boisé* ●
1996 MOLINARD HOMME III   *Water / Marine* ●●●

1996 VANITECK *Dry Woods / Chypre Cuir* ●●●●

MOLYNEUX
1932/95 LE CHIC* *Soft Floral / Fleuri Aldéhydé* ●●
1971 VIVRE *Soft Floral / Fleuri Aldéhydé* ●●
1977 QUARTZ *Floral / Florale* ●
1980 GAULOISE* *Mossy Woods / Chypre Boisé* ●
1990 INITIATION* *Floral Oriental / Fleuri Oriental* ●●●
1998 I LOVE YOU *Floral / Florale* ●
1999 MODERN QUARTZ *Floral / Florale* ●
1975 CAPTAIN* *Aromatic / Fougère* ●●
1988 LORD* *Dry Woods / Chypre Cuir* ●●
1996 QUARTZ POUR HOMME *Citrus / Hespéridé* ●●

MONDI
1991 MONDI PURSENSE *Woody Oriental / Oriental Boisé* ●

MONSOON
1994 MONSOON *Floral / Florale* ●●
1996 SHIMÓ *Floral Oriental / Fleuri Oriental* ●●
1997 MONSOON EAU *Water / Marine* ●●

MONT ST MICHEL
1920 MONT ST MICHEL ♂ *Citrus / Hespéridé* ●●●
1920 EAU DE LAVANDE ♂ *Floral / Florale* ●●●

MONTANA
1986 MONTANA PARFUM DE PEAU *Dry Woods / Chypre Cuir* ●●●●
1990 MONTANA PARFUM D'ELLE* *Mossy Woods / Chypre Boisé* ●
1994 SUGGESTION EAU CUIVRÉE *Floral Oriental / Fleuri Oriental* ●●●
1994 SUGGESTION EAU D'ARGENT *Floral / Florale* ●●
1994 SUGGESTION EAU D'OR *Floral / Florale* ●●
1997 JUST ME *Woody Oriental / Oriental Boisé* ●●
1989 MONTANA POUR HOMME *Woody Oriental / Oriental Boisé* ●●

MONTEIL
1995 L'EAU DE MONTEIL *Floral / Florale* ●●●●

MONTEIL / ROYAL SECRET → ROYAL SECRET

MORABITO
1987 MON CLASSIQUE *Floral / Florale* ●●
1992 TURQUOISE *Citrus / Hespéridé* ●●●●
1995 SOIR D'ÉTÉ *Mossy Woods / Chypre Boisé* ●●●
1996 MISS MORABITO *Floral / Florale* ●
1997 UN MATIN D'ÉTÉ *Floral / Florale* ●●
1998 FLEUR *Floral / Florale* ●
1998 ON AIR FEMME *Floral / Florale* ●●
1989 M de MORABITO *Woody Oriental / Oriental Boisé* ●●●●
1994 MONSIEUR MORABITO *Aromatic / Fougère* ●
1998 ON AIR HOMME *Aromatic / Fougère* ●

MORENI → POPY MORENI

MORGANE LE FAY
1997 MORGANE LE FAY *Floral / Florale* ●

MOSCHINO
1987 MOSCHINO *Oriental / Oriental* ●●●
1995 CHEAP & CHIC *Floral / Florale* ●
1996 OH! DE MOSCHINO *Soft Floral / Fleuri Aldéhydé* ●
1991 MOSCHINO POUR HOMME *Dry Woods / Chypre Cuir* ●●
1997 UOMO? MOSCHINO *Woody Oriental / Oriental Boisé* ●

MUELHENS
1792 4711 ORIGINAL ♂ *Citrus / Hespéridé* ●●●
1921 TOSCA *Soft Floral / Fleuri Aldéhydé* ●●●
1976 EXTASE MUSK WOMAN *Oriental / Oriental* ●●●
1994 EXTASE DEVOTION WOMAN *Woody Oriental / Oriental Boisé* ●
1996 EXTASE BODY TALK ♂ *Citrus / Hespéridé* ●
1997 EXTASE EXOTIC NATURE *Floral / Florale* ●●
1997 VIVA DI TOSCA *Floral Oriental / Fleuri Oriental* ●●●
1998 BELLA FIRENZE *Floral Oriental / Fleuri Oriental* ●
1999 SUMATRA RAIN WOMAN *Floral Oriental / Fleuri Oriental* ●
1969 SIR IRISH MOSS *Mossy Woods / Chypre Boisé* ●●
1985 EXTASE MUSK MAN *Oriental / Oriental* ●●●●
1993 EXTASE MAGMA MAN *Woody Oriental / Oriental Boisé* ●●●

1993 SUMATRA RAIN *Aromatic / Fougère* ●●
1995 GALILEO DE VIENTO *Aromatic / Fougère* ●●
1997 EXTASE EXOTIC NATURE MAN *Aromatic / Fougère* ●●
1997 GALILEO 21st CENTURY *Aromatic / Fougère* ●
1997 PUMA INDEPENDENCE *Aromatic / Fougère* ●
1997 SUMATRA RAIN FRESH *Aromatic / Fougère* ●
1998 PUMA CHALLENGE *Aromatic / Fougère* ●●
1998 SUMATRA RAIN WOOD *Woody Oriental / Oriental Boisé* ●●

MUGLER → THIERRY MUGLER

MULBERRY
1997 MULBERRY *Soft Oriental / Oriental Doux* ●●●
1966 MULBERRY FOR MEN *Dry Woods / Chypre Cuir* ●●

MYRURGIA
1916 LAVANDA ♂ *Floral / Florale* ●●●
1921 MAJA *Soft Oriental / Oriental Doux* ●●●
1996 TRIANGLE* *Floral / Florale* ●●

NAF NAF
1991 UNE TOUCHE DE NAF NAF *Floral / Florale* ●
1995 GRAFFITI VANILLA *Woody Oriental / Oriental Boisé* ●●

NAOMI CAMPBELL
1999 NAOMI CAMPBELL *Woody Oriental / Oriental Boisé* ●●●●

NAPA VALLEY
1998 CIELO *Mossy Woods / Chypre Boisé* ●

NAPOLEON
1999 LAPIS *Woody Oriental / Oriental Boisé* ●●

NATIO
1999 U *Floral / Florale* ●

NAUTICA
1997 NAUTICA WOMAN *Floral / Florale* ●
1992 NAUTICA *Water / Marine* ●
1997 NAUTICA COMPETITION *Woody Oriental / Oriental Boisé* ●●

NAUTILUS
1998 NAUTILUS AQUA *Water / Marine* ●●●●

NICOLE MILLER
1993 NICOLE MILLER *Floral Oriental / Fleuri Oriental* ●●
1998 NICOLE *Floral / Florale* ●
1994 NICOLE MILLER FOR MEN *Woody Oriental / Oriental Boisé* ●●

NIKE COSMETICS
1991 NIKE *Aromatic / Fougère* ●●
1997 NK *Aromatic / Fougère* ●

NIKI DE ST PHALLE
1982 NIKI DE SAINT PHALLE *Mossy Woods / Chypre Boisé* ●

NIKOS
1994 SCULPTURE *Floral Oriental / Fleuri Oriental* ●
1995 SCULPTURE HOMME *Woody Oriental / Oriental Boisé* ●●

NINA RICCI
1946 COEUR JOIE *Soft Floral / Fleuri Aldéhydé* ●●●
1948 L'AIR DU TEMPS *Floral / Florale* ●●●
1952 FILLE D'EVE *Mossy Woods / Chypre Boisé* ●●●
1961 CAPRICCI *Floral / Florale* ●●●
1974 FAROUCHE *Soft Floral / Fleuri Aldéhydé* ●●
1980/82 FLEUR DE FLEURS *Soft Floral / Fleuri Aldéhydé* ●
1987 NINA *Soft Floral / Fleuri Aldéhydé* ●●
1994 DECI DELÀ *Mossy Woods / Chypre Boisé* ●●
1996 LIBERTÉ ACIDULÉE (LES BELLES DE RICCI) *Floral / Florale* ●
1999 AMOUR D'AMANDIER *Floral / Florale* ●●
1999 DÉLICE D'ÉPICES *Floral Oriental / Fleuri Oriental* ●●●
1975 SIGNORICCI *Citrus / Hespéridé* ●●●
1989 RICCI-CLUB *Woody Oriental / Oriental Boisé* ●●

NINO CERRUTI → CERRUTI

Index des Maisons

NORELL
1968 NORELL *Floral / Florale* ●●

OLD ENGLAND
1999 CHELSEA DREAMS *Floral / Florale* ●●

OLEG CASSINI
1990 CASSINI *Mossy Woods / Chypre Boisé* ●●
1998 BLACK TIE *Woody Oriental / Oriental Boisé* ●
1995 CASSINI FOR MEN *Aromatic / Fougère* ●

OLIVIER DE KERSAUSON
1992 LATITUDE *Aromatic / Fougère* ●●
1997 LATITUDE SPORT *Water / Marine* ●●●

OMAR SHARIF
1989 OMAR SHARIF *Floral / Florale* ●●●
1994 NUBIADE *Woody Oriental / Oriental Boisé* ●●●
1998 CONVICTION *Floral Oriental / Fleuri Oriental* ●
1992 OMAR SHARIF POUR HOMME *Aromatic / Fougère* ●●
1994 IGNIS *Dry Woods / Chypre Cuir* ●●●
1999 CONVICTION MEN *Woody Oriental / Oriental Boisé* ●●

ORIGINS
1995 SPRING FEVER *Floral / Florale* ●●

ORLANE
1983 FLEURS D'ORLANE *Floral / Florale* ●
1992 EAU D'ORLANE *Citrus / Hespéridé* ●
1978 / 80 DERRICK *Woody Oriental / Oriental Boisé* ●●●

OSCAR DE LA RENTA
1977 OSCAR DE LA RENTA *Floral Oriental / Fleuri Oriental* ●●●
1992 VOLUPTÉ *Floral Oriental / Fleuri Oriental* ●●
1997 SO DE LA RENTA *Floral / Florale* ●
1980 OSCAR DE LA RENTA POUR LUI *Dry Woods / Chypre Cuir* ●●
1999 OSCAR FOR MEN *Dry Woods / Chypre Cuir* ●●

OTTO KERN
1990 NOA NOA* *Floral Oriental / Fleuri Oriental* ●●
1994 YPNO* *Woody Oriental / Oriental Boisé* ●●
1991 CYCLE* *Aromatic / Fougère* ●

OZBEK → RIFAT OZBEK

PACO RABANNE
1969 CALANDRE *Soft Floral / Fleuri Aldéhydé* ●●
1979 MÉTAL *Soft Floral / Fleuri Aldéhydé* ●
1985 LA NUIT *Dry Woods / Chypre Cuir* ●●●●
1994 XS POUR ELLE *Floral / Florale* ●
1996 PACO ♂ *Citrus / Hespéridé* ●
1998 PACO ENERGY ♂ *Citrus / Hespéridé* ●●
1999 ULTRAVIOLET *Floral Oriental / Fleuri Oriental* ●
1973 PACO RABANNE POUR HOMME *Aromatic / Fougère* ●●
1986 SPORT DE PACO RABANNE *Citrus / Hespéridé* ●●
1988 TÉNÉRÉ *Floral / Florale* ●●●●
1993 XS POUR HOMME *Aromatic / Fougère* ●

PALLADIO / KITON
1997 KITON DONNA *Floral / Florale* ●●
1996 KITON MEN *Mossy Woods / Chypre Boisé* ●
1998 KITON NAPOLI *Woody Oriental / Oriental Boisé* ●

PAGLIERI
1920 FELCE AZZURRA *Soft Oriental / Oriental Doux* ●●●

PALOMA PICASSO
1984 PALOMA PICASSO *Mossy Woods / Chypre Boisé* ●●●
1996 TENTATIONS *Woody Oriental / Oriental Boisé* ●●●
1992 MINOTAURE *Woody Oriental / Oriental Boisé* ●●

PARAH
1996 PARAH *Floral / Florale* ●●●●
1998 REALLY PARAH *Soft Floral / Fleuri Aldéhydé* ●●
1999 ESSENZA DI MEDITERRANEÒ DONNA *Floral / Florale* ●
1999 ESSENZA DI MEDITERRANEÒ UOMO *Dry Woods / Chypre Cuir* ●

PARFUMS BLEU
1975 BLUE STRATOS *Aromatic / Fougère* ●
1983 GOLD *Aromatic / Fougère* ●
1985 CLASSIC *Mossy Woods / Chypre Boisé* ●●●
1989 ENGLISH BLAZER *Aromatic / Fougère* ●●
1997 BLUE *Aromatic / Fougère* ●

PARIS BLEU
1995 GALICE *Floral Oriental / Fleuri Oriental* ●●
1998 COEUR D'OR *Woody Oriental / Oriental Boisé* ●

PARLUX
1984 ANNE KLEIN* *Soft Floral / Fleuri Aldéhydé* ●
1985 DÉCADENCE* *Floral / Florale* ●●
1986 ANNE KLEIN II* *Oriental / Oriental* ●
1987 ANIMALE *Mossy Woods / Chypre Boisé* ●●●●
1988 PHANTOM OF THE OPERA* *Floral Oriental / Fleuri Oriental* ●●
1993 ANIMALE ANIMALE *Floral Oriental / Fleuri Oriental* ●●
1997 INSTINCT D'ANIMALE *Mossy Woods / Chypre Boisé* ●●●
1993 ANIMALE FOR MEN *Aromatic / Fougère* ●●
1994 ANIMALE ANIMALE FOR MEN *Woody Oriental / Oriental Boisé* ●

PAROUR
1997 FIORA *Dry Woods / Chypre Cuir* ●●
1994 ARIOS *Aromatic / Fougère* ●●●●

PARQUET / DANA → DANA
PATOU → JEAN PATOU

PATRICIA DE NICOLAÏ
1989 COLOGNE SOLOGNE ♂ *Citrus / Hespéridé* ●●●
1989 LE TEMPS D'UNE FÊTE *Floral / Florale* ●
1989 NUMBER ONE *Floral / Florale* ●●
1989 ODALISQUE *Floral / Florale* ●
1992 EAU DE CHEVERNY ♂ *Mossy Woods / Chypre Boisé* ●●●
1992 EAU DE PROVENCE ♂ *Floral / Florale* ●●●
1992 JARDIN SECRET *Mossy Woods / Chypre Boisé* ●
1992 MIMOSAÏQUE *Floral / Florale* ●●
1993 SACREBLEU! *Floral Oriental / Fleuri Oriental* ●●●
1996 JUSTE UN RÊVE *Woody Oriental / Oriental Boisé* ●●
1997 EAU D'ÉTÉ *Citrus / Hespéridé* ●●
1997 VANILLE-TONKA *Oriental / Oriental* ●●●
1998 ROSE-PIVOINE *Floral / Florale* ●●●
1989 NEW YORK *Woody Oriental / Oriental Boisé* ●●
1994 BALADIN *Dry Woods / Chypre Cuir* ●●●
1995 CARRÉ D'AS *Aromatic / Fougère* ●

PAUL DJIRKALI
1998 VERTIGO FOR WOMEN *Aromatic / Fougère* ●●
1995 VERTIGO FOR MEN *Aromatic / Fougère* ●

PAUL SEBASTIAN
1985 DESIGN *Soft Floral / Fleuri Aldéhydé* ●
1995 CASUAL *Floral / Florale* ●
1979 PS *Soft Oriental / Oriental Doux* ●●●
1995 DESIGN FOR MEN *Aromatic / Fougère* ●

PAVAROTTI
1995 PAVAROTTI DONNA *Mossy Woods / Chypre Boisé* ●●
1994 LUCIANO PAVAROTTI *Dry Woods / Chypre Cuir* ●●●
1999 LUCIANO *Aromatic / Fougère* ●

PAYOT
1977 PAVLOVA *Floral / Florale* ●●●●

PENHALIGON'S
1911 ENGLISH FERN ♂ *Aromatic / Fougère* ●●●
1927 EAU DE COLOGNE ♂ *Citrus / Hespéridé* ●●●
1949 EAU DE VERVEINE ♂ *Citrus / Hespéridé* ●●●●
1963 EXTRACT OF LIMES ♂ *Citrus / Hespéridé* ●●●●
1976 ESPRIT DE LAVANDE ♂ *Aromatic / Fougère* ●
1976 GARDENIA *Floral / Florale* ●●
1976 LILY OF THE VALLEY *Floral / Florale* ●
1976 NIGHT SCENTED STOCK *Floral / Florale* ●●●●
1976 ORANGE BLOSSOM *Floral* ●●●●
1976 PRIMROSE *Floral / Florale* ●●●
1976 VIOLETTA *Floral / Florale* ●●●●

1977 ORMOLU *Woody Oriental / Oriental Boisé* ●●
1978 BLUEBELL *Floral / Florale* ●
1979 VICTORIAN POSY *Floral / Florale* ●●●●
1984 ELISABETHAN ROSE *Floral / Florale* ●●●
1989 ESPRIT DU ROI ♂ *Citrus / Hespéridé* ●●
1991 CORNUBIA *Floral Oriental / Fleuri Oriental* ●●●
1992 EAU SANS PAREIL ♂ *Aromatic / Fougère* ●●
1996 QUERCUS ♂ *Citrus / Hespéridé* ●
1998 LP N° 9 *Floral Oriental / Fleuri Oriental* ●
1999 PENHALIGON'S CASTILE ♂ *Citrus / Hespéridé* ●●●
1872 HAMMAM BOUQUET *Woody Oriental / Oriental Boisé* ●●●
1902 BLENHEIM BOUQUET *Citrus / Hespéridé* ●●●
1911 LORDS *Citrus / Hespéridé* ●●●●
1989 RACQUETS FORMULA *Aromatic / Fougère* ●●●
1999 LP N° 9 FOR MEN *Woody Oriental / Oriental Boisé* ●●●

PERFUMER'S WORKSHOP
1972 TEA ROSE *Floral / Florale* ●●●
1987 SAMBA *Floral / Florale* ●●
1992 SAMBA NOVA *Mossy Woods / Chypre Boisé* ●
1996 SAMBA NATURAL *Water / Marine* ●●
1998 UNZIPPED *Woody Oriental / Oriental Boisé* ●
1999 SAMBA RED WOMAN *Soft Floral / Fleuri Aldéhydé* ●●
1999 UNZIPPED SPORT *Floral / Florale* ●
1999 UNZIPPED UNIVERSE *Floral Oriental / Fleuri Oriental* ●
1990 SAMBA FOR MEN *Citrus / Hespéridé* ●●●●
1993 SAMBA NOVA HOMME *Woody Oriental / Oriental Boisé* ●●
1997 SAMBA NATURAL MAN *Aromatic / Fougère* ●
1998 ZIPPED *Citrus / Hespéridé* ●●
1999 SAMBA RED MAN *Mossy Woods / Chypre Boisé* ●●
1999 ZIPPED SPORTS *Aromatic / Fougère* ●
1999 ZIPPED UNIVERSE *Woody Oriental / Oriental Boisé* ●●

PERLIER
1995 NATURE'S ONE FREESIA *Floral / Florale* ●●
1994 NATURE'S ONE GARDENIA *Floral / Florale* ●●

PERRY ELLIS
1985/96 PERRY ELLIS FOR WOMEN *Soft Floral / Fleuri Aldéhydé* ●●
1993 360° FOR WOMEN *Floral / Florale* ●●
1996 AMERICA FOR WOMEN *Floral / Florale* ●
1985/96 PERRY ELLIS FOR MEN *Dry Woods / Chypre Cuir* ●●●
1995 360° FOR MEN *Aromatic / Fougère* ●
1996 AMERICA FOR MEN *Aromatic / Fougère* ●
1997 PERRY ELLIS RESERVE *Aromatic / Fougère* ●
1999 PERRY ELLIS PORTFOLIO *Aromatic / Fougère* ●

PHILIPPE VENET
1965/96 VENET *Floral Oriental / Fleuri Oriental* ●●●
1998 EAU DE COUTURE *Soft Floral / Fleuri Aldéhydé* ●●●●

PIERRE BALMAIN
1947/90 VENT VERT *Green / Vert* ●●●
1953/92 JOLIE MADAME *Woody Oriental / Oriental Boisé* ●●
1967 MISS BALMAIN *Dry Woods / Chypre Cuir* ●●●
1980 IVOIRE *Soft Floral / Fleuri Aldéhydé* ●
1998 BALMAIN *Mossy Woods / Chypre Boisé* ●
1964/90 MONSIEUR BALMAIN *Citrus / Hespéridé* ●●●●
1983 ÉBÈNE *Aromatic / Fougère* ●●

PIERRE CARDIN
1981 CHOC *Mossy Woods / Chypre Boisé* ●
1990 ROSE CARDIN *Mossy Woods / Chypre Boisé* ●●●
1995 OPHÉLIE *Soft Floral / Fleuri Aldéhydé* ●●●
1965/98 BLEU MARINE *Woody Oriental / Oriental Boisé* ●
1972 PIERRE CARDIN POUR MONSIEUR *Soft Oriental / Oriental Doux* ●
1987 PIERRE CARDIN MUSK *Aromatic / Fougère* ●●●●
1992 ENIGME *Aromatic / Fougère* ●●
1995 INSATIABLE *Aromatic / Fougère* ●
1996 CENTAURE CUIR AMBRE *Woody Oriental / Oriental Boisé* ●●
1996 CENTAURE CUIR BLANC *Mossy Woods / Chypre Boisé* ●●
1996 CENTAURE CUIR CASAQUE *Aromatic / Fougère* ●●
1996 CENTAURE CUIR ÉTALON *Dry Woods / Chypre Cuir* ●●●
1996 CENTAURE CUIR FOUGÈRE *Aromatic / Fougère* ●
1996 SPORTIF *Aromatic / Fougère* ●
1998 CENTAURE DIAMANT NOIR *Aromatic / Fougère* ●●
1998 CENTAURE TÊTE D'OR *Aromatic / Fougère* ●●

PIERRE RENÉ
1980 JACQUI *Soft Oriental / Oriental Doux* ●●●
1981 ÉVÉ *Soft Oriental / Oriental Doux* ●●●

PIERRE WULFF
1985 GILDA *Woody Oriental / Oriental Boisé* ●

PIGUET → ROBERT PIGUET

PINO SILVESTRE - MAVIVE
1996 GREEN GENERATION ♂ *Aromatic / Fougère* ●●
1998 GREEN GENERATION HER *Floral / Florale* ●
1955 PINO SILVESTRE ORIGINAL *Mossy Woods / Chypre Boisé* ●●●
1992 ICE WATER* *Aromatic / Fougère* ●
1998 GREEN GENERATION HIM *Aromatic / Fougère* ●
1998 PINO SILVESTRE EXTREME *Citrus / Hespéridé* ●●●●

PIVER → L.T. PIVER

Pol
1995 VERDI 800 *Woody Oriental / Oriental Boisé* ●●●

POLICE
1998 POLICE *Aromatic / Fougère* ●●●

POPY MORENI
1996 POPY MORENI *Woody Oriental / Oriental Boisé* ●
1998 POPY MORENI DE FÊTE *Floral / Florale* ●●
1999 LE CIRQUE DE POPY MORENI *Soft Floral / Fleuri Aldéhydé* ●

PRECISE INTERNATIONAL
1996 SWISS ARMY *Aromatic / Fougère* ●

PRESCRIPTIVES
1986 CALYX *Floral / Florale* ●
1998 FLIRT *Floral / Florale* ●●

PRINCE MATCHABELLI
1953 WIND SONG *Floral / Florale* ●●●
1970 CACHET* (Original) *Dry Woods / Chypre Cuir* ●●●
1997 UNRULY *Floral Oriental / Fleuri Oriental* ●●●●

PRISCILLA PRESLEY
1990 MOMENTS *Woody Oriental / Oriental Boisé* ●●●
1993 EXPERIENCES *Floral / Florale* ●●●●
1996 INDIAN SUMMER *Floral Oriental / Fleuri Oriental* ●
1998 ROSES AND MORE *Floral / Florale* ●●●
1999 GOLDEN MOMENT *Floral Oriental / Fleuri Oriental* ●

PUIG
1940 AGUA LAVANDA ♂ *Floral / Florale* ●●●
1975 ESTIVALIA *Citrus / Hespéridé* ●●
1989 ANOUCK *Floral / Florale* ●
1996 THAÏS *Floral / Florale* ●
1968 AGUA BRAVA *Mossy Woods / Chypre Boisé* ●●●
1982 QUORUM *Dry Woods / Chypre Cuir* ●●●
1988 SYBARIS *Woody Oriental / Oriental Boisé* ●●
1989 BOSTON MAN *Aromatic / Fougère* ●●
1993 SPRINGFIELD *Dry Woods / Chypre Cuir* ●
1994 AQUA QUORUM *Aromatic / Fougère* ●

PUPA
1996 FIORILU EN FLEURS *Floral / Florale* ●●
1997 PLUMES *Floral / Florale* ●

RABANNE → PACO RABANNE

RALPH LAUREN
1978 LAUREN *Floral / Florale* ●●
1990 SAFARI *Soft Floral / Fleuri Aldéhydé* ●
1996 POLO SPORT WOMAN *Water / Marine* ●●
1998 ROMANCE *Floral / Florale* ●●●
1978 POLO *Dry Woods / Chypre Cuir* ●●
1979 CHAPS *Woody Oriental / Oriental Boisé* ●●●
1985 CHAPS MUSK *Woody Oriental / Oriental Boisé* ●●●
1991 POLO CREST *Dry Woods / Chypre Cuir* ●●
1992 SAFARI FOR MEN *Aromatic / Fougère* ●

1994 POLO SPORT   *Aromatic / Fougère* ●
1998 POLO SPORT EXTREME   *Dry Woods / Chypre Cuir* ●●
1999 ROMANCE MEN   *Aromatic / Fougère* ●

RAPHAËL
1947 RÉPLIQUE*   *Mossy Woods / Chypre Boisé* ●●●

RAVELLO
1997 RAVELLO   *Floral Oriental / Fleuri Oriental* ●●●

RED PEARL
1999 RED PEARL   *Floral Oriental / Fleuri Oriental* ●●

RÉGINE'S
1989 RÉGINE'S   *Woody Oriental / Oriental Boisé* ●●●
1992 ZOA   *Floral / Florale* ●●
1995 PALACE   *Soft Floral / Fleuri Aldéhydé* ●●
1991 JIMMY'Z   *Woody Oriental / Oriental Boisé* ●●
1993 RÉGINE'S FOR MEN   *Woody Oriental / Oriental Boisé* ●

RÉMY LATOUR
1989 SI TENDRE   *Soft Floral / Fleuri Aldéhydé* ●
1993 LUNE D'ÉTÉ   *Woody Oriental / Oriental Boisé* ●
1994 SI FLEURI   *Floral / Florale* ●●
1998 L'ELUE   *Floral Oriental / Fleuri Oriental* ●●
1990 MANÈS   *Woody Oriental / Oriental Boisé* ●●
1994 KRYIAZ   *Aromatic / Fougère* ●
1996 CIGAR   *Woody Oriental / Oriental Boisé* ●●
1996 CIGARILLO   *Dry Woods / Chypre Cuir* ●●●●
1997 MANÈS ICE   *Aromatic / Fougère* ●
1999 PRESSURE   *Aromatic / Fougère* ●●

RÉMY MARQUIS
1999 MARQUIS POUR FEMME   *Woody Oriental / Oriental Boisé* ●
1999 RÉMY FOR WOMAN   *Floral / Florale* ●●
1999 MARQUIS   *Aromatic / Fougère* ●
1999 RÉMY   *Woody Oriental / Oriental Boisé* ●●

RENAUD DE LUSTRAC
1989 EXCEPTION   *Oriental / Oriental* ●

REPLAY
1996 REPLAY   *Woody Oriental / Oriental Boisé* ●

RÉVILLON
1953/94 DETCHÉMA   *Soft Floral / Fleuri Aldéhydé* ●●●●
1981 TURBULENCES   *Mossy Woods / Chypre Boisé* ●●●●
1994 ANOUCHKA   *Mossy Woods / Chypre Boisé* ●●
1998 EAU DE RÉVILLON   *Floral / Florale* ●
1995 R   *Mossy Woods / Chypre Boisé* ●

REVLON
1955 INTIMATE*   *Mossy Woods / Chypre Boisé* ●
1970 MOONDROPS   *Floral / Florale* ●●●●
1973 CHARLIE   *Floral / Florale* ●●
1973 CIARA   *Oriental / Oriental* ●●●●
1975 JONTUE   *Floral / Florale* ●●●●
1978 ENJOLI   *Floral / Florale* ●●●●
1984 ENJOLI MIDNIGHT   *Soft Oriental / Oriental Doux* ●●●
1984 FOREVER KRYSTLE   *Floral Oriental / Fleuri Oriental* ●●●
1985 MAROC*   *Mossy Woods / Chypre Boisé* ●●●●
1987 XI'A XI'ANG*   *Floral Oriental / Fleuri Oriental* ●●
1990 UNFORGETTABLE   *Woody Oriental / Oriental Boisé* ●●●●
1993 CHARLIE RED   *Floral / Florale* ●●
1994 CHARLIE WHITE   *Water / Marine* ●
1994 FIRE & ICE   *Oriental / Oriental* ●
1995 CHARLIE GOLD   *Floral Oriental / Fleuri Oriental* ●
1995 CIARA FEMME FATALE*   *Floral Oriental / Fleuri Oriental* ●●
1995 LASTING   *Floral / Florale* ●●
1996 CHERISH   *Floral / Florale* ●
1996 FIRE & ICE COOL   *Citrus / Hespéridé* ●
1996 JONTUE MOONLIGHT*   *Floral / Florale* ●
1997 CHARLIE SUNSHINE   *Floral / Florale* ●
1997 CHARLIE WHITE MUSK   *Soft Floral / Fleuri Aldéhydé* ●
1997 SHE*   *Floral / Florale* ●●
1998 CHARLIE SILVER   *Floral / Florale* ●
1999 FIRE & ICE SMOULDER FOR HER   *Woody Oriental / Oriental Boisé* ●

1958/89 THAT MAN   *Citrus / Hespéridé* ●●●●
1965 PUB   *Aromatic / Fougère* ●●●
1994 FIRE & ICE FOR MEN   *Aromatic / Fougère* ●
1999 FIRE & ICE SMOULDER FOR HIM   *Mossy Woods / Chypre Boisé* ●●

REYNALD KATZ
1998 REYNALD KATZ ♂   *Citrus / Hespéridé* ●

RICCI → NINA RICCI

RIFAT OZBEK
1995 OZBEK   *Floral / Florale* ●●●
1999 OZBEK 1001   *Oriental / Oriental* ●

RITZ
1935 JEAN NATÉ   *Aromatic / Fougère* ●●●

ROBERT ISABELL
1996 ATTAR   *Oriental / Oriental* ●●●●
1996 CALLA   *Soft Oriental / Oriental Doux* ●●●
1996 CEYLON   *Citrus / Hespéridé* ●●
1996 MANDARIN   *Floral / Florale* ●●●●
1996 SAVANNA   *Floral / Florale* ●●

ROBERT PIGUET
1944 BANDIT   *Dry Woods / Chypre Cuir* ●●●
1948 FRACAS   *Floral / Florale* ●●●●

ROBERTO CAPUCCI
1963 PARCE QUE!*   *Soft Floral / Fleuri Aldéhydé* ●●●
1974 YENDI*   *Soft Floral / Fleuri Aldéhydé* ●●●●
1987 CAPUCCI DE CAPUCCI   *Woody Oriental / Oriental Boisé* ●●
1965 CAPUCCI POUR HOMME   *Citrus / Hespéridé* ●●
1985 R de CAPUCCI   *Aromatic / Fougère* ●

ROBERTO VERINO
1992 VERINO   *Floral Oriental / Fleuri Oriental* ●●
1995 EAU DE VERINO   *Floral / Florale* ●
1999 VERINO POUR HOMME   *Aromatic / Fougère* ●●

ROCCOBAROCCO
1994 ROCCOBAROCCO TRE   *Floral / Florale* ●●
1995 SILVER JEANS FEMME   *Floral / Florale* ●
1997 GOLD JEANS FEMME   *Citrus / Hespéridé* ●
1997 PIAZZA DI SPAGNA   *Floral / Florale* ●
1998 BLACK JEANS FEMME   *Floral / Florale* ●●●●
1989 ROCCOBAROCCO*   *Aromatic / Fougère* ●●●●
1995 SILVER JEANS HOMME   *Aromatic / Fougère* ●
1997 GOLD JEANS HOMME   *Aromatic / Fougère* ●●
1998 BLACK JEANS HOMME   *Woody Oriental / Oriental Boisé* ●●
1998 PIAZZA DI SPAGNA UOMO   *Aromatic / Fougère* ●

ROCHAS
1944/89 FEMME   *Mossy Woods / Chypre Boisé* ●●●
1960/89 MADAME ROCHAS   *Soft Floral / Fleuri Aldéhydé* ●●●●
1970 EAU DE ROCHAS   *Citrus / Hespéridé* ●●●
1978 MYSTÈRE   *Woody Oriental / Oriental Boisé* ●●
1984 LUMIÈRE   *Floral / Florale* ●
1987 BYZANCE   *Floral Oriental / Fleuri Oriental* ●●
1994 TOCADE   *Floral Oriental / Fleuri Oriental* ●●●
1995 BYZANTINE   *Floral Oriental / Fleuri Oriental* ●
1996 FLEUR D'EAU   *Floral / Florale* ●
1997 TOCADILLY   *Floral / Florale* ●●
1998 ALCHIMIE   *Floral Oriental / Fleuri Oriental* ●●
1948 MOUSTACHE   *Mossy Woods / Chypre Boisé* ●●
1969 MONSIEUR ROCHAS   *Aromatic / Fougère* ●●
1980 MACASSAR   *Dry Woods / Chypre Cuir* ●●●●
1990 GLOBE*   *Aromatic / Fougère* ●●
1993 EAU DE ROCHAS HOMME   *Citrus / Hespéridé* ●●●●
1999 ROCHAS MAN   *Woody Oriental / Oriental Boisé* ●●

RODIER
1998 RODIER   *Woody Oriental / Oriental Boisé* ●
1999 COLÈRE DE RODIER   *Woody Oriental / Oriental Boisé* ●
1999 GOURMANDISE DE RODIER   *Citrus / Hespéridé* ●
1999 ORGUEIL DE RODIER   *Floral Oriental / Fleuri Oriental* ●
1999 PARESSE DE RODIER   *Soft Floral / Fleuri Aldéhydé* ●

1999 PASSION D'HOMME *Woody Oriental / Oriental Boisé* ●●

ROGER & GALLET
1806 JEAN-MARIE FARINA ♂ *Citrus / Hespéridé* ●●●
1991 BOUQUET IMPÉRIAL ♂ *Citrus / Hespéridé* ●●●●
1991 ROGER & GALLET EXTRA-VIEILLE ♂ *Citrus / Hespéridé* ●●●
1991 LAVANDE ROYALE *Floral / Florale* ●●●
1992 NATURE SYSTEM ♂ *Citrus / Hespéridé* ●●
1993 POUR UNE FEMME *Floral / Florale* ●
1999 EAU POUR SOI *Floral / Florale* ●
1974/91 VÉTYVER *Mossy Woods / Chypre Boisé* ●●●
1980 L'HOMME *Aromatic / Fougère* ●●
1985 OPEN *Aromatic / Fougère* ●●
1993 POUR L'HOMME *Citrus / Hespéridé* ●●

ROMEO GIGLI
1989 ROMEO *Floral / Florale* ●●
1994 G GIGLI* *Soft Floral / Fleuri Aldéhydé* ●
1999 DI ROMEO GIGLI *Soft Floral / Fleuri Aldéhydé* ●●●●
1991 GIGLI PER UOMO *Woody Oriental / Oriental Boisé* ●●
1995 SUD EST *Aromatic / Fougère* ●

ROSINE
1991 LA ROSE DE ROSINE *Soft Floral / Fleuri Aldéhydé* ●●●●
1993 LA COUPE D'OR *Floral Oriental / Fleuri Oriental* ●●
1994 MEA CULPA *Floral / Florale* ●●
1996 LE MUGUET DE ROSINE *Floral / Florale* ●
1997 ROSE D'ÉTÉ *Floral / Florale* ●
1997 ROSEBERRY *Soft Floral / Fleuri Aldéhydé* ●●

ROYAL COPENHAGEN
1970 ROYAL COPENHAGEN *Woody Oriental / Oriental Boisé* ●●●
1976 ROYAL COPENHAGEN MUSK *Soft Oriental / Oriental Doux* ●●●●
1996 ROYAL COPENHAGEN SPORT* *Aromatic / Fougère* ●
1999 VIKING *Aromatic / Fougère* ●

ROYAL DOULTON
1998 DOULTON *Floral Oriental / Fleuri Oriental* ●●

ROYAL SECRET
1958 ROYAL SECRET *Oriental / Oriental* ●●●
1964 GALORÉ *Floral Oriental / Fleuri Oriental* ●●●
1990 ROMANCE *Floral / Florale* ●●●●
1999 ROYAL SECRET II *Woody Oriental / Oriental Boisé* ●●

RYKIEL → SONIA RYKIEL
SABATINI → GABRIELA SABATINI
SAINT LAURENT → YVES SAINT LAURENT

SALLE
1997 REBEL *Citrus / Hespéridé* ●

SALVADOR DALI
1983 SALVADOR DALI *Soft Oriental / Oriental Doux* ●●●
1991 LAGUNA *Floral Oriental / Fleuri Oriental* ●
1994 DALISSIME *Floral / Florale* ●●
1995 EAU DE DALI *Floral / Florale* ●
1996 DALIMIX ♂ *Citrus / Hespéridé* ●
1997 DALIMIX GOLD ♂ *Green / Vert* ●
1997 LE ROY SOLEIL *Soft Oriental / Oriental Doux* ●●
1999 DALIMANIA *Floral Oriental / Fleuri Oriental* ●●
1987 SALVADOR DALI POUR HOMME *Woody Oriental / Oriental Boisé* ●●
1992 SALVADOR *Aromatic / Fougère* ●●
1996 DALI *Aromatic / Fougère* ●
1998 LE ROY SOLEIL HOMME *Mossy Woods / Chypre Boisé* ●●

SALVATORE FERRAGAMO
1998 SALVATORE FERRAGAMO *Floral / Florale* ●●
1999 SALVATORE FERRAGAMO POUR HOMME *Mossy Woods / Chypre Boisé* ●

SAMBA → PERFUMER'S WORKSHOP
SANDER → JILL SANDER

SCAASI
1989 SCAASI *Floral / Florale* ●●

SCANNON
1966 KANØN *Woody Oriental / Oriental Boisé* ●●●

SCAPA OF SCOTLAND
1991 SCAPA *Citrus / Hespéridé* ●●
1999 INTENSE DE SCAPA *Citrus / Hespéridé* ●●●●
1994 SCAPA POUR HOMME *Aromatic / Fougère* ●●

SCHERRER → JEAN-LOUIS SCHERRER

SCHIAPARELLI
1937/97 SHOCKING *Oriental / Oriental* ●●●
1937/97 ZUT *Woody Oriental / Oriental Boisé* ●

SCHIAPPARELLI PIKENZ
1995 JOHNNY LAMBS *Woody Oriental / Oriental Boisé* ●●

SEA WORLD
1998 IMPLICITE *Soft Floral / Fleuri Aldéhydé* ●
1998 IMPLICITE HOMME *Mossy Woods / Chypre Boisé* ●●

SEBASTIAN → PAUL SEBASTIAN

SERGIO TACCHINI
1998 SERGIO TACCHINI DONNA *Water / Marine* ●●
1987 SERGIO TACCHINI *Aromatic / Fougère* ●●
1993 SERGIO TACCHINI SPORT EXTREME *Aromatic / Fougère* ●
1996 SERGIO TACCHINI UOMO *Aromatic / Fougère* ●●

SEVE BALLESTEROS
1992 ROYAL GREEN *Aromatic / Fougère* ●

SHISEIDO
1964 ZEN *Floral / Florale* ●●●
1976 INOUÏ *Green / Vert* ●●●
1980 MURASAKI *Soft Floral / Fleuri Aldéhydé* ●
1986 SPIRIT OF ZEN *Floral / Florale* ●●
1992 FEMINITÉ DU BOIS *Woody Oriental / Oriental Boisé* ●●●
1997 RELAXING FRAGRANCE *Floral / Florale* ●
1997 VOCALISE *Floral Oriental / Fleuri Oriental* ●
1999 ENERGIZING FRAGRANCE *Soft Floral / Fleuri Aldéhydé* ●●
1979 TACTICS *Green / Vert* ●●●●
1993 BASALA *Aromatic / Fougère* ●●●●

SHULTON / H&BF → HEALTH & BEAUTY FOCUS
SHULTON / PARFUMS BLEU → PARFUMS BLEU

SHULTON / P&G
1937 OLD SPICE *Soft Oriental / Oriental Doux* ●●●
1997 OLD SPICE WHITEWATER *Aromatic / Fougère* ●●

SISLEY
1974 EAU DE CAMPAGNE ♂ *Green / Vert* ●●●
1990 EAU DU SOIR *Mossy Woods / Chypre Boisé* ●●●

SLAVA ZAÏTSEV
1992 MAROUSSIA *Floral Oriental / Fleuri Oriental* ●●●
1996 AUTHENTIC MAROUSSIA *Floral Oriental / Fleuri Oriental* ●

SMALTO → FRANCESCO SMALTO

SOLO SOPRANI
1995 SOLO SOPRANI ♂ *Citrus / Hespéridé* ●
1999 SOLO FIORI FREESIA *Floral / Florale* ●●
1999 SOLO FIORI JASMINE *Floral / Florale* ●●
1999 SOLO FIORI LILY OF THE VALLEY *Floral / Florale* ●
1999 SOLO FIORI ROSE *Floral / Florale* ●●●
1999 SOLO FIORI TUBEROSE *Floral / Florale* ●●●●
1999 SOLO FIORI VIOLET *Floral / Florale* ●●●●

SOPRANI → LUCIANO SOPRANI

SONIA RYKIEL
1993 LE PARFUM *Woody Oriental / Oriental Boisé* ●●
1997 SONIA RYKIEL *Woody Oriental / Oriental Boisé* ●
1998 L'EAU DE SONIA RYKIEL *Floral / Florale* ●
1999 RYKIEL HOMME *Aromatic / Fougère* ●

S.T.DUPONT
1998 S.T.DUPONT FEMME   *Floral / Florale* ●
1998 S.T.DUPONT HOMME   *Dry Woods / Chypre Cuir* ●●●●

ST JOHN
1994 ST JOHN   *Floral Oriental / Fleuri Oriental* ●●●●
1998 WHITE CAMELLIA   *Floral / Florale* ●

STENDHAL
1960 CHARTREUSE DE PARME   *Floral / Florale* ●●●●

STÉPHANIE DE MONACO
1989 STÉPHANIE   *Woody Oriental / Oriental Boisé* ●●●
1991 L'INSAISISSABLE   *Floral / Florale* ●●

SUCCÈS DE PARIS
1994 DREAMING PRINCESS   *Floral Oriental / Fleuri Oriental* ●●
1995 BEST LADY   *Floral / Florale* ●●●
1995 FUJIYAMA ♂   *Citrus / Hespéridé* ●
1997 L'EAU DE SUCCÈS   *Floral / Florale* ●●
1999 POLEMIC!   *Floral Oriental / Fleuri Oriental* ●
1995 BEST MAN   *Woody Oriental / Oriental Boisé* ●

SWANK / REGENCY
1964 JADE EAST   *Aromatic / Fougère* ●●●

SYLVIE CHANTECAILLE
1997 FRANGIPANE   *Floral / Florale* ●●●●
1997 TIARÉ   *Floral / Florale* ●●
1997 WISTERIA   *Floral / Florale* ●●
1999 DARBY ROSE   *Floral / Florale* ●●●

TACCHINI → SERGIO TACCHINI

TED BAKER
1998 TED BAKER   *Citrus / Hespéridé* ●●●●

TED LAPIDUS
1984 CRÉATION   *Mossy Woods / Chypre Boisé* ●
1992 FANTASME   *Floral Oriental / Fleuri Oriental* ●●
1997 FOU D'ELLE   *Floral / Florale* ●●
1987 LAPIDUS POUR HOMME   *Aromatic / Fougère* ●●●●
1999 TED   *Woody Oriental / Oriental Boisé* ●●

TERRY ELLIS
1997 SOUTHERN EXPOSURE   *Citrus / Hespéridé* ●●

THIERRY MUGLER
1992 ANGEL   *Woody Oriental / Oriental Boisé* ●
1998 ANGEL INNOCENT   *Woody Oriental / Oriental Boisé* ●
1996 A*MEN / ANGEL MEN   *Woody Oriental / Oriental Boisé* ●●

TIFFANY
1987 TIFFANY   *Floral / Florale* ●●●●
1995 TRUESTE   *Soft Floral / Fleuri Aldéhydé* ●
1999 SHEER TIFFANY   *Floral / Florale* ●
1989 TIFFANY FOR MEN   *Woody Oriental / Oriental Boisé* ●●●
1998 TIFFANY FOR MEN SPORT   *Green / Vert* ●

TODD OLDHAM
1995 TODD OLDHAM*   *Woody Oriental / Oriental Boisé* ●

TOMMY HILFIGER
1996 TOMMY GIRL   *Floral / Florale* ●
1999 FREEDOM FOR HER   *Floral / Florale* ●
1995 TOMMY   *Aromatic / Fougère* ●
1998 HILFIGER ATHLETICS   *Citrus / Hespéridé* ●
1999 FREEDOM FOR HIM   *Aromatic / Fougère* ●●

TOSCA / MUELHENS → MUELHENS

TOVA BORGNINE
1989 TOVA   *Soft Floral / Fleuri Aldéhydé* ●●●●

TRISH McEVOY
1997 TRISH McEVOY 1   *Citrus / Hespéridé* ●●●●
1997 TRISH McEVOY 2   *Floral / Florale* ●

1998 TRISH McEVOY 3   *Floral / Florale* ●

TRUSSARDI
1982 TRUSSARDI   *Dry Woods / Chypre Cuir* ●●●
1989 ACTION*   *Green / Vert* ●●
1993 DONNA TRUSSARDI   *Mossy Woods / Chypre Boisé* ●●●
1997 LIGHT HER   *Floral / Florale* ●●
1999 PYTHON   *Woody Oriental / Oriental Boisé* ●●●
1990 ACTION UOMO*   *Aromatic / Fougère* ●
1993 ACTION SPORT   *Citrus / Hespéridé* ●●●●
1995 L'UOMO TRUSSARDI   *Aromatic / Fougère* ●
1997 LIGHT HIM   *Woody Oriental / Oriental Boisé* ●
1999 TRUSSARDI UOMO FRESH   *Dry Woods / Chypre Cuir* ●●

TSUMURA
1988 SANTA FE FOR MEN   *Woody Oriental / Oriental Boisé* ●

TUVACHÉ / COTY → COTY

ULRIC DE VARENS
1986 CYANE*   *Woody Oriental / Oriental Boisé* ●
1992 OTTOMANE   *Woody Oriental / Oriental Boisé* ●●
1994 VARENSIA   *Mossy Woods / Chypre Boisé* ●●
1995 PLEINE LUNE   *Woody Oriental / Oriental Boisé* ●
1996 RUE PEROGLÈSE   *Mossy Woods / Chypre Boisé* ●●
1997 EAU DE VARENS N° 2 ♂   *Citrus / Hespéridé* ●
1997 EAU DE VARENS N° 3 ♂   *Citrus / Hespéridé* ●●
1998 EAU DE VARENS N° 4 ♂   *Citrus / Hespéridé* ●●●●
1999 U de V POUR ELLE   *Floral / Florale* ●●
1993 U de V   *Aromatic / Fougère* ●
1995 VERSION HOMME*   *Mossy Woods / Chypre Boisé* ●●
1999 U de V N° 2   *Woody Oriental / Oriental Boisé* ●●

ULTIMA II
1990 U II SHEER SCENT   *Mossy Woods / Chypre Boisé* ●
1994 HEAD OVER HEELS   *Floral / Florale* ●
1996 MADLY   *Floral / Florale* ●●

UNGARO
1977/90 UNGARO   *Woody Oriental / Oriental Boisé* ●●●●
1983 DIVA   *Mossy Woods / Chypre Boisé* ●●●●
1987/92 SENSO   *Floral / Florale* ●●
1997 FLEUR DE DIVA   *Floral / Florale* ●
1991 UNGARO POUR L'HOMME I*   *Woody Oriental / Oriental Boisé* ●●
1992 UNGARO POUR L'HOMME II*   *Citrus / Hespéridé* ●●●●
1993 UNGARO POUR L'HOMME III   *Aromatic / Fougère* ●

UN MONDE NOUVEAU
1993/98 CHERRY MUSK   *Floral / Florale* ●●
1993 SAVAGE VANILLA   *Woody Oriental / Oriental Boisé* ●●
1993/98 WHITE SPELL   *Floral / Florale* ●
1995/98 LOVIN' GIRL   *Citrus / Hespéridé* ●●

VALENTINO
1977/86 VALENTINO   *Floral / Florale* ●●
1991 VENDETTA*   *Woody Oriental / Oriental Boisé* ●
1997 VERY VALENTINO   *Oriental / Oriental* ●
1991 VENDETTA POUR HOMME*   *Dry Woods / Chypre Cuir* ●●
1999 VERY VALENTINO POUR HOMME   *Woody Oriental / Oriental Boisé* ●●

VALERIA MAZZA
1998 VALERIA   *Floral / Florale* ●●

VAN CLEEF & ARPELS
1976 FIRST   *Soft Floral / Fleuri Aldéhydé* ●●●●
1987 GEM   *Woody Oriental / Oriental Boisé* ●●●●
1993 VAN CLEEF   *Floral Oriental / Fleuri Oriental* ●●
1994 MISS ARPELS   *Floral / Florale* ●
1999 BIRMANE   *Floral / Florale* ●●
1978 VAN CLEEF & ARPELS POUR HOMME   *Dry Woods / Chypre Cuir* ●●●●
1989 TSAR   *Aromatic / Fougère* ●
1998 EAU DU TSAR   *Aromatic / Fougère* ●

VAN GILS
1988 VAN GILS   *Aromatic / Fougère* ●●●●

VENTILO

1997 VENTILO *Floral Oriental / Fleuri Oriental* ●●
1998 L'ÉTÉ DE VENTILO *Floral Oriental / Fleuri Oriental* ●
1998 L'HOMME DE VENTILO *Dry Woods / Chypre Cuir* ●●●●

VENTURI → GIAN MARCO VENTURI
VERINO → ROBERTO VERINO

VERSACE

1982 GIANNI VERSACE *Mossy Woods / Chypre Boisé* ●●●●
1989 V'E VERSACE *Mossy Woods / Chypre Boisé* ●●
1991 VERSUS DONNA *Floral Oriental / Fleuri Oriental* ●●
1994 RED JEANS *Floral / Florale* ●●
1995 VERSACE'S BLONDE *Floral / Florale* ●●●●
1996 YELLOW JEANS *Floral / Florale* ●
1997 WHITE JEANS *Mossy Woods / Chypre Boisé* ●●●
1998 V/S *Floral / Florale* ●
1984 VERSACE L'HOMME *Woody Oriental / Oriental Boisé* ●●●
1990 VERSUS UOMO *Woody Oriental / Oriental Boisé* ●
1994 BLUE JEANS *Woody Oriental / Oriental Boisé* ●●
1996 GREEN JEANS *Aromatic / Fougère* ●
1996 THE DREAMER *Woody Oriental / Oriental Boisé* ●●
1997 BLACK JEANS *Aromatic / Fougère* ●●

VIALE!

1995 TOM TAILOR *Citrus / Hespéridé* ●
1997 BAD BOYS *Aromatic / Fougère* ●●

VIA PARIS

1998 SEAWEST *Water / Marine* ●

VICKY TIEL

1990 VICKY TIEL ORIGINALÉ *Floral / Florale* ●●●●
1994 SIRÈNE *Floral Oriental / Fleuri Oriental* ●●
1997 VÉNUS DE L'AMOUR *Floral Oriental / Fleuri Oriental* ●●●
1999 ÉTHÉRÉ *Floral / Florale* ●
1998 ULYSSE *Woody Oriental / Oriental Boisé* ●

VICTOR

1946 SILVESTRE *Mossy Woods / Chypre Boisé* ●●●
1949 ACQUA DI SELVA *Mossy Woods / Chypre Boisé* ●●●

VICTORIA CHALON

1993 EMOTIONS *Floral Oriental / Fleuri Oriental* ●●●
1994 FLEUR D'AMOUR *Floral / Florale* ●●

VISARI

1999 FLEURAGE *Soft Floral / Fleuri Aldéhydé* ●●

VIVIENNE WESTWOOD

1998 BOUDOIR *Floral Oriental / Fleuri Oriental* ●●●

VUARNET

1999 VUARNET *Aromatic / Fougère* ●

WEIL

1928 ZIBELINE *Mossy Woods / Chypre Boisé* ●●●
1933/96 SECRET DE VÉNUS *Woody Oriental / Oriental Boisé* ●●●
1945 ANTILOPE *Mossy Woods / Chypre Boisé* ●●●
1961/93 WEIL EAU DE FRAÎCHEUR ♂ *Citrus / Hespéridé* ●
1971 WEIL DE WEIL *Green / Vert* ●●●
1984/91 BAMBOU *Floral / Florale* ●●
1995 FLEUR DE WEIL* *Floral / Florale* ●
1980/97 WEIL POUR HOMME *Aromatic / Fougère* ●●
1986 KIPLING *Woody Oriental / Oriental Boisé* ●●

WILKES BASHFORD

1999 WILKES SAN FRANCISCO *Aromatic / Fougère* ●

WILLIAMS

1935 AQUA VELVA ICE BLUE *Mossy Woods / Chypre Boisé* ●●

WOODS OF WINDSOR

1974 HONEYSUCKLE *Floral / Florale* ●●
1974 LAVENDER *Floral / Florale* ●●●
1974 WILD ROSE *Floral / Florale* ●●●
1978 LILY OF THE VALLEY *Floral / Florale* ●

1982 FORGET ME NOT *Soft Floral / Fleuri Aldéhydé* ●●●
1997 MIMOSA *Floral / Florale* ●●
1998 VIOLET *Floral / Florale* ●●●●
1999 FREESIA *Floral / Florale* ●●
1981 FOR GENTLEMEN *Mossy Woods / Chypre Boisé* ●●●

WORTH

1925/95 SANS ADIEU *Water / Marine* ●●
1932 JE REVIENS *Soft Floral / Fleuri Aldéhydé* ●●●●
1977 MISS WORTH *Floral / Florale* ●●●●
1981 WORTH POUR HOMME *Aromatic / Fougère* ●●

XAN KIM

1999 MERGE ♂ *Aromatic / Fougère* ●

YARDLEY

1873 ENGLISH LAVENDER *Floral / Florale* ●●●
1913 APRIL VIOLETS *Floral / Florale* ●●●●
1970/94 ROSE* *Soft Floral / Fleuri Aldéhydé* ●●
1973 YOU'RE THE FIRE FOR WOMEN *Soft Oriental / Oriental Doux* ●●●
1980/94 LILY OF THE VALLEY *Floral / Florale* ●
1982/88 ESP STAFAST *Floral / Florale* ●●●●
1982 PURE SILK* *Mossy Woods / Chypre Boisé* ●●●
1984 ENGLISH FINE COLOGNE ♂ *Citrus / Hespéridé* ●●●
1991 FOREVER* *Floral Oriental / Fleuri Oriental* ●●
1994 JASMINE* *Floral / Florale* ●●●
1995 ORCHID* *Floral / Florale* ●●●
1995 WHITE LAVENDER *Floral / Florale* ●●
1996 BAROQUE *Floral Oriental / Fleuri Oriental* ●●
1996 IMPERIAL VETYVER ♂ *Mossy Woods / Chypre Boisé* ●●●
1996 SANDALWOOD ♂ *Woody Oriental / Oriental Boisé* ●●●
1997 ENGLISH ROSE *Floral / Florale* ●●●
1983 YARDLEY GOLD *Aromatic / Fougère* ●
1985 YARDLEY CLASSIC *Mossy Woods / Chypre Boisé* ●●●
1989 YOU'RE THE FIRE FOR MEN *Dry Woods / Chypre Cuir* ●●●
1992 YARDLEY ORIGINAL *Aromatic / Fougère* ●

YARDLEY / BOND STREET

1994 SO...? *Woody Oriental / Oriental Boisé* ●●●
1997 SO...? INSPIRED *Floral / Florale* ●
1998 SO...FOR HIM *Aromatic / Fougère* ●

YARDLEY / FFC
→ FFC – FINE FRAGRANCES & COSMETICS

YARDLEY / PARFUMS BLEU → PARFUMS BLEU

YOHJI YAMAMOTO

1996 YOHJI *Oriental / Oriental* ●●
1998 YOHJI ESSENTIAL *Mossy Woods / Chypre Boisé* ●●
1999 YOHJI HOMME *Aromatic / Fougère* ●●●●

YVES SAINT LAURENT

1964 Y *Mossy Woods / Chypre Boisé* ●
1971 RIVE GAUCHE *Soft Floral / Fleuri Aldéhydé* ●●
1977 OPIUM *Soft Oriental / Oriental Doux* ●●●
1983 PARIS *Floral / Florale* ●●●
1993 YVRESSE (CHAMPAGNE) *Mossy Woods / Chypre Boisé* ●
1998 IN LOVE AGAIN ⓛ *Floral / Florale* ●
1999 BABY DOLL PARIS *Floral / Florale* ●
1999 VICE VERSA ⓛ *Floral / Florale* ●●
1971 YSL POUR HOMME *Citrus / Hespéridé* ●●●●
1981 KOUROS *Aromatic / Fougère* ●●●●
1988 JAZZ *Aromatic / Fougère* ●
1993 KOUROS FRAÎCHEUR *Aromatic / Fougère* ●●
1995 OPIUM POUR HOMME *Woody Oriental / Oriental Boisé* ●●
1998 LIVE JAZZ *Aromatic / Fougère* ●
2000 BODY KOUROS *Woody Oriental / Oriental Boisé* ●

ZAHAROFF

1997 ZAHAROFF *Floral Oriental / Fleuri Oriental* ●
1999 ZAHAROFF POUR HOMME *Woody Oriental / Oriental Boisé* ●●●●

ZEGNA → ERMENEGILDO ZEGNA

Fragrances of the World

Parfums du Monde

Publisher *Editeur*
Michael Edwards & Co. Pty Ltd
ACN 002 639 241
PO Box 14, Blakehurst
Sydney 2221
Australia

Fragrance evaluation
Michael Edwards
in consultation with the perfumers
and/or senior evaluators of the Houses

Evaluation des parfums
Michael Edwards
aidé par les créateurs de parfums et/ou
les principaux évaluateurs des maisons
de parfumerie

Editor *Editrice*
Fiona Stewart

Coordination
Margaret Khoury

Technical consultant
Conseiller technique
Guy Robert

Translation *Traduction*
Guy Robert
Brigitte Carcenac de Torné

Art direction
Direction artistique
Béatrice Torrente, Patrick Lébédeff
Emphase, Paris

Images
Michel Roudnitska

Production
Peter Bowen, Jackie Welch
Production Art Services, Sydney
K&H Lithographics, Sydney

Printer *Imprimeur*
The Pot Still Press, Sydney

ORDER FORM

	US $	FF	UK £	NZ $	AUS $*	Order units	Order value
Fragrances of the World 2000 Parfums du Monde	49.50	295	29.50	75	64.90		
Fragrance Adviser CD ROM *English software for in-store use*	395	2590	295	625	544.50		
Perfume Legends *English edition*	120	590	75	175	159.50		
Parfums de Légende *French edition*	120	590	75	235	203.50		
Fragrances of the World 2001 Parfums du Monde *Released February 2001*	49.50	295	29.50	75	64.90		
Add International Airmail per unit	9	100	10	24	11		
Please ✓ currency ❏ US $ ❏ FF ❏ UK£ ❏ NZ $ ❏ AUS $							TOTAL

*Includes GST   Prices subject to change without notice

Please charge . . . . to my ❏ MasterCard ❏ Visa Card

CARD NUMBER

Expiry date   /   Name on Card

Signature

Billing Address

DELIVER TO (please print and allow up to 21 days for delivery)

Name

Address

City / State / Zip or Postcode

Country

Fax /Tel #   E-mail

ORDER FORM

	US $	FF	UK £	NZ $	AUS $*	Order units	Order value
Fragrances of the World 2000 Parfums du Monde	49.50	295	29.50	75	64.90		
Fragrance Adviser CD ROM *English software for in-store use*	395	2590	295	625	544.50		
Perfume Legends *English edition*	120	590	75	175	159.50		
Parfums de Légende *French edition*	120	590	75	235	203.50		
Fragrances of the World 2001 Parfums du Monde *Released February 2001*	49.50	295	29.50	75	64.90		
Add International Airmail per unit	9	100	10	24	11		
Please ✓ currency ❏ US $ ❏ FF ❏ UK£ ❏ NZ $ ❏ AUS $							TOTAL

*Includes GST   Prices subject to change without notice

Please charge . . . . to my ❏ MasterCard ❏ Visa Card

CARD NUMBER

Expiry date   /   Name on Card

Signature

Billing Address

DELIVER TO (please print and allow up to 21 days for delivery)

Name

Address

City / State / Zip or Postcode

Country

Fax /Tel #   E-mail

ORDER FORM

	US $	FF	UK £	NZ $	AUS $*	Order units	Order value
Fragrances of the World 2000 Parfums du Monde	49.50	295	29.50	75	64.90		
Fragrance Adviser CD ROM *English software for in-store use*	395	2590	295	625	544.50		
Perfume Legends *English edition*	120	590	75	175	159.50		
Parfums de Légende *French edition*	120	590	75	235	203.50		
Fragrances of the World 2001 Parfums du Monde *Released February 2001*	49.50	295	29.50	75	64.90		
Add International Airmail per unit	9	100	10	24	11		
Please ✓ currency ❏ US $ ❏ FF ❏ UK£ ❏ NZ $ ❏ AUS $							TOTAL

*Includes GST   Prices subject to change without notice

Please charge . . . . to my ❏ MasterCard ❏ Visa Card

CARD NUMBER

Expiry date   /   Name on Card

Signature

Billing Address

DELIVER TO (please print and allow up to 21 days for delivery)

Name

Address

City / State / Zip or Postcode

Country

Fax /Tel #   E-mail

TO ORDER

USA and Canada	Please telephone 1 800 426 8986 *or* fax this order form to (847) 677 1338
European Union	Please complete and fax this order form to +61 2 9546 8067 *or* e-mail orders@fragranceadviser.com *or* post to: Michael Edwards & Co PO Box 14, Blakehurst, 2221, Sydney, Australia
Australia and New Zealand	Please complete and fax this order form to 02 9546 8067 (+61 2 9546 8067) *or* e-mail orders@fragranceadviser.com *or* post to: Michael Edwards & Co PO Box 14, Blakehurst, 2221, Sydney, Australia

Other countries	For current prices, please fax +61 2 9546 8067 *or* e-mail orders@fragranceadviser.com
Quantity discounts and queries	Please fax +61 2 9546 8067 *or* e-mail orders@fragranceadviser.com

Please tick here if you would like to receive more information on:

❏ Perfume Legends

❏ Fragrance Adviser CD-ROM Software

TO ORDER

USA and Canada	Please telephone 1 800 426 8986 *or* fax this order form to (847) 677 1338
European Union	Please complete and fax this order form to +61 2 9546 8067 *or* e-mail orders@fragranceadviser.com *or* post to: Michael Edwards & Co PO Box 14, Blakehurst, 2221, Sydney, Australia
Australia and New Zealand	Please complete and fax this order form to 02 9546 8067 (+61 2 9546 8067) *or* e-mail orders@fragranceadviser.com *or* post to: Michael Edwards & Co PO Box 14, Blakehurst, 2221, Sydney, Australia

Other countries	For current prices, please fax +61 2 9546 8067 *or* e-mail orders@fragranceadviser.com
Quantity discounts and queries	Please fax +61 2 9546 8067 *or* e-mail orders@fragranceadviser.com

Please tick here if you would like to receive more information on:

❏ Perfume Legends

❏ Fragrance Adviser CD-ROM Software

TO ORDER

USA and Canada	Please telephone 1 800 426 8986 *or* fax this order form to (847) 677 1338
European Union	Please complete and fax this order form to +61 2 9546 8067 *or* e-mail orders@fragranceadviser.com *or* post to: Michael Edwards & Co PO Box 14, Blakehurst, 2221, Sydney, Australia
Australia and New Zealand	Please complete and fax this order form to 02 9546 8067 (+61 2 9546 8067) *or* e-mail orders@fragranceadviser.com *or* post to: Michael Edwards & Co PO Box 14, Blakehurst, 2221, Sydney, Australia

Other countries	For current prices, please fax +61 2 9546 8067 *or* e-mail orders@fragranceadviser.com
Quantity discounts and queries	Please fax +61 2 9546 8067 *or* e-mail orders@fragranceadviser.com

Please tick here if you would like to receive more information on:

❏ Perfume Legends

❏ Fragrance Adviser CD-ROM Software